THE
STOLEN
YEARS

THE
STOLEN
YEARS

BY ROGER TOUHY

with Ray Brennan

 PENNINGTON PRESS

To innocent men and women in prison, or otherwise deprived of their liberties, this book is dedicated.

Roger Touhy

Acknowledgments

There are many persons to whom my debt of gratitude is great.

First and foremost, I wish to bow my head in reverence to the memory of the late John P. Barnes, former Chicago federal court judge. He was devoted to justice. He had the courage to find me innocent.

To Robert B. Johnstone, a brilliant and resourceful lawyer, my deepest thanks. He sacrificed a law practice and impaired his health in my behalf.

The loyalty and devotion of my family—my wife, Clara, our two sons and my sisters, Ethel and Eleanor—was a bottomless well of encouragement for me.

To Governor William G. Stratton and the members of the Illinois Pardon and Parole Board, I give thanks for their mercy and understanding.

To the many lawyers who believed in me and fought for me, including: Daniel C. Ahern, Homer Atkins, Howard Bryant, Frank Ferlic, Frank J. Gagen, Jr., Kevin J. Gillogly, Joseph Harrington, Thomas Marshall, Thomas McMeekin and Charles P. Megan.

To the newspaper, radio and television people who brought the truth about me to the public when truth was what I needed desperately.

They include: Earl Aykroid, Julian Bentley, Ray Brennan, Elgar Brown, Tom Duggan, Gladys Erickson, William Gorman, Jim Hurlbut, James P. Lally, Clem Lane, Robert T. Loughran, John J. Madigan, Milton Mayer, John J. McPhaul, Len O'Connor and Karin Walsh.

A number of police officers assisted me. Among them were Bernard Gerard, Thomas Maloney and Walter Miller. Without the dilligence of Morris Green, my innocence might never have been established.

To State's Attorney Benjamin S. Adamowski, my special thanks for telling the Pardon and Parole Board that he believed I should be freed.

Roger Touhy

CONTENTS:

THE COURT *is of the opinion and finds and holds that the writ issued out of the Criminal Court of Cook County, Illinois, whereunder Relator Roger Touhy is held for the period of ninety-nine years for the crime of kidnaping for ransom is void because issued on a judgment of that court which is void because the proceedings in that court antecedent to said judgment and said judgment were violative of the Due Process of Law Clause of the Fourteenth Amendment of the Constitution of the United States in that said judgment was procured by means of the use of testimony known by the prosecuting officers to be perjured and because the Relator was deprived in a capital case of the effective assistance of counsel devoted exclusively to protection of Relator's interests and compelled against his will and over his protests to accept the services of counsel who was compelled to serve adverse interests.*

Judge John P. Barnes
United States District Court
Northern District of Illinois

August 9, 1954

The Sharpest Thief
in Stateville

The best thief I ever knew, in or out of prison, was Gene O'Connor. He was doing his stealing when I first knew him in Illinois' biggest and toughest penitentiary, Stateville, near Joliet. A wheelbarrow was all the thievery equipment he had; that and a lot of good will.

O'Connor was a little man—smaller than I am, which is five feet six inches. He had an engaging grin and a disarming manner, and he was thinking all the time. Escaping was what he thought about mostly.

He was on a prison yard detail, which gave him the run of the joint. He buzzed in and out of the storerooms, the shops, the kitchen and the cell houses like a fly through a window with the screen left out.

I was working in the kitchen as a steward and clerk, and he would come around to mooch a cup of coffee, an apple, a handful of raisins or whatever he could glom. He hinted about escaping, but I didn't pay much heed. There were 3,000 cons in Stateville, and all of them had crazy ideas about going over the wall.

"You're too busy stealing in here to take time to escape,"

I told O'Connor. "You're doing better in stir than you could on the outside."

Two or three times a week I would see him pushing his wheelbarrow across the yard toward one or another of the guard towers. He would be trundling a quarter of beef, steaks, slabs of bacon, a 100-pound sack of sugar, or bags of coffee.

He stole the stuff out of the storehouses and peddled it to the guards in the towers.

Those towers are perched on top of the prison wall, which is 33 feet high, of solid concrete and steel, and nine feet thick at the base. Each guard up there has a cubicle to sit in, with windows looking down on the yard and a catwalk for exercise along the top of the wall.

The only square way to reach a tower is by an enclosed stairway on the *outside* of the wall with a solid door kept locked at the bottom.

When O'Connor reached the inside base of the wall at one of the towers, he would call up to the man on duty. The screw would lower a rope and Gene would tie on the loot for the trip. Up would go beef, coffee, bacon or sugar.

The tower screws dropped a dollar or two for Gene now and then, or mailed letters to his outside connections for him. But mostly he was making friends and building up good will.

The year was 1942 and the guards were old parties brought in to replace younger men who left for the armed services or for big-paying jobs in war plants. They probably never understood what a hell of a chance they were taking with O'Connor. The damnedest prison break that ever happened at Stateville was in the making.

Gene kept giving me reports about the jolly, larcenous friends he was making in the towers, and the "influence" he was building up. Wartime rationing was on and the guards were getting big money—considering the starvation wages paid in all prisons—by selling O'Connor's meats and groceries in the Joliet and Chicago black markets.

"One old character up there is treating me like a son," O'Connor told me. "I said to him this morning that I was coming up to visit him some day. He told me to come right ahead and bring my friends. He said he never shot anybody in his life and he wasn't aiming to start now."

I didn't want to know about such things and I told O'Connor so. Convicts have a saying that goes: "If three guys know a secret, that makes four, counting the warden." I didn't relish getting a rap as one of the three guys who got word to the fourth.

Anyway, O'Connor kept on stealing everything that wasn't nailed down, and some things that were. He got away with it because we had a dull warden and a lot of new guards. And he kept needling me to throw in with him on the escape. I was a good candidate for a break, by his standards.

First and foremost, I was under a sentence of 99 years. I would have to serve a third of it, or 33 years, before even being allowed to apply for parole. I had a minimum of 25 years left to go before parole, and I didn't want to stay alive that long in prison—even if I could. So what did I have to lose by going over the wall—or getting killed trying?

Also, I had been railroaded to prison. I was innocent. I had been convicted of a fake kidnaping that never happened. I had been sworn into prison on false testimony. I was a fall guy for the Chicago Capone mob.

I was rotting in prison on the falsified testimony of a swindler and ex-convict, John "Jake the Barber" Factor.

A distinguished former federal judge, the late John P. Barnes, subsequently ruled that the kidnaping was a hoax. I had been railroaded to prison under an unjust conviction. Even so, I should have continued to be deaf when Gene O'Connor talked to me. Instead, I was dumb—stupid dumb.

He came to me one day in early summer, and he was grinning with good news. I was in the kitchen and he was pushing that silly wheelbarrow. It was half full of sand. They were drilling a well in the yard and some of the sand from the hole was going into the bottoms of decorative tanks of goldfish in the big dining hall.

O'Connor sidled up to me and whispered: "We got

two guns into the joint last night, Rog. Old Percy Campbell carried 'em in wrapped up in the flag."

I was shocked and scared. Guns in a prison are like a firebug in a high octane gasoline refinery. I backed off from Gene and told him to keep the hell away from me.

There was no reason for me to be thinking seriously about a break at that time. I had something going for me, and I wasn't hopeless. Not even desperate. I figured I had some percentage on my side.

John P. Lally, a *Chicago Daily News* writer, had made up his mind that I was innocent. He was one of the first of many to realize the truth. He worked day and night on my case, digging up evidence. He had visited me a few months before with this message: "Rog, you never will spend another Christmas in this place."

One of Lally's *Daily News* co-workers, William Gorman, had written a long magazine story on my case. I had read the story. It was a good one, and it showed my innocence. When it was published, Gorman and I figured, public opinion wouldn't allow me to remain in prison any longer. I had the greatest possible confidence in the article.

After O'Connor dropped the word about the guns and left me, I stood in the kitchen doorway for quite a while. It was the first really fine day of early summer.

Acres and acres of flowers were blooming in the prison yard, where Warden Joseph E. Ragen had had them planted before the politicians got rid of him, temporarily —and I, Roger Touhy, got him back. In Joliet, down the road a piece, the pretty girls would be out in their sleeveless, summer dresses.

It was the kind of day when convicts, all 3,000 of us in Stateville, began to get restless. Nature makes guys that way in the spring, I guess.

I was thinking of my wife, Clara, the little brunette I had courted by telegraph when we both were youngsters working opposite ends of a Morse wire for Western Union in Chicago. Our two sons now were high-school age. They weren't having it easy, I knew. This was my eighth year away from them; a hell of a long eternity when you measure it on a penitentiary calendar.

As I stood there in the doorway, birds were singing from every direction, from the flower beds, the shrubbery, and from trees in the yard. There were thousands of birds in Stateville, and more every year because the cons fed and protected them.

We envied them, too, and sometimes our feelings got pretty close to hatred. A bird can go over those 33-foot walls faster than a tower screw's rifle can follow and be miles away in minutes. The cons protected the birds, and any hungry cat caught sneaking up on a robin or a bluejay could expect a kick in the tail in Stateville.

Still—with the temptations of birds, family, springtime and all—I had no thought of joining Gene O'Connor. I had faith in Gorman and his magazine story. I remembered the promise that I'd be out by Christmas.

All through the hot summer and into the fall, O'Connor needled me. The two guns were hidden somewhere in the prison, he kept saying. The break couldn't miss. Basil Banghart was going along. The old tower screw wouldn't shoot.

Gene's news bulletin about Banghart impressed me. Basil was a shrewd, fast-thinking con. Everybody called him "The Owl" for two reasons. He had big, slow-blinking eyes, and he was wise. He wouldn't go on a break unless the gamble was a good one. I had met him for the first time in Stateville.

The Owl had been sentenced to 99 years for the Factor kidnap fake, as I had. He was a resourceful and courageous man. He could run a locomotive or fly an airplane, and he was better than a green hand at opening up an armored mail truck or persuading a bank guard not to step on the robbery alarm button.

O'Connor was no slouch, either. He had beat Stateville twice on breaks. Once he got into the powerhouse at night, pulled a switch that doused every light in the prison, got a ladder from the carpenters' shop, and whisked over the wall in darkness. Another time he had himself nailed inside a furniture crate being shipped to Joliet, and rode through the gates in a truck.

"This is going to be a high-class break, with no dummies

allowed in the group," O'Connor assured me. Sometimes he talked like those Ivy League Madison Avenue boys who started getting into Stateville after they lowered the entrance requirements to include Phi Beta Kappa men. He also explained the exact way in which the two guns had been smuggled in.

Percy Campbell was an old trusty who pottered around outside the main gate, tending the flower beds, watering the grass, sweeping the walks and tidying up the visitors' parking area. He also had the job of carrying in the American flag at sundown every day.

The guns were left at the base of the flagpole one night and Percy carried them in next evening, wrapped up in Old Glory. He got a grand total of thirty bucks for this errand. Whatever his other talents might have been, Campbell was an amateur at collective bargaining. I guess Percy did it mainly for meanness. He had put in 17 years on a one-to-life term, and he should have been paroled long before.

I was an unwilling listener while Gene talked, but that was all. O'Connor wanted me along so bad that his urging got to be a nuisance. I had friends and political connections on the outside. I could raise money and arrange for hideouts, he figured. I just shook my head "no" and grinned.

And then the bad news began hitting me.

First it was Lally, of the *Chicago Daily News*. He died of cancer of the throat. Not only had I lost a good friend, but one of my last two legal chances to get out of Stateville was gone. I had some outside people send flowers to John's funeral. That was all I could do.

John died without ever telling anybody what evidence he had found: why he was so certain I never would spend another Christmas in prison. He wanted his story to be exclusive and, like any good newspaperman, he kept buttoned up.

Chance No. 2 blew up when Gorman came to see me. I knew at once that something had gone wrong. He was carrying a large brown envelope, and his face was long. "I'd rather be kicked all the way back to Chicago than tell you this, Rog," he said. He dumped the contents of the envelope in front of me. Magazine rejection slips, dozens of them.

"No magazine will take the story," Gorman said. I read a few of the slips. Some of the editors wrote that they were interested only in articles with a war angle. Others said that the story of my doublecross was too fantastic, that readers wouldn't believe it. One editor commented coldly that all prison inmates claimed to be innocent and that most of them were trying to get their alibis into print.

I mumbled my thanks to Gorman for all of his wasted work. I stumbled back to my cell. I was seeing through a sort of haze. My last hope was gone. The United States Supreme Court earlier had turned me down for a hearing. I wasn't a man any more. I was a dead thing.

I stayed awake until dawn in my cell, thinking. I was without hope. I was buried alive in prison and I would die there. I couldn't see a light ahead anywhere. Nothing but darkness and loneliness and desperation.

The world had forgotten me, after eight years. I was a nothing. Well, there was one way I could focus public attention on my misery. I could escape. I would be caught, of course, but the break would show my terrible situation.

What cockeyed thinking that was. The only thing I could do by going over the wall would be to destroy almost every chance I might have for decent justice at some future time. But a man in my spot isn't reasonable, of course.

My mental attitude was a mess, I later came to realize.

I hadn't seen my wife, Clara, for four years, but I couldn't forget her last visit. It had been an ordeal rather than the usual delight. She had worn a white hat and gloves and a dark tailored suit, I remembered. It might be a long time before I saw her again, and maybe never.

At that time, in 1938, I had been disconsolate. I had figured that I couldn't be a drag on Clara and our two sons for all of their lives. So I had given her a direct order for the first time in our 18 years of marriage:

"Take all the money you can raise and go to Florida. Change your name. Take the kids with you, of course.

Start them out in a new school down there under new names. This is something you must do.

"I'll be in prison for a long time. I want you to make a fresh start for all of us in Florida."

I gave her the names of a couple of people she could trust completely in Chicago and in Miami. They would help her get started in this new life. I would send word to her and the boys through the contacts, and get messages from her.

Her eyes filled with tears, but she didn't cry and she didn't ask a lot of questions, either. Giving her that order was the most difficult thing I ever did. But it had to be done, I thought.

She had only one question to ask as she sat across the long table in the visiting room, forbidden by the rules to so much as reach across and touch my hand for a goodbye. "When should the boys and I leave for Florida?" she wanted to know. I told her right away, the next day, if it was possible.

The visit was over, and when I looked back from the door, she was staring at me. I think she was crying, but somehow she put on a smile.

Anyway, after my last hope collapsed in 1942, I decided to throw in on the escape. I was thankful then that Clara and the boys were out of the way, living in obscurity under the name of Turner in the Florida town of Deland.

Once I was over the wall, or killed trying to get there, the publicity would be monstrous, with newspaper headlines the size of boxcars. I didn't want my wife and kids hounded by the police or the FBI. I wouldn't be able to see my family, anyway. They would be watched, if the law could find them. Their mail and telephone would be checked. I would have to avoid them like yellow fever wherever they were—Chicago or Florida or the other side of the world.

After making up my mind to go AWOL, I passed Gene O'Connor in the yard and told him: "I'm going with you."

He didn't seem a bit surprised then, or later, in the kitchen, when he gave me a rundown on the program. He pointed to one of the guard towers and said that was where we would go over the wall. He set the time for one p.m. on October sixth.

"The screw up there is the old guy who says he won't shoot anybody," Gene said. "I'll promise him the day before the break to bring him some meat and groceries. That way he'll be sure to have his car beside the wall outside, to take home the stuff. We're using his car."

O'Connor explained exactly what I had to do, and it didn't sound too tough. But not easy, either.

October sixth was three days away, the longest three days I ever lived. I ate and pretended to sleep and acted like I was interested in the radio broadcasts. And all the time the only thing on my mind was how a rifle bullet from one of the guard towers would feel drilling into my back.

Then, with only ten minutes notice, O'Connor called everything off for another three days. The new date, October ninth, was the one he had in mind all along. I had jittered for three days for nothing.

I asked him the reason for the fake date and time, and he explained. It had been a pretty clever idea, at that—he had been testing the security of the plan.

"Suppose somebody had stooled to the warden that the break was coming off on the sixth," he said. "The warden would have cancelled all days off for the screws, and I would know he was wise. Then I could have nosed around, found out who talked too much, dealt him out of the break and made a scheme to use the guns later in some other way."

Gene could have been a great commanding general or an international spy, if he hadn't preferred being a thief.

I asked him then for the first time who was going on the break and he told me—Banghart, Eddie Darlak, Martlick Nelson, Ed Stewart and St. Clair McInerney, plus the two of us. Ours were names that were to hit the headlines for nearly three months.

Eddie Darlak was a Chicago man doing 199 years for murder in a cop-killing conviction. I knew him slightly. He had to go with us, Gene said, because his brother had delivered the guns to the flagpole. That sounded okay;

and I was in favor of "The Owl" being with us, of course.

Nelson, Stewart and McInerney meant nothing to me, but I might have seen them around Stateville. It was impossible to know 3,000 men, all dressed the same way, and without identifying marks such as mustaches, or preferences in neckties.

A short time after lunch on the big day, I was standing at the back door of the kitchen, following out Gene's plan. A truck came rolling along on the daily round, picking up garbage to be hauled to the prison hog farm outside the wall. I was trembling like a kid on the way to the woodshed for a whipping.

I walked up beside the driver and asked him for the truck keys. He looked at me like I was crazy—and he wasn't far wrong. "Give me the goddam keys," I told him, and it surprised me to hear my voice and realize I was yelling. He pointed to the truck's instrument panel; the keys were hanging from the ignition switch. I pushed and pulled him out of the cab.

The driver said later that I waved a big scissors from the tailor shop at him. That wasn't true, but I didn't blame him for saying it. He might have got hooked on a phony aiding-and-abetting-to-escape charge if he hadn't told a real good story.

I drove the truck along, slowly and carefully, getting the feel of driving after eight years. There was a steel mesh cyclone fence running across that part of the yard and I had to get through a gate where a con was on duty.

After about 75 yards, I approached the gate and beeped the horn. The gate swung open at once. The inmate waved me on and closed the gate. To him, this was just the garbage truck making a routine run.

I stepped on the gas a little. Straight ahead of me was the mechanical store, a building with a vehicle ramp leading down under it. The prison coal supply and a lot of equipment was there. I made a U-turn and backed the truck down the ramp.

O'Connor, Banghart, Darlak and the other three were waiting for me. So, it seemed to me at first, was about half the rest of Stateville's population, although there really were only about 300 cons crowded around.

Two of our guys—Darlak and Banghart, I think— were holding guns, and they had a complication. A guard and a staff lieutenant were down in that passageway under the building. They were standing with their hands at their sides and their faces were white. We were no more scared than they were, really, and for good reason: many a guard held as a hostage has been killed in a prison break.

Somebody handed me one of the guns, a .45. The others loaded a heavy ladder in two extension sections onto the back of the truck. We put the lieutenant and the guard on top to act as ballast and hold down the ladders. I climbed up with them.

Stewart was behind the wheel of the truck and I heard the starter grind a couple of times. The engine didn't start. I jumped off the back of the truck and took Stewart's place. It still wouldn't turn over and I hollered: "The goddam thing is stuck on center! Push it, you guys."

Those convicts down there with us grabbed the truck in every place there was a handhold. They pushed it and rocked it, anxious to help. The motor came off dead center and started at last with a roar.

I drove up the runway and aimed the truck at the tower where the old father-and-son screw was on duty. It seemed to me that we were going 90 miles an hour, bucketing across the yard. The convicts who had helped start the truck cheered and waved to us. Two 50-gallon oil drums, for garbage, were on the truck. I hit a big bump and those drums shot out across the yard like depth charges from a Navy destroyer. It was a crazy trip, and things were going to get crazier.

Chapter 2

Over the Wall

I skidded the truck to a stop near the wall tower. We unloaded the ladder, and then things went comical. Nobody knew how to fit the two extension lengths together. Each guy tried to do it in a different way at the same time, with everybody swearing at each other.

Another guard lieutenant came ambling up. He seemed upset, but not much. "You sonsabitches," he said, "don't you know them tower windows ain't supposed to be washed from the inside?" I started laughing so hard I could hardly hold the .45 on him.

He finally saw the gun. His mouth fell open and he went over and stood with the other lieutenant and guard. One of the screws kept saying, over and over: "Let 'em go. Don't interfere. They'll kill us for sure."

The three of them were helpless against us. Guards and officers went unarmed, except for blackjacks and clubs, inside Stateville. They used to have weapons, but the state lost too many guns that way, with the cons taking them away from the screws.

But the old lad up in the tower had plenty of firepower,

and I got to thinking about him. The way we were flubbing around with the ladder might give him brave ideas. He might get hurt and so might we, which I didn't want.

He was standing over to one side of the tower at the end of the walkway, doing nothing. He wasn't holding a gun, but he didn't have far to reach for one.

I decided a little noise might make things safer for everybody, including him. So I fired two shots and knocked out the glass of a window at the opposite end of the tower. He raised his hands and hollered that he was going to behave.

We got the ladder in place, at last, and I scrambled up with the .45. The other six men in the escape party followed, with the two lieutenants and the guard spaced in between us. With the screws along, we had less danger of drawing fire, although maybe that precaution wasn't needed.

Not a shot came from any other tower. Either the screws weren't looking, or else they were remembering all those meats and groceries from O'Connor's wheelbarrows.

It was pretty crowded when all of us got to the tower house, which was only a cubicle. The guard handed over his keys to his sonny boy, Gene, and croaked at him: "Please don't take me with you. I'm an old man." A couple of other guys got his weapons—a 30.30 rifle and an automatic handgun.

On the floor of the tower were packages of meat and other stolen stuff that O'Connor had delivered a few hours before. The tower man's Ford sedan was standing on the roadway outside the wall waiting to haul the loot home— but now the script was changed. It was going to carry us far, far away, if our luck held.

The grandpappy guard had a scratch on his face, from flying glass, I guess. He sure as hell wasn't shot, as some people tried to claim later.

The next thing that happened all but panicked me. Gene gave the ladder a kick and it clattered down to the ground inside the wall. I started to yell that now we were trapped in the tower. Without the ladder, we could break our legs or necks dropping that 33 feet to the outside.

Sure, there was a stairway leading down, but the door

at the bottom would be locked, and there was a keyhole only on the outside. But O'Connor had covered that angle, too. "Thorough" was his middle name that day.

He dropped his grocery delivery rope over the side and somebody—Nelson, as I remember—shinnied down it. Then O'Connor dropped him a key, taken from the old guard, to the door below.

Some one of the guys tore the tower telephone out by the roots. That would delay the alarm getting to the warden's office and from there to the Illinois Highway Patrol. Then we tumbled down the stairs, locked the door behind us and piled into the guard's Ford.

I looked at my watch. It had been just 17 minutes since I took the garbage truck away from the driver—but it seemed like it'd been some time back in my childhood.

Banghart gunned our getaway car, and I looked back. The two lieutenants and two guards were gazing after us from the wall. They couldn't do a thing except yell for help. We had the tower arsenal, plus the two pistols that Darlak's brother had delivered to the flagpole.

We were on Highway 66 for a while, but mostly we hit the country side roads. After a while we pulled into a patch of woods to talk things over.

"Where do we go from here?" I asked. "Where's the hideout?"

There was a long silence. I began feeling silly, then alarmed and finally, downright mad. The situation was obvious—and awful.

We didn't have any place to go. There wasn't any hideout. O'Connor, the master mind, hadn't set up even one single goddam contact to help us. We were in a mess.

We had just pulled off one of the slickest prison breaks in history. And now we were as unprotected as a stranger turned loose at noon without clothes in downtown Chicago.

Seven of us were jammed into a small car. All of us were wearing prison uniforms. We had guns, but what good would they be against the army of cops who soon would be looking for us? What a fugitive needs is a place to hide, not firepower.

I had taken it for granted that O'Connor had made

arrangements, at least for a few days, on the outside. He hadn't. Well, there was no sense in bellyaching. We took stock. Together we had $120, mostly money that Gene had picked up from his meat-and-grocery route.

What we needed was darkness, and it was hours away. In the meantime, we had to keep moving. The news would be on the radio soon, and every farmer or small town rube in Illinois would be phoning the cops upon seeing a parked car with a lot of guys in it.

So we drove. We kept to the dirt and gravel roads, driving carefully and slowly. When we met a car, some of us crouched down so we wouldn't seem to be so overcrowded.

The car had no radio so we couldn't hear the news about ourselves. But one thing was good. The Ford had a full gas tank, so we didn't need a filling station stop. Nature's demands we handled in the trees and bushes. Everything was aimless. I remember noticing that we passed through one village four times. The name of the place was Barkley, and I got mighty weary of it.

When darkness hit, we pulled into a Forest Preserve grove near Lombard, a suburb to the west of Chicago. We had driven more than 150 miles and we still weren't anyplace.

We did some scrounging and one of the guys got into a garage at the rear of a house. He came back with a tattered suit jacket and an old raincoat. The clothes fit Banghart pretty well, so he wore them into a grocery store to shop. We ate bread, cheese and cold meat, washed down with milk. It felt fine to eat without a gun pointed at you from a dining-hall tower. "You should have brought a side of prison beef along," Darlak told O'Connor, "and we could have had a barbecue."

We had to have help, but where to try for it was a terrible problem.

The prison had complete lists, with addresses, of our relatives, of visitors we had had at Stateville, of people we had corresponded with. They would be watched, with taps on their telephones. Former cell mates and friends on parole would be covered like a floor with wall-to-wall carpeting. Anybody who did help us could be prosecuted for harboring criminal fugitives.

There was one possibility among all the hundreds of people I knew in Chicago. He was a legitimate business-man and he had been my friend since we were boys. He never had been in trouble with the law, and there was nothing kinky in his background. But, most important, we never had communicated when I was in Stateville, so the prison had no line on him. I felt sure he would help us if we could get to him.

The Owl, wearing the tattered jacket and old raincoat, rode a bus into Chicago. I gave him instructions on how to telephone the man I had in mind. I couldn't make the trip because the clothes from the garage were acres too big for me.

The rest of us waited through the night. It was bitter cold, even for October in the Chicago area. We couldn't take a chance on lighting a fire. "If Banghart doesn't score," McInerney said, "we might as well go back to the main gate at Stateville and apply for readmittance."

But The Owl didn't fail us, and neither did my friend. Soon after dawn Banghart was back. He was driving a car and carrying $500, both loaned to him for me by the Chicago businessman. And in the car were pants, jackets, shirts and neckties—nobody ever expects to see a necktie on a con—enough so we all got a good enough fit.

We dressed and were ready to take off for Chicago in the borrowed car. But Gene got to feeling sorry for the old tower guard and his Ford sedan. If we left the Ford in the grove, O'Connor said, it might not be found for a long time. What would the screw do for transportation?

"I'll drive the car up on the main drag of Lombard and park it there," our master-mind said. "That way it will be spotted in a couple of days. You follow me and pick me up."

In a couple of days, it would be spotted, he said! Less than a couple of minutes! The license numbers of that Ford had been going out over the police radio every ten minutes all night long. Every cop in the Midwest was looking for it, slavering frothily for a reward and dreaming of becoming a hero. That car was hotter than a jet plane's after-burner.

We had no more than turned the corner after O'Connor parked the guard's heap and rejoined us when there came the big "w-o-o-o—woooo" of a police car siren. A suburban squad had spotted the license. But by that time we were out of sight.

I turned on the radio in the new car and got the police wavelength. The broadcasts made us feel real good. We had been reported seen in St. Louis, Indianapolis, Kansas City, Peoria, and 14 different places in Chicago. The cops had us pinpointed just about everyplace in the Midwest except where we really were.

All the way into Chicago we didn't see so much as one police car. If the police had us blocked off, as the radio kept on saying, then somebody had left a great big hole in the roadblock.

"I got more good news for you," Banghart said, as we turned in on Ogden Avenue, the diagonal street leading from Joliet and the Chicago Midway Airport into the Loop. "Rog's friend has lined us up for an apartment. We can move in right away."

We went there, and what a miserable dump it was. A basement flat near 13th and Damen. I knew the neighborhood like a penitentiary screw knows his stool pigeons. I had played stickball in the streets out there as a kid, pestered the hurdy-gurdy man, and opened the fire hydrants for cooling off on those 100-degree August days.

We went into the apartment. Warden Ragen wouldn't allow a pig from the Stateville farm to set one cloven hoof in the place. The walls were sweating with dampness. The kitchen crackled everywhere we stepped. Roaches were a carpet on the floor.

And the rats! They were as big as tiger cubs and twice as nasty. Banghart claimed that one of them—a stallion rat, he said—stood up on his hind legs, doubled up one fist, pulled a switchblade knife in the other and told him, with the authority of a Stateville guard captain: "Get outa here, you bastard, and take your friends with you.

I've been boss of this cellar for 20 years and you ain't going to muscle in on me."

I believed The Owl. And the rat, too. But we had nowhere else to go. We stayed, after Banghart said: "We'll plug up the holes in the floors and the walls with steel wool, and let the goddam rats tear out their claws and teeth trying to burrow through." A great strategist, Banghart was—except when it came to staying out of prison.

The landlord of the building was an elderly man who lived in a cottage at the rear. We told him we were from downstate Illinois, in Chicago to go to work in a war plant. He took $65 for a month's rent and told us where we could buy cheap furniture in a second-hand store somewhere on Madison Street.

We got in some groceries and, for the first time, we saw the newspapers, all editions of them since the previous afternoon. Our escape was the biggest news anywhere in the world, so far as Chicago was concerned. We had pushed the war off page one. The big, screaming headlines would make you think we had murdered half the guards in Stateville.

The Owl and I got the biggest play, because we had been in the headlines for our conviction in the fake Jake the Barber Factor kidnaping. Our pictures were plastered all over the papers, but they were eight years old or more and we had aged a lot in prison. O'Connor killed my optimism along that line by saying:

"Sure, you guys are older, but you're just as homely, if not more so. Any cop could recognize you from the photos, and don't forget there'll be rewards out for all of us soon."

In its very first story of the break, one of the papers had dug up the tag of "Terrible" Touhy for me. That fitted me like calling Calvin Coolidge an anarchist.

The only conviction I ever had in my life, up to the time of the Factor frameup, was for parking my car too close to a fireplug. And now the papers were speculating on how soon I would lead my "mob of terrorists" into robbing a bank or kidnaping somebody.

Out in California, on a fancy estate built out of swindling people, Jake the Barber was bleating like a lost lamb and trying to look twice as innocent. He was scared as hell that Banghart and I would kill him, he said, and the FBI was guarding him. Huh! I wouldn't *spit* in his direction, much less touch him.

Factor then was under indictment, but on bond, for swindling Catholic priests in another of his fancy con games. He later served a prison term in the case, too.

My silly idea of bringing my case before the public for justice was rebounding in the newspapers like a screw's club off a convict's head. Instead of getting fair treatment, I was being crucified. There wasn't one mention in any of the papers that day that I might be innocent—although there were plenty of working reporters, even then, who believed in me.

Later there was a story by Bill Gorman in the *Daily News,* saying there probably had been no kidnaping, but nobody seemed to pay much heed.

I gave up reading and went for a walk. It was my first jaunt around Chicago since getting free. I looked at the show window displays, dropped in at a couple of joints for a beer and saw a movie. The thing I enjoyed most was looking at the people, free people.

Heading back toward the apartment, I went into a Pixley & Ehler's Restaurant, one of a cafeteria chain specializing in baked beans. I got a crock of beans, Boston brown bread and coffee at the counter, went to a table, and started to eat. But I didn't relish the beans for long.

In the door came three of the biggest, toughest-looking coppers I ever saw. I froze. There wasn't any back door. I was like a mouse in the wainscoting with a cat plonked at the only exit.

The cops picked out their food and brought it to the table next to mine. One of them sat sipping coffee and looking at the *Chicago Times,* a tabloid. My picture covered practically all the front page. He squinted at the photo for a while.

"This guy Touhy would be a fine pinch," he said, and lit into his grub. He could have reached out and grabbed me almost as easily as he picked up his coffee cup.

I finished my food, paid my check and left. A fine sense

of well-being hit me. I wasn't scared any more, and I wouldn't be again. The experience had shaken the hell out of me, but, at the same time, it had given me back my courage.

Now, I knew, I really was free. Nobody knows freedom, of course, if he has fear, but I had never thought of that before.

Back at the apartment, things weren't good. McInerney, Nelson and Stewart had brought in whiskey and they were getting drunk and noisy. They were talking about going out to look for women. I told them to quiet down and act careful.

McInerney got mean and sneering. "Big shot, eh?" he said. "Think you're going to run everything, do you?"

I put it on the line for them. Noise, whiskey and women would bring trouble. Not only for them, but for me, too, if I was living with them.

It was my money, part of the $500 I had borrowed, that they were drinking up. I wasn't being tough, but unless they stopped behaving like reform-school sophomores I was moving out.

I went to bed after that, but the next day I gave our situation a lot of thought. I wasn't going to gamble on going back to Stateville on a drunk-and-disorderly pickup. Anyway, living with six other convicts in a small apartment was too much like prison for me. I wanted solitude: a life of my own without unnecessary danger.

For another thing, the men who escaped with me still had the guns we brought from the penitentiary. Suppose a cop came nosing around the apartment and one of the guys let loose with a pistol. A lot of people could get killed, and I might be one of them.

So I set up a life for myself. I was going to stay outside the wall just as long as I could. I would enjoy my freedom in my own way. I wouldn't carry a gun, and, when the time came, as it must for every fugitive, I would give up. I wasn't going to have anything to do with any shooting.

I found a furnished flat behind a bank building at Madison and Ogden on the West Side. It was small, and the toilet-bath was a share-it proposition down the hall. But the joint had two exits, which was essential to sound sleep for me. And the location gave me a boot. My, how those bankers would have shook if they knew "Terrible" Touhy was living only a few feet from their building!

When I got back to the basement apartment that evening, a drunken argument was going on. McInerney wanted to fight. I jollied him along and then said, in a nice way, that I was leaving for a place of my own. It was only fair to them that I move out, I told them.

The newspapers were running pictures of me every day. I was hot as a depot stove. If I got caught, so would the rest of them if they were living with me.

I didn't really believe that guff, but it got me out of the basement without a fight. I made a deal with Banghart for contacts. To hell with the rest of them.

For a couple of days, I just sat around my new place, admiring the loneliness. It was terrific not to have some con snoring or whimpering or yelling in his sleep in the same cell, or the next one. And no guard peering through the door with a stool pigeon pencil in his hand. The greatest pleasure in life is to be unregimented, your own boss. Prison teaches you that—though it isn't the easiest way to learn it.

I needed a substantial bankroll, just in case I had to pay off a bribe or get out of Chicago. My best source was my brother, Eddie. He owned a roadhouse, Eddie's Wonder Bar, near the State Fair Grounds outside of Madison, Wisconsin.

I had put up the money for the place, and Eddie would come up with any reasonable amount I needed.

But making a meet with him was almost as tricky as getting out of Stateville. The FBI would be sticking as close to him as hogs to a swill barrel. His phones would be tapped. If he got caught with me, it would be a harboring rap for him.

So I called my friend, the businessman who had loaned me the car and the $500. We met in mid-afternoon at the Morrison Hotel bar and had a drink at a quiet table. I explained what I wanted and he set me up with a guy. I'll call him Simpson, but that wasn't his name.

Simpson was an ex-convict, and eager to pick up a quick buck. I explained what I wanted and even drew a map for him.

He drove up across the state line to Wisconsin, parked his car in downtown Madison so his license wouldn't get spotted and took a bus out to my brother Eddie's place. I figured I needed $1,500, but Eddie said to make it $2,500. He would get it from the bank next day and send it by messenger to Chicago.

Simpson came back to Chicago and he was itchy about the set-up in Wisconsin.

"There are a lot of guys acting like surveyors around your brother's club," he said. "They got spyglasses set up on tripods so as to get a fix if you try sneaking up to the joint across the fields or through the fairgrounds.

"They're FBI men. They hang around Eddie's bar and peek through the windows of his living quarters at night. I told him to have your messenger make damn sure he isn't tailed when he comes to Chicago."

I got the $2,500 next day. An ex-convict working at the Wisconsin Fair Grounds brought it to me at my apartment, and he wouldn't take a dime for his trouble. Eddie was paying him, he said.

He also brought word that Eddie wanted to fix me up with a hideout in Arizona. To hell with that, I said. I wasn't going to bury myself in some hole in the desert. I was staying in Chicago.

I had plenty of money now and things should go better. But a lot of problems and troubles were ahead.

Chapter 3

82 Days AWOL

A convict on the lam absolutely must have a set of identification papers. A Social Security card. A driver's
license. And—back in 1942, when I was loose—a draft
card.

With such papers, a man usually can talk himself out
of a routine arrest. Without them, he is up against a trip
to a police station—with identification by fingerprinting—
for any trifling thing the cops may ask about.

I was living in a semi-Skid Row section of Chicago, los-
ing myself among thousands of men trying to be forgotten
for reasons of wife-trouble, personal disgrace, a permanent
knockout by booze, or just plain shiftlessness.

This jungle of men gave me a fine protective coloring,
but there were drawbacks. The cops might collar a man
—me, for instance—at any time for a few questions. The
FBI was looking for draft dodgers and the military authorities for wartime deserters.

Also, I needed a car to get around, and passing a traffic
sign could mean a return ticket to Stateville unless I had a
driver's license.

I hit on the deal that a pickpocket could fix me up, and

I knew where to find one. He was a skinny little guy, and I had seen him get run out of a Monroe Street joint by a saloonkeeper who hollered at him: "Get out of here, Slim, and stay out. You've lifted your last wallet off my customers."

I watched for this character and saw him about a week later as he waited for a streetcar. When I asked for a word with him, he held his arms out from his sides and said: "Okay, officer, give me the frisk. I'm clean. Haven't made a touch in months."

It took a little talking to persuade him that I wasn't a detective, and then we went into a little restaurant for coffee. I told him a tale—one he obviously didn't swallow —that I had walked out on my wife and that I needed driver's license, Social Security and draft registration cards.

He wanted to know how much, and I offered $100, if the cards fit me on age and general description. He wanted $500 and we settled at $200. "Okay, meet me here Friday at the same time," he said, and skittered out to the street.

I met him that Friday and he had a set of cards that came close to me on description. But I wasn't quite satisfied, and he aimed to please. Before we finished dickering I had examined 18 sets—and finally I had myself a tailor-made fit.

My name was Jackson. I was five feet six inches tall, weighed 160, had gray eyes and wavy hair. I was 4-F in the draft for physical reasons and I had a job in a war plant. My new papers said so, and who was I to argue?

As more camouflage, I bought a round tin badge in a novelty store. It said "Inspector" and looked like the identity discs issued to some war workers. I wore this thing pinned to my shirt.

Cons in Stateville, the screws and some of my visitors often asked me later how I dodged the law on the outside. The truth is that I didn't dodge. I lived like hundreds of other men, only they were working stiffs and I was a fugitive.

I wore good enough clothes, but nothing gaudy. My hat came down well on my forehead. I wore glasses, issued to me in prison, and the old photographs of me in the paper showed me without them. If that adds up to a disguise, I'm Mary Margaret McBride in a cell.

My new papers made it easy for me to buy a cheap used car. I drove around Chicago and out into the country through the Forest Preserves. I saw movies, dozens of them. I drank nothing more than a beer or two now and then, but a few bartenders became friendly.

Coming out of the Tivoli Theater late one afternoon, I had one of my biggest starts. Under the bright lights of the marquee, I met two ex-cons from Stateville. They whooped at me, shook my hand, clapped me on the back and wanted me to go on a celebration.

I got away from there fast. They were good guys, but one of them might take a pinch some day or get picked up up for parole violating. It might be too much of a temptation for him to talk himself out of trouble by telling where Roger Touhy was.

About six weeks passed and I never saw any of the guys who went over the wall with me. The Owl was the only one who knew where I lived. One evening he came calling. With him were Stewart and Nelson, and that didn't sit well with me. I didn't want those trouble makers to know where I was.

"Thanksgiving is coming up, Rog, and we all ought to be together," Banghart said. "We got two nice apartments out near Broadway and Wilson. Come out and stay with us, at least for the holiday."

It didn't sound too bad. Living like a hermit was getting dreary. There wasn't much point in it any longer, now that Stewart and Nelson knew my address. I packed up, went with them and moved into one of the apartments with Banghart and O'Conner.

No dice. On the second night, all seven of us were drinking beer and playing cards when a rumble started. Darlak wanted to move into the apartment where I was. I said no; that it was crowded enough with three of us. I insisted on a room by myself.

Nelson was a little drunk and got mean. I tried pacifying him and Stewart, who was pretty soggy, jumped in. I gave him a slap in the mouth and left. I had the telephone number of the flat, and I told Gene and The Owl: "I'll keep in touch with you, but if you ever again tell those other three bastards where I am, I'm through with all of you."

My next stop was a room with an old lady on Wood off Madison, back near the Skid Row belt again. I had a line on her because she had a son who did time in Stateville and now was in the can in another state up north. She didn't know me from the name on my Social Security card, but she took me in when I mentioned the son.

"Terrible" Touhy still made headlines in the papers. An armored car carrying a $20,000 candy company payroll got robbed out in the suburbs, and they blamed me and my gang of "escaped terrorists" for that one. In the next edition there was a story saying I had bribed my way to South America ten days earlier. I was reported seen all over Chicago—at times, in two places simultaneously.

The FBI was making things tighter for me all the time. I learned that when I went out to suburban Des Plaines one evening to look at the house with swimming pool, where I had lived with my wife and sons so many years ago.

I was feeling sloppy sentimental and I remembered that I had an old friend, a square, in the village of Cumberland nearby. I drove over there and rang his bell. He opened the door, looked at me, winked and did an acting job that would have won laurels on Broadway. "Yes, sir?" he said, in the tone people have for door-to-door salesmen. "What can I do for you?"

I looked past him into the living room. Two young guys in bankers' gray suits and Arrow collars were sitting there with briefcases beside their chairs. FBI agents, sure as J. Edgar Hoover has jowls.

It was my cue, and I blabbered something about hearing he was in the market for a good used car. My friend said, "No, thank you," and shut the door in my face. I got out to the street and around the corner to where my car was parked.

The federals took a couple of minutes to get the polite looks off their faces, and then took out after me. I was long gone, threading my car through alleys and side-streets, but I had learned something. The FBI was everywhere.

Another time I pulled into a filling station at North and Damen Avenues for gas. A car was at the next pump and the driver—a city cop in uniform and wearing a gun—was standing beside it.

He came walking toward me, and I was sort of mesmerized. He didn't reach for his gun, but I was willing to give up. He leaned in the open window of my car. He grinned and I flinched. Then came the goddamnedest one-way conversation I ever heard:

"Hello, Mr. Touhy. I was wondering if I'd run into you. I'd like to repay a big favor. When you were running beer, back in '29, I was in an accident and laid up in the hospital. Things were tough for my wife and kids, until you put me on your payroll.

"Can I help you now? Need any money?"

I couldn't speak, but I managed to shake my head. He reached out a big paw and shook my hand. The station attendant finished filling my tank, and the policeman paid him for me—which made the attendant almost as dumfounded as I was. Quite a few Chicago cops collect easy; but they usually pay under protest, I had learned years before.

It was all I could do to squeak out a "thanks" to my benefactor. He told me to phone him any time I needed anything, and gave me the number of his district station. I drove away.

I sat in my room that night and wondered. If that copper had arrested me, I wouldn't have given him a bit of trouble. I didn't have a gun and I wouldn't have resisted. Pinching me would have gotten him a promotion and the award of hero cop of the year, probably. But he had remembered a favor. And I hadn't even remembered the guy, say nothing of the favor!

The time was getting close for capture. The friendly cop and those FBI men in my friend's home in Cumberland village proved that. I was covered too tight to stay on the streets for long. But what was the difference? Capture had to be sometime.

I had made my big protest against false imprisonment. My escape should get a lot of people wondering whether I really might be innocent. No longer would I be a man buried alive. After my capture, the newspapers would print my side of the story. That was the silliest hope I ever had!

When the law moved in on me, I would come out with my hands up. I would go back to prison, but I wouldn't betray the people who had helped me and I wouldn't squeal on the other six who went over the wall with me.

I had telephoned Banghart a few times in their hideaway, but that didn't seem smart. Some day the FBI might be there, waiting for the phone to ring after catching or killing the others. They would trace my call and I would be next.

So I set up a meet with Banghart—a strange meet for two of the most wanted men in America. It was St. Charles Roman Catholic Church at 12th and Cypress, where I had received my first communion.

Every Tuesday evening at six o'clock, the bell tolled in the steeple at St. Charles. It was a call to confession for people of the parish, an unusual custom for that day of the week, I guess. I would be walking up the steps as the bell started clanging.

In the church would be women with shawls over their heads. People were too poor in that neighborhood for the womenfolk to buy hats. They would be praying and going to confession in order to take communion next day for their dead or for sons, sweethearts or husbands in the war. I had strayed away from religion a long, long time ago, but the holiness of the place still got me.

I would sit in a vacant pew. Banghart would slip in beside me and we would whisper, exchanging word on whether any of us needed help. Then we would leave, separately. If The Owl was more than five minutes late, I would leave.

Banghart, O'Connor, Darlak, McInerney, Nelson and

Stewart were getting along okay. They hadn't committed any crimes, The Owl said. All of them were getting help from relatives or friends. They were being discreet about women and liquor. Sometimes they worked at odd jobs for walking-around money.

"I don't think they'll ever catch us," The Owl said. But I didn't agree. Pitch a needle into the biggest haystack in the world, and it'll be found if enough people look for it long enough, I told him.

The Christmas season came along and I spent hours walking on State Street, looking in the windows. Christmas is always a lonely business in prison, but it was worse for me that year on the outside. I did manage to get a message through to my wife and kids in Florida, with a few gifts. I thought of visiting them, but that would be nuts. Even if I got away with it, which was unlikely, the tear of parting would be too much.

My old landlady had me in her living room on Christmas Eve to look at her tree. It was scrawny, with the lights flickering on and off, and she was sniffling about her son in prison. I got out of there.

Almost everybody knows the gag about "lonely as a whorehouse on Christmas Eve." Well, I lived it—in a sidestreet saloon, that is, listening to the Christmas carols on the radio and drinking beer for beer with a white-haired bartender.

The next day I went to the Empire Room in the Palmer House, got a table in a corner and ate a big dinner. I was halfway through the meal before I began to realize that the turkey didn't taste much better than it had at Stateville. Freedom was beginning to pall on me, I guess.

When I got home that evening, there was a holiday-wrapped package on my bureau. It was a necktie, a gift from the landlady. I had put a box of candy under her scrawny tree, and now she was paying off.

Every day I left my room early in the morning and took my car out of a garage on Adams Street. I would drive around or go to a movie or take long walks in the Forest Preserves. In the late afternoon, I would be back, like a working man finishing his day. The tin "inspector" badge on my shirt helped that fakery along.

And then I felt the roof creaking, as a hunted man gets to sense. It was going to fall in on me unless I moved fast.

I came home on a Tuesday afternoon and started for my room. The old lady heard me and called to me from the living room. She had three or four guests in there, having coffee and cake. I went in and she introduced me by my phony name. "This man is a friend of my son," she said. "I want him to have refreshments with us. He gave me such a nice box of chocolates for Christmas."

The lights were bright. Across the room I saw a dried-up looking guy peering at me. I knew he had me made. He was almost drooling at the chops over his fat reward in the near future. I went around the room, deadpan as Buster Keaton, shaking hands. The character I suspected had a moist, hot hand. Excitement? Anticipation? Greed for reward? Anxiety to become a hero by stooling on "Terrible" Touhy?

I got the hell out of there fast, after mumbling excuses. In my room, I packed up and used a towel to wipe every surface that might hold a fingerprint. The old lady—she was probably 75—didn't deserve a harboring rap. Then I back-doored the joint.

My hunch was right, too. A Chicago copper, John Nolan, told me after my capture that a telephone stoolie had called the police, left his name, and squealed that Roger Touhy was hanging around Wood and Madison, where I had been living. He wanted a reward, the stoolie said. But I foxed him.

Leaving the old lady's house, I ran to my garage on Adams, tossed my suitcase into my car and headed for St. Charles Church. I dashed up the steps—almost falling on the ice—and got inside. The bell stopped tolling just as I pulled open the heavy doors.

Banghart was sitting in a pew. The candlelight flickering on his widow's peak, his big eyes and his beakish nose, made him look more like an owl than usual. I got next to him and whispered: "Basil, they got me made. I'm in bad trouble. No place to go."

"Never mind," Banghart said. "I got things all fixed up. Come on."

We left the church and sat in my car. The Owl explained. He and Darlak had a big apartment out on Kenmore Avenue, near Lawrence Avenue. Everything was as quiet and well behaved as an 82-year-old spinster with a displaced cervical vertebra.

"Move in with us," he invited. "We don't have any guns, liquor or women around the place. Any playing we do, we get away from the neighborhood. O'Connor and McInerney have an apartment a few blocks from us."

Nelson and Stewart, he went on, had broken away from them. Probably left town, he said, and that news didn't exactly make a weeping ruin out of me. Those two guys were no assets to any of us.

We went out to the Kenmore flat and up the back stairway after I had parked about a block away. Darlak, always a good enough mope, was there. But the joint felt creepy to me, and I prowled around, uneasy as an alley tomcat at midnight mating time, and peered out the windows.

I saw a man stop briefly and talk with another man. He walked a half block and stopped to chat with a second fellow. That was it! Men don't hold sidewalk conversations with other men at night—with girls, yes, but not with men. These men must be cops. I told Banghart and Darlak that we ought to clear out of there.

The Owl laughed at me. "It's that kind of a neighborhood," he said. "Dope addicts and peddlers. They meet on the streets to make deals." I accepted that explanation and decided to stay. It was the lousiest goddam decision I ever made—aside from joining the break in the first place. This is what happened . . .

I was sleeping like dead when a hoarse, bellowing voice awakened me. I thought at first that Banghart or Darlak had turned on the radio. It was that kind of voice.

Then the room lit up, brighter than the sunniest day you ever saw, with a pure white light. It stung my eyes, and I started to yell for somebody to turn it off. But the light wasn't in the apartment. It was blasting through the windows.

The voice came on again. And now I knew what it was. Somebody was talking over a loudspeaker from the street outside. It was the voice of doom—the reveille bugle calling us back to Stateville.

"Touhy! Banghart! Darlak!" the voice said, with an ungodly tone that must have been heard a half mile away. "Touhy! Banghart! Darlak!

"This is the Federal Bureau of Investigation. You are surrounded. You cannot escape. Come out with your hands up—immediately. If you resist, you will be killed."

There was a minute or so of silence, while the spotlights played against our windows. Then the voice resumed:

"You, Banghart, come out first. Hold your hands over your head and walk backwards down the stairs."

The game was up. We all knew it. Banghart looked at me, with those big owl eyes blinking. Then he opened the door and, without a word, backed out through it. Darlak followed him, and then I did. Half way down the stairs there was a gun in my back, and then the handcuffs were on. Just like old times, it was.

Our next stop was the FBI headquarters on the 19th floor of the Bankers Building in downtown Chicago. They questioned us separately, in pairs, and all three together. We didn't chirp about anyone who had harbored us, of course. And we soon got the pitch on how the law had caught up with us.

Nelson had turned himself in to the FBI in St. Paul, Minnesota, and Stewart had been picked up in a fleabag hotel on State Street in Chicago. They had squealed on us.

During all the questioning in those early hours, nobody asked about O'Connor and McInerney, I noticed. There was an astounding lack of curiosity about them. I began to scent, in a vague sort of way, the attar of embalming fluid. An FBI man confirmed it for me.

"We killed O'Connor and McInerney," he said. "They opened fire and we had to shoot them."

The news of the death of O'Connor, particularly, shook me up. McInerney never had meant much to me, except for wondering why his parents hung the first name of St. Clair on him.

All I said was that I hoped Gene would have that wheelbarrow and rope with him, wherever he was. The FBI kids looked at me blankly—a habit of theirs.

That was it. The big escape was all done. The date was December 29th. We had been free for 82 days. Two of us were dead and, although we weren't aware of it yet, the other five were in a hell of a fix.

The FBI and the Chicago police yammered at us for most of two days. They tried to get us to rat on people who had helped us, but we dummied up. As for blaming the $20,000 candy-company payroll job on me, that was strictly police guff. I had had nothing to do with any robberies or other crimes, and there was no evidence of any kind against any of us.

The time had come to go home; home to prison. I glanced toward a doorway in the FBI suite and there stood a man I knew well. He was Joseph E. Ragen, one of the most widely known prison wardens in America. He was my boss, and a stern disciplinarian. There was an ironical story behind my association, as a convict, with Ragen, the warden.

Back in 1941, Ragen had resigned as warden of Stateville because of a political upheaval in Illinois. My escape, with Banghart and our five companions, had created the most whopping prison scandal of its kind in Illinois penitentiary history. The politicans had gone whining to Ragen, begging him to return and take charge.

He had agreed, but only after being guaranteed absolute freedom from politics. My escape had made him, in effect, the most independent state prison warden in the United States. I looked at him as we met again and said: "Well, Warden, I see I got your job back for you."

The warden looked a bit startled, then chuckled and said: "Yes, Touhy, you did." They tell me Warden Ragen told that story hundreds of times in the years that followed.

We rode back to Stateville in style, with a bigger police escort than they give to the St. Patrick's Day parade. I spent New Year's Eve getting dressed back into prison, but I didn't feel too unhappy about it. I had made my big protest as an innocent man. What had it cost me personally? Not too much, I thought.

Illinois law, strangely enough, provided no prosecution or penalty at that time for inmates who broke out of prison. That sounds cockeyed, I know, but it wasn't a crime then to escape from custody, provided you didn't kill or hurt somebody in doing so. It wasn't until 1949 that the Illinois General Assembly passed a law making it a felony to bust out of a jail or a penitentiary.

All I could lose, personally, I thought at the time I went over the wall, was time off earned for good behavior. And that was a damnably insignificant item against 99 years. It was much more important, I had convinced myself, to make a big public protest against false imprisonment.

A Chicago lawyer, Joseph Harrington, came to see me a few days after I was back in Stateville. My family had retained him. I asked him if I was correct in believing they couldn't prosecute me for escaping. Oh, yes, he said, I was right. Absolutely right. But hiding away in the pubic bushes of the law was a little angle that I had overlooked.

There was a clause saying that a person who aids or abets another in escaping can be prosecuted and, if found guilty, be sentenced to the same number of years which the escapee had been serving. It is an archaic law, and judges time and again had called it unfair and barbaric.

"In your case," Harrington said, "I have a hunch they're going to try to pin Darlak's 199 years on you."

I recalled, as Harrington spoke, that Captain Daniel A. "Tubbo" Gilbert—often called "the world's richest cop"—had been lurking around after the FBI had picked me up in Chicago. Gilbert had been a central figure in my being sent to prison.

It would be a terrible injustice to hook me with Darlak's time, of course. I hadn't aided or abetted anybody to escape. Darlak's brother had smuggled the guns and the whole caper had been planned for months before I talked myself—with Gene O'Connor's persuasion—into going along.

But I strongly suspected that Gilbert would be delighted if the law saddled me with Darlak's 199 years. Tubbo had helped send me to prison for the Factor sham in the first place, as Judge Barnes later ruled. To bury me in prison forever might be Gilbert's idea of personal triumph.

To understand the case of Dan Gilbert vs Roger Touhy, it is necessary to go back a lot of years. I had known him for a long time, back to the days when my truck drivers were running beer through his Chicago district.

Chapter 4

My Father was a Cop

M y father was a Chicago policeman. An honest one. Otherwise, he would have had a hell of a lot less trouble getting up the grocery and rent money. And I might have managed to get farther in school than to squeak through the eighth grade.

I was born in 1898, although the prison records say '97, in a house at 822 South Robie Street, not far from one of the places where I hid out while on the lam in 1942. There were seven of us kids, two girls and five boys.

We lived in an area of working people, big families and low incomes. My father's pay as a policeman wasn't enough to keep the wolf off the front porch but, at least, he never made it in to eat the potatoes and meat—when we had meat, that is—off the table.

Some of Chicago's most notorious gangsters came out of that part of the city. So did business leaders, college professors, clergymen and a couple of mayors. I was doing all right myself until the big Factor frameup came along.

My mother died when I was ten. She was fatally burned when a kitchen stove exploded. After that, my father, my two sisters and I moved to Downers Grove, a suburb. The older boys stayed in Chicago, living with relatives and friends. I graduated from the St. Joseph Roman Catholic Parochial School in Downers Grove when I was thirteen.

It was a good enough boyhood. I played baseball and raised the usual amount of the devil and got teased because my hair was curly. If I had anything to gripe about, I didn't realize it, because other boys didn't have any more than I did, generally speaking.

I often thought in prison of the priest in charge of the school, a Father Goodwin. My family couldn't afford to pay tuition for me, so I was a sort of handyman around the school and the church. I mowed the lawns, served mass as an altar boy, tended the furnace, ran errands and did a little janitor work. It was fun.

Once or twice a week, Father Goodwin rented a horse and buggy from a livery and went calling on his parishioners. I was his driver. At whatever house we stopped, there would be refreshments—apple pies, lemonade, thick sandwiches, salads, pickles, ice cream. Father waved the food away, but I ate fit to bust a gut.

In the church there was a big oil painting, a copy of The Last Supper. Father Goodwin explained it to me, saying that a man called Judas had betrayed Jesus Christ for thirty pieces of silver. A thing like that can have a remarkable influence on a kid.

I began thinking of Judas as a stool pigeon, a word I knew, as did all youngsters. While sweeping up the church and dusting the pews, I would stop and look for a long time at the painting. I picked out the face of a man I figured was Judas, and I would stand there hating him.

I thought of cutting the face of the man I concluded to be Judas out of the picture, but that would have ruined the painting and Father Goodwin would have been unhappy. So I just went on despising Judas—something which I never told the "bug doctors," which is what psychologists and psychiatrists are called in prison.

My contempt for informers grew on me as the years passed. When I later got into the labor union movement, I despised the company finks. After a few years in prison, I got to distrust everybody around me, except for a few convicts. Too many inmates are stoolies; the bug doctors can call my attitude antisocial if they want to.

My feeling about informers can be summed up by an anecdote which seems very, very apt to me. Funny, too.

I once knew a confidence man called Yiddles Miller. He spoke with a Weber and Fields Dutch accent, but he was a shrewd operator. Con men are, I learned in prison, the elite of all lawbreakers, in the opinion of other felons. They never tattle on each other.

Well, Yiddles and another bunco expert, Gus London, were sharing a twin-bed hotel room in Pittsburgh. Each of them folded his pants across the back of the chair near his single bed. Each fell asleep, but in the middle of the night Yiddles, a light sleeper, was awakened by a prowler in the room. London slept on, snoring a bit.

The thief took London's pants from a chair at the bed nearest the door. He then moved toward the second chair. Yiddles, feigning sleep, stirred and pretended to be awakening. The burglar left, taking only London's pants, with $3,-000 in the pockets. Yiddles got out of bed, double-locked the door, propped the back of a chair under the doorknob for added security and went back to sleep.

In the morning London awakened, demanded to know whether his pants had walked away with his $3,000, and was told by Yiddles: "A burglar came in and stole your trousers." London was indignant, demanding to know why Yiddles hadn't awakened him, summoned the hotel house officer, or called the police.

Yiddles propped himself up on an elbow, stared in astonishment at his comrade in larceny and demanded: "What do you think I am, a stool pigeon?"

London thought over the questionable ethics involved, agreed that Yiddles was right, and apologized for having suggested calling in the law.

Whatever the moral, or immoral, angles of the story may be, I always have despised stoolies, and I always will. The only thing worse is a perjurer. I have had more than my share of troubles from both.

When I got out of the eighth grade, it was hunt-a-job for me. Only rich kids went to high school back then, and I didn't qualify. I had a little edge on other youngsters, because my hobby was ham radio, or wireless as it was called. I had built my own set at home, and I knew the International code.

I tried for a job as a wireless operator, but there wasn't a chance at my age. Too young for responsibility, I was told. So I ran my feet down halfway to my ankles as an office and stockroom boy for a few months and then hooked on with Western Union. They made me manager of a little residential section branch office. A real big dealer, I was. Salary: $12 a week.

I lied about my age to get the job, but it was easy to get by. My hair was gray at the sides of my head —maybe I worried as an infant—before I got out of knee pants, and every day I would have a five o'clock shadow by lunch time.

Western Union gave me a chance to learn the Morse code which wasn't too difficult because I already knew the International. They moved me to the main office downtown and I was an operator.

My father went into retirement about that time, and he liked to play the horses. He would bet fifty cents, or one or two bucks on a race, and only one race a day, when he had the cash to spare. And now I was in a position to be his personal tout.

The stable owners, trainers and jockeys would send messages on the chances of their horses over the wires. I tipped off my father. He had nine winners, mostly long shots, in a row. He would have broken half the bookies in Chicago if he had started with ten bucks and parlayed it. But no, he never risked more than two.

But the really important thing that happened to me— back then in 1915—was that a dark-haired Irish girl went to work for Western Union in the company's branch office in Chicago's finest hotel, the Blackstone.

She was sixteen, and fresh out of telegraph school. From the main office, I sent the Blackstone's messages to her and received the ones she transmitted. She sent better than she copied, but she wasn't so good at either. I tried to help her.

Since she worked from four p.m. to midnight, I could drop in and see her evenings after my day shift ended. The first time I called only to help her with telegraphy. After that I courted her by the Western Union's wires between the main office and the Blackstone. And in person, too.

I'd take her home now and then when she finished work at midnight, but she always had a chaperon. Another pretty girl, Emily Ivins, was night telephone operator at the hotel and she made certain that everything was proper on those late-at-night-ride-home dates.

Miss Ivins, incidentally, was to be an important witness in trying, many years later, to keep me out of prison on the Jake the Barber hoax. She was to tell the truth, but it wasn't good enough against the screen of lies behind which Factor and his friends stood grinning.

I would have been a telegrapher for the rest of my life but, odd as it sounds, I was too damn honest. The Commercial Telegraphers Union of America was trying to organize Western Union and the Postal Telegraph Company. I didn't know anything about unionization and I wasn't interested, but I knew some of the operators in the office had joined.

Every hour, the operators got a ten-minute "short," or relief, and we would go into the men's lounge for a smoke. One of the CTU boys scattered organization pamphlets around the room. I picked up one and, like a dummy, read it right out in the open. A company fink saw me and within an hour I was on the pad in the superintendent's office. He had a lot of questions to ask.

Did I belong to ther union? No. Did I know any men who did belong? Yes, I did. Would I give him their names? No, I would not. Did I have any plans for joining the union? "Well," I said, "if I decide the union is a good thing, 1 probably will take out a card."

Whammo! I was fired and out on the street. A company guard escorted me to the door and told me never to come back. Now, I'm not rapping Western Union after all these years. Every employer fought the unions then, and the

National Labor Relations Act was nearly 20 years in the future as the bosses' nightmare. I would have been fired anywhere for giving the same answers about unionization.

I should have lied to the superintendent, of course. Honesty was my downfall. A CTU organizer came to visit me at home that evening. He brought along an armful of union literature and a paid-up card in the union for six months.

"You're all through as a telegrapher, Touhy," he said. "By this time, your name is on the blackball list. No telegraph company or brokerage office will hire you. But if you want a job with us as a union organizer, we'll hire you."

I didn't believe him about the blackball, but he was right. Nobody would accept an application from me, much less give me a job. The hiring boss at the Associated Press needed operators, but he turned pale and looked ready to climb the wall when he heard my name. I could have been a bearded bolshevik with a bomb under my coat.

I read the union literature and got impressed with the rights of the working man. I took the job as an organizer, which was a lot of hard work and a smattering of prankish fun. We would call up Western Union and Postal, dictate long telegrams to fake addresses in distant cities and send them collect. We kept the companies' messenger services jumping with requests to pick up telegrams from vacant lots.

One of the union men telephoned the non-union Associated Press, posed as the AP's reporter at Rockford, Illinois, and turned in a long, fake story about a hotel fire that had killed twenty people. The story would have got on the wires, too, but some smartie called Rockford to check it.

It wasn't too difficult to sign up telegraphers in the union. The working hours were long, the pay was skinflint and the bosses were nasty. The trouble was that as soon as a key-pounder signed a secret union application card he was fired. I figured we had a stool pigeon in the CTU offices and I suspected one of our office secretaries.

So we forged the names of ten Western Union finks to application blanks and gave them to the secretary. Sure enough, all ten of the informers were fired, including the one who had squealed on me. We got rid of the girl we suspected and things went better.

Unions didn't have big enough treasuries to hire meeting halls, so we usually met in saloons. I got to know the big, tough, two-fisted pioneers of unionism. There were Pete Shaunnessey of the bricklayers, Tom Reynolds and Tom Malloy of the movie projection operators, Steve Sumner of the milk wagon drivers, Umbrella Mike Boyle of the electricians, Big Tim Lynch, Con Shea and Paddy Burrell of the teamsters, Bill Rooney of the flat janitors, and Art Wallace of the painters.

Those men were to figure, innocently, in my being railroaded to prison. Their names will crop up later in this story. Some of them were honest enough to get murdered and others were so crooked they could sleep comfortably only on a circular stairway.

Their faces were scar-tissued from fighting hired strikebreakers on picket lines. Their skulls were permanently creased from bumping their heads on the tops of police paddywagon doorways. Their knuckles, sometimes, were driven halfway up to their wrists from past impacts. I admired their courage and I made lifelong friendships with them—short as some of their lives were.

Con Shea was an erudite character who delighted in using fancy words. I recall his saying to me one night at the bar at the Ansonia Saloon: "Roger, a divided or deviated septum is an occupational hazard of the profession of union organization." I nodded wisely, not wanting to appear dumb. When I got to a dictionary, I learned that he was talking about a busted nose.

Union organizing was fascinating, but there didn't seem to be a secure future in it. Anyway, I liked telegraphy. I joined the Order of Railroad Telegraphers, went west and wangled a job from the Denver & Rio Grande Railroad. The pay was magnificent—$185 a month.

Everywhere the Denver & Rio Grande went, it seemed to parallel streams alive with big, fighting mountain trout. I learned about game fishing there. Also, I became acquainted with ranching, horseback riding and financial security. I worked in small towns where living costs were low, and I sent half my pay home to help out the family.

I wrote long letters and sent small gifts to Clara, the girl telegrapher back in Chicago who was going to be my wife. I was sure of that even then, although I never had proposed to her.

I worked in the depots, with their round-bellied wood-burning stoves in Buena Vista, Glenwood Springs and Eagle, Colorado. In Eagle, I got my first warning of western bad-man danger when a local merchant told me: "You won't be here long, sonny. We got a rancher, Clyde Nottingham, who runs depot agents out of town. He carries a gun. Guess he don't like you depot agent dudes."

It was cold that first night in Eagle and I had the stove red hot as I jiggled the telegraph key, handling freight car, stock car and personal messages. The waiting room door opened and in came a big man in cowboy clothes and a sheepskin coat. He spat on the potbellied stove. *Sizzle, sizzle,* the stove went.

I walked to the ticket window, looked out and saw the caller was carrying a .45. He didn't look pleasant, but damned if he was going to run me out of town. "Mr. Nottingham?" I asked. He nodded and I said: "Mr. Nottingham, any time you want to spit on the stove, go right ahead. But come back next day after the stove cools, and polish it. I ain't going to do it."

He stared at me for a long time. My proposition was reasonable to him, I guess. He came to my window, reached into an inner pocket and handed me a half dozen letters. He asked me if I would put them in the slot of the mail car on the late train.

I made another proposition: "I put your letters on the train and you stop spitting on the stove? Right?"

"That's the idea, young fellow," he said. "Only reason I been running depot agents out of town is they don't want to mail my letters for me."

A fine friendship started right away. He invited me out to his ranch. He had a ten-year-old daughter called "Toots," and I always get along well with kids. The three of us went fishing and hunting and horseback riding together.

Meeting Nottingham taught me a lot, as a young fellow away from home. I learned from the incident in the depot that the town bad man—or later, the rioting con in prison —pretty often isn't bad at all. His trouble is that he can't make himself understood to the depot agent, or the yard screw, or to his family—and he gets sore at people as a result.

Being with Nottingham and his kid gave me a sense of belonging, of being liked and being part of something. Second to my own wife and sons, I thought a lot about the Nottinghams at night in Stateville.

But nothing could be permanent back then. A war was going on in Europe, and then the United States stepped in and it was World War 1.

I got patriotic and headed back for Chicago to enlist in the Navy. The Nottinghams saw me off at the station and I tried to make Toots stop crying by promising to bring her back half of Kaiser Bill's waxed mustache.

I didn't win the war, or have any active part in it, but the war did something for me. It gave grounds for me, a boy from the eighth grade, to say honestly to cops, bootleggers, convicts, prison screws and interviewers: "I've been to Harvard." It was the truth, too. I taught telegraphy at Harvard to classes of enlisted men and officers.

After my discharge from the Navy, I spent a couple of weeks with my father, living in Franklin Park, a Chicago suburb. I saw that cute little girl telegrapher a few times, but I had a job of getting back on my financial feet before becoming serious about marriage.

I drifted out to a small Iowa town near Des Moines, on a telegraphing job for the Rock Island Lines, then to Kansas City, figuring I might go back to Colorado. But I met one of my Morse code students from Harvard.

He was a bright young man, a lawyer, although I hadn't been able to pound telegraphy into his head. He just didn't have an ear for Morse signals. I'll call him Collins, for the good reason that he had a different name.

Collins was heading for Cushing, Oklahoma, where his

brother had an interest in a hotel. The two brothers also had a tire shop in Oklahoma, and I wound up as manager of the store. There wasn't enough money in that job, but it was a stopgap.

The oil business was boiling and busting and gushing in Oklahoma. A guy could make a million overnight. That was the line for me, particularly when I thought of my little Irish telegrapher back in Chicago. Marriage was on my mind.

I didn't know any more about the oil business than a mink knows of sex hygiene, but I could learn. For a bottle of bootleg corn, I got an oil field engineer to give me a couple of hours of instruction in engineering. Now, all I can remember of what he taught me is: "Don't bump your skull against an overhead valve and smash your goddam brains out."

I went to a field at Drummond, Oklahoma, told the superintendent I was an engineer, and went to work. I was short on technical skill, but long on bluff. And I knew where to buy corn whiskey to give the mechanics for doing my work when something went wrong with the pumps or engines.

My next on-the-job training in oil was as a telegrapher for the Empire Pipe Line Company at Ardmore, Oklahoma, and there I learned the big words about petroleum —plus a few names to drop.

The Sinclair Oil people, in a moment of laxity, hired me as a scout.

The experience I had had in that line was confined to watching silent western movies in which Army scouts killed Indians. But what the hell, I was an oil field engineer, wasn't I? And I could talk as good a gusher as the original Carbon Petroleum Dubbs.

Word came to me that a famous New York geologist, Dick Raymond, needed a helper. He had located oil fields all over the world. I went after the job and got it. It put me in the big money.

Raymond and I drove all through southwest Oklahoma. At each county seat town, we would get a plat, or diagram, on oil leases, along with figures on production of wildcat wells. Raymond would study those things, look over the terrain and decide whether any of the land was worth leasing from the owners, who were mostly Indians and cattle ranchers.

I had about $1,000 saved, and there was nothing against my buying leases that Raymond recommended. I took a gamble on 150 acres at two dollars an acre in Jefferson County. Three oil companies were bidding on my lease within a month, and I made $2,000 on the deal. I bought and sold about 20 leases, and never lost on any of them.

The money was good, but I was a guy who liked the city. And my mind was on the girl at the telegraph key in the Blackstone in Chicago. I went back home with $25,-000 in cash, a fortune in 1920, and it had taken me less than a year to earn it.

Clara and I were married on April 22nd, 1922. I had figured on returning to the west, but Chicago looked too good to me, and there was a lot of money around. Everybody was buying cars and trucks and that was the business for me.

A boyhood friend, John Powell, had an auto sales agency on Madison Street. He was a politician, and later he became an Illinois state legislator and went blind. But at that time he was a real rouser. Powell was a six-footer, and he had a black bear that was just as tall when it stood on its hind legs. When Powell went night clubbing, the bear went along, and both of them would drink bourbon with beer chasers. It was a race between them as to who got drunk first.

I went to work for him (Powell, not the bear) as a car and truck salesman, at no pay. My idea was to learn how to buy and sell, and then go into business for myself.

My wife and I were living in an apartment in Oak Park, a sedate suburb where every man was a municipal disgrace if he wasn't a deacon, or at least a pillar of a church. To get away from that mad social gaiety, and to keep my bankroll intact, I bought a taxicab and drove it nights in Chicago. I learned things in the cab I never heard at Harvard.

In a few months, I opened my own garage and auto sales place, with a capacity of 15 cars, and did pretty well.

I sold it and moved to a bigger place on North Avenue. I was becoming a tycoon, in a minor league way, in the auto business. I should have stayed in that league.

My brother, Tommy, and I bought our father a two-flat building at California and Warren, where he could be independent and make a small bet now and then. He died in 1926 on a trip to California, the same year Clara's and my first son was born. That's nature's way of evening things up, I guess; like when one guy goes into the penitentiary and another guy gets paroled to make room for him.

My wife and I moved from Oak Park to another suburb, Des Plaines. I bought a place that some of the newspapers later called a "mansion" or a "gang fortress." It was a six-room bungalow and later I put a 60-foot swimming pool in the back. The only gang I ever had around there was a guard with a shotgun after the Capone mob tried to kidnap my kids.

A bargain in trucks got me into the prohibition beer business by chance. I bought eight of them, sold six, and wound up with two sitting around my garage, using up space and showing no profit.

It happened that I knew most of the bootleggers and saloon owners in my area. Why not? They were the guys who had money to buy fancy cars. If Chicago's best stores catered to them and their wives, why shouldn't Roger Touhy?

I called on a few saloonkeepers and then made a deal with two young lads who would work hard to make a buck or two. Also, I fixed it to buy beer from two breweries which turned out legal one-half of one per cent prohibition beer—and sneaked good brew out the back door.

My trucks hauled the beer, the drivers made a profit of twenty dollars a barrel, they paid me a percentage on the purchase price of the trucks and everybody was happy.

The police generally expected a payoff of $5 a barrel for beer being run into any given district. I didn't pay it and neither did my drivers. Our operation was too small for the law to bother much with us.

And then Tubbo Gilbert stepped into the picture. I had known him for a long time, first as a labor skate and later as a ward politician. We never got along well and, later on, he swore that he couldn't remember having seen me until July 19th, 1933, an important date in my life.

Anyway, Tubbo, a sergeant at the time, stopped one of my beer trucks, carrying three barrels of beer, arrested the driver and took the beer to his stationhouse.

The payoff was that the beer in the barrels was legal stuff—a half of one per cent. It was no more illegal than lollypops or baby Pablum, and it carried about the same kick. He had to release the driver, the beer and the truck, of course.

I circulated the story around Chicago and the back of Tubbo's neck turned red as a gobbler turkey's wattles in mating season.

Gilbert liked me even less after that. It took him a long time to get even with me, but he finally did—99 years of even.

One of my friends at the time of Tubbo's near-beer humiliation was Matt Kolb, a bootleg beer distributor with a saloon on California Avenue, not far from my garage. He was a fat, gentle old gent who weighed about 220 pounds, beer belly and all. Anybody who thought all bootleggers were gangsters with machines guns and gun molls had only to meet Matt. He would run away from a ten-year-old kid armed with a flyswatter.

I sold Kolb a car, giving him a good deal and splitting the commission with him, a thing all dealers did then to promote sales. Matt came to me a few months later with a proposition. He had a partner, but they weren't getting along. I could buy out the partner for $10,000. Kolb once had been tied up with the Capone mob, but violence had scared him away.

My automobile business then was bringing me in from $50,000 to $60,000 a year. But the big money was in alcoholic beverages. Everybody in the racket was getting rich. How could the bootleggers miss, with a short ounce of gagging moonshine selling for $1.25, or an eight-ounce glass of nauseating beer going at 75 cents?

I drew $10,000 from the bank, handed it to Kolb and said: "You got a new partner."

Chapter 5

My Beer Was Bootleg
—But Good

C harlie Wilson said that the way to be a success was to make a superior product. He made a giant out of General Motors that way. Henry Ford said it before Wilson, and his business became pretty gigantic, too.

I had the same idea when I went into the bootleg beer business. I didn't become a giant in the racket, but you might say I was one of the biggest midgets who ever scoffed at the Volstead Law.

Matt Kolb's beer was awful. One time it would be as flat as pond water with a green scum on it, and the next batch would have enough gas to blow up the Empire State. It could be as bitter as biting into a green persimmon, or as sweet as the smell of a Greek candy kitchen. In only one characteristic was it consistent. All of it was bad—nasty bad, usually.

I set out to make a superior product, and the first person I consulted was a chemist who worked for the City of Chicago, counting the germs in test tubes of sewage water and such delicate tasks. I asked him how to make good beer and, after giving me a lot of long words about enzymes and such, he said:

"Good water, you want first of all. Fine pure water. Water is the big thing in all good beverages, from soda pop on up."

I told him to go find the right kind of water, and he did. He tested water all over northern Illinois. Samples from my home town of Des Plaines were pretty good. There was better stuff in a creek out at St. Charles. But the elixir of all beer-base water was from an artesian well near Roselle, he said.

I built a wort plant out there and put my brother Eddie, who years later came through with the $2,500 while I was on the loose, in charge.

Wort was an entirely legal product. It is used for making rye bread. Before I was through, I was producing enough wort for all the bread baked in a dozen states. It was a big enterprise, and I paid fifteen cents tax on every gallon I made.

Into the wort I persuaded Matt to put the finest malt, white flakes of corn, rice and hops, domestic and imported, that we could buy. And I went to the American Brewmasters' Institute and hired the best man they could recommend.

"Matt, we're not going to need any salesmen," I told my partner. "We're going to put out the best beer in America. The saloonkeepers will come to us begging to buy it."

To make beer, all we needed was to put the wort into vats, under proper temperature control, add brewer's yeast and water. What happened then was like introducing a pretty, eager girl to a handsome lad and handing them the key to a motel room. Nature took care of the rest.

The mixture stood in open vats for twelve days to ferment while the brewmaster pottered around sniffing, sipping and testing the stuff. If it didn't come up to the highest standards, he dumped it. That was my order. We never peddled a poor-quality barrel of beer.

After twelve days, the brewmaster dropped the temperature to thirty degrees and let the brew mellow. The last step was putting it into barrels, with carbolic gas carbonation added as it went in. Chill it, tap it and fill up a foaming glass—my, my, it was fine beer!

This was an illegal operation, in violation of a federal law which everyone regarded with the same fondness as a swift kick with a Number 11 boot. Clergymen, bankers, mayors, U.S. senators, newspaper publishers, blue-nose reformers and the guy in the corner grocery all drank our beer. They enjoyed it, and I was proud.

In addition to being outside the law, our enterprise was a big one. At peak production, we had ten fermenting plants, each one a small brewery in itself. It was too big a gamble to have the complete works in one place, which the federal prohibition agents might raid and chop to ruins with axes.

Each little brewery had to have refrigeration and an ice-making machine for proper temperature control. Every vat and other piece of equipment had to be laboratory-clean or else the beer would be rancid nasty. I had $50,000 tied up in the business before the first stein of beer gushed out of a tap.

It was an efficient, well-run business; not a matter of messing around in basements or bathtubs to run up a few gallons or hundred gallons of sickening stuff.

Barrels were a big trouble, with leaks springing to release the carbonation and, sometimes, the beer itself. So we set up our own cooperage in Schiller Park, hiring all union-labor craftsmen to handle that end. It paid off big, because saloonkeepers who bought from us weren't carping about "leakers" from our deliveries.

I bought a half dozen tank trucks, and had them painted like those used by the Texaco Oil Company, to haul bulk beer. The trucks could load 100 gallons a minute, with the engine throttled down and operating a pump from a six-inch feed.

At the top of the season—beer really was a six-months-a-year proposition, with many people turning to rotgut whiskey during cold weather—we peddled 1,000 barrels a week. The price was $55 a barrel to the saloon owners, and it doesn't take much arithmetic to figure our weekly gross.

As for net profit, the brew cost us $4.50 a barrel to produce, using the finest ingredients, plus wort tax and delivery expense. Water is cheap, and there's a lot of it in beer.

We sold beer to about 200 roadhouses, night clubs and saloons, all outside of Chicago, to the west and northwest of the city. Our boundaries were from the city line west to Elgin and from North Avenue to the Lake County, Illinois line. We could have expanded, but Matt and I never were hogs for money.

One question always comes up when people talk with me about bootlegging. How much graft did we pay? How many policemen and politicians did we have to bribe, or put on our payroll?

The payoff, surprisingly, wasn't big.

First and foremost, Matt and I were working the suburbs and Cook County towns. We didn't have to fill the pockets of money-hungry Chicago cops. The small-town police were happy with a ham, a turkey or a $20 bill at Christmas time.

Our business was scattered over a lot of mileage. A barrel here and a barrel there. Nobody realized that Matt and I were grossing about $1,000,000 a year from beer alone. That's right, a million dollars. So the politicians and the fuzz didn't expect big handouts.

The federal agents stuck pretty well to big towns like Chicago, and our local law was mostly the Cook County Highway Patrol. I figured out an angle to keep the roads open for us, with top priority for our beer trucks.

Whenever we had a job open as truck driver or what not, I hired a cop away from the highway patrol to fill it. The arrangement was a splendid one.

We paid no man less than $100 a week, which was more than triple what the patrol guys got for longer hours. There soon was a waiting list of applicant cops to drive our trucks. A cop looking for a good-paying job wouldn't interfere with us any more than he would pinch a former fellow-cop working for us.

As for the politicians, the payoff for them was largely in beer. A small town mayor or justice of the peace would be as happy as a juvenile delinquent with a pile of rocks and an empty greenhouse for a target if we rolled a barrel of brew up on his back porch every few months.

The big-time boys at the trough wanted more, to be sure. Tony Cermak was an example. He was then chairman of the Cook County Board of Commissioners which made him a powerhouse in the county outside of Chicago, where our beer trucks rolled. Later he became mayor of Chicago, and was killed by a bullet fired by a nut as he stood beside Franklin D. Roosevelt in Miami.

Tony put on a big picnic, to raise political campaign funds, every summer in the Forest Preserves. My contribution would be 100 barrels of beer. The cost of the beer didn't lose me any sleep, but Tony's boys made a good thing by selling it at a buck a mug.

I built up good will that way, like Gene O'Connor with his wheelbarrow at Stateville.

Beer bought you more sunshine friends than money did, I realized, so we set up a bottling plant, and it wasn't cheap. The bottle washer alone cost $4,500, I recall, and the pasteurizer was even more expensive.

We bottled 750 cases, or 18,000 bottles, of brew a week. That was all the pasteurizer would handle. And we never sold so much as one bottle of that beer. It all went for friendship, jolly friendship. A case of that stuff, and it was good, meant more to some pols and cops than a $500 bill.

"Try a bottle of this," the guy lucky enough to have some of it would say to his big shot friends on a Saturday night. "Finest beer in America. Roger Touhy sent it along as a token of his friendship. Fine fellow, Rog."

I lived quietly with my family during those big money years. I put a workshop, office and bar in my basement. There was a playhouse for the kids in the backyard. My wife got along well with our neighbors. There wasn't any stigma to selling beer. It was a great public service, most people thought—and the U.S. government finally agreed, you'll recall.

My hobby was making fishing rods from split bamboo in my shop, along with lures and baits. Fishing, from my days along the Denver & Rio Grande as a telegrapher, was my sport. Northern Wisconsin, Minnesota, Canada, Florida, and Montauk Point, Long Island, for weakfish and blue-fish, were my vacation spots. I hunted, too, and was a good shot. Which reminds me. . . .

One afternoon in a Wisconsin lake, I hooked a thirty-pound muskie. I tried working him up to the boat, but he fought like Jack Dempsey in the last round of a tough bout. The fish pulled away, broke water, danced on his tail and shook his head. My reel jammed and left me with only one thing to do.

I took a .25 revolver from my pocket, kept there for the purpose, and shot the muskie through the head.

In the boat with me was an Indian guide, Joe St. Germaine, who was better than a green hand with a gun. He was amazed when I boated the fish and showed him the bullet hole. "Nobody can shoot that good," he said. "You were lucky."

We had drunk a dozen bottles of beer in the boat, and now he started throwing the empties out on the choppy waves twenty-five or thirty feet away. I sat there in the rocking boat and smashed all twelve bottles with thirteen shots. Which brings up, to me, an important point:

If I had been aiming to hit, would I have missed that old guard in the Stateville tower, from a range of thirty-three feet, on the day of the escape? Nonsense! He was a lot bigger target than a muskie or a beer bottle, the range was shorter and the firing conditions were ideal.

But those two shots through the tower window had a big part, back in a ridiculous trial in 1943, in getting me tagged for an additional 199 years for aiding and abetting. . . .

Getting back to the late '20s, Matt and I had another bonanza going, in addition to beer. Ah, those lovely slot machines!

They were against the law, technically, but they stood openly and invitingly in practically every roadhouse, drug store, saloon, gas station and grocery in outlying Cook County. The only places you wouldn't find them were in churches, schools, hospitals, post offices and public libraries.

My partner and I had 225 of them in choice locations, and the only way to make money faster is to have a license to counterfeit the stuff.

The businessman in whose place the machine was set up got forty per cent of the coins. Matt and I split the remaining sixty per cent. My cut would add up to about twenty dollars a week for each machine, or $4,500 weekly, and the costs of upkeep and replacement of machines were far from high.

I met Al Capone about a half dozen times back then, mostly in Florida on fishing trips. He offered to let me use his yacht or stay in his big house, surrounded by a wall about as thick as Stateville's, on Palm Island in Biscayne Bay, between Miami and Miami Beach. I didn't accept.

Capone wasn't my kind of person. People around him— or against him—were all the time getting murdered. He surrounded himself with gunsels. That wasn't right in my let-everybody-make-a-living way of thinking. I never carried a gun, except on my hunting or muskie-fishing trips. And I had a rule that none of my employees could tote arms.

Back in about 1927, I had two business deals with Capone. The prohibs had knocked off a couple of his Chicago breweries and he had trouble getting enough beer for his Chicago and suburban Cicero speakeasies. His brother, Ralph, was in charge of beer for the syndicate, but Al himself telephoned me and asked me to sell him five hundred barrels.

We had a surplus at the time, so I agreed. I told him to send his trucks, with five hundred empties, out to our Schiller Park cooperage. We exchanged five hundred barrels of good beer—a lot better than he ever made—for his empties. I gave him a discount price of $37.50 a barrel because of the big order.

The brew must have sold well. He called me a few days later and asked for three hundred more. I said okay and told him that Tuesday—the day I collected from all my customers and paid off my help—would be the day I wanted my money.

On Monday, he called me with a beef. "Fifty of those

barrels were leakers," he said. "I'll pay you for 750. Okay?"

I laughed at him. I knew there couldn't be so much as one leaker. Not with the crew of craftsmen I had in the cooperage. They tested every barrel under powerful air pressure before it was filled. Al was trying to chisel me out of fifty barrels, and I let him know that I knew what his pitch was.

"You owe me for eight hundred," I said, "and I expect to get paid for eight hundred."

His voice was a little lame as he replied: "Well, the boys told me there were fifty leakers. I'll check on it."

Check on it? Pfui! He knew what he owed me and he paid it—$30,000 in cash. He could afford to have paid three times as much, with the prices his speakeasy clipjoints were getting in Chicago. If there had been even one leaker among those eight hundred barrels, I would have gotten a new crew in the cooperage.

He called me again in a week or so and asked to buy another five hundred barrels. I told him no, that my regular customers were taking all my output. That wasn't exactly true, but what was the use of needling him by saying I didn't do business with weasels?

Chapter 6

Al Capone Didn't Like Me

A s the years rolled along, I got to be as popular with the Capone mob as a police squad raiding a gambling hall on a busy Saturday night. Al Capone had good reason to be jealous and resentful of me. I was making a pile of money and I was practically unknown to the newspapers.

My partner, Matt Kolb, had the reputation for being the top man in beer running and slot machines in our part of Cook County. He sort of liked the limelight and I didn't mind his having the notoriety. I enjoyed being a quiet family man.

Even when the Chicago syndicate murdered Matt in 1931, my name wasn't mentioned prominently in the papers. Capone envied me my anonymity and he begrudged me my income. He wanted to open up the suburbs for brothels and big-money gambling. He sent his torpedoes out to see me, and among the first were Frank Rio and Willie Heeney.

Capone made the appointment by telephone and I set up the meeting at a roadhouse I owned, The Arch, in Schiller Park. When the Capone tough guys arrived, I was in a setting that looked like a grade Z gangster program on television. On the walls of the office in the joint I hung hunting rifles, shotguns and target pistols from my gun collection. A friend on the county highway police had borrowed two machine guns for me. I didn't know how to load or fire them, and I wasn't planning to learn. I just stashed them in an open closet for window dressing.

I owned a gas station on the property and the attendant could see me plainly in the office through the windows. I arranged signals with the attendant. Every time I scratched my head, blew my nose or stood up from my chair, he was to telephone the office from the pay phone in the station. "Don't pay any attention to what I tell you when you call," I told him. "I'm only playing a joke on some friends."

Rio and Heeney came in swaggering, but they got sedate when they saw the weapons on the walls. They were downright meek after they looked through the open doorway of the closet and saw the two choppers.

Heeney was the spokesman. He said that Capone wanted to open the county for brothels, taxi-dance halls, alcohol stills and a punchboard racket to rob school kids of their lunch money. "Al wants you to go along on this deal, and he means business," Heeney said, sort of blusteringly.

I pulled out my handkerchief, blew my nose, and in a minute or two the telephone rang. I pretended to listen, put on a scowl like a silent-movie villain and barked an order: "Send some of the boys over there and take care of it. Nobody can hijack our slots."

After I had apologized for the interruption, Heeney went on: "Al says this is virgin territory out here for whorehouses." I started to laugh politely at the remark, but my callers seemed to see nothing funny about it. They showed me a map of Cook County, with the locations pinpointed where brothels would be located. I coughed loudly and, on signal, one of my "deviated septum" boys—a former county cop—came striding into the office from the bar.

He grabbed the machine guns out of the closet and said to me: "Louie and I are going over to give those bastards a good scare—or maybe worse, boss." I told him: "Do what you think best, Joe, but don't let them bluff you."

He walked out, taking the guns back to the police arsenal from where they had been borrowed.

I apologized again to my visitors and told them that prostitution in the county was impossible. "The suburbanites and the farmers out here won't hold still for bawdy houses," I said. "Beer and slots are okay, but not girls." Which was true.

They kept talking. The telephone rang constantly, and I made gangster-type remarks into the mouthpiece. I acted like a one-man Murder Incorporated, and Heeney and Rio got a little pale around their noses and mouths. They said they would go back and report to Capone. I waved them cheerily on their way.

In the weeks that followed, I had a parade of Capone mob proposition guys. Two of them were Louis Campagna, called "Short Pants" or "Little New York," and "Machine-gun Jack" McGurn, both killers. Campagna gave me a sales talk along this line:

" 'Snorky' [a code name for Capone] is in trouble. The 'G' [federal prohibition agents] is knocking off his breweries and stills before the beer can be barreled or the alcohol put in the delivery cans. He wants to expand a little out in the country, but he doesn't plan to compete with you."

As Campagna talked, I kept scratching, blowing my nose, rising from my chair, answering the telephone and making like Little Caesar. It was a lot of nonsense, of course. In my years of beer peddling and slot machine operating, I never had a man involved in a shooting, or had a brewery raided, or a beer truck confiscated, either.

I kept stalling Capone's messengers, telling them the local people were dead set against prostitution or casinos. Of course, I knew I would be put out of business soon after the Chicago mob got a foot in the door. I went to the local chiefs of police and explained frankly that I wanted to stay in business, but added:

"If the Capone mob gets into your towns, there will be no law left. The mobsters will be killing each other on your streets. You'll have a cathouse in every block. I'm trying to bring up two sons out here in a decent way, and you law enforcement people have families, too. We must protect ourselves."

The argument was valid, even coming from me, a beer runner. I had a pretty good standing in the community. I lived quietly, paid my taxes, contributed liberally to charities and was a leader in the Des Plaines Elks Club and other organizations. A group of businessmen had at one time even tried to get me to run for mayor.

The word passed along through the suburbs, and my advice was followed. As a starter, Capone's agents tried to install punchboards in the stores and shops. The effort was a complete failure. The merchants wouldn't buy the boards. Capone must have known I was monkey-wrenching his machine. I was making a powerful enemy—and I was going to pay for it.

The Chicago hoods kept pressuring me. Three of them— Rio, Frank Diamond, a brother-in-law of Capone, and Sam Hunt, called "Golf Bag," because of the way he carried machine guns and shotguns—were at The Arch one afternoon. The ex-cops and brawny farmers on my payroll clomped in and out of the place.

"You got a big organization, huh, Rog?" Rio said. "Lotta good guys, I guess."

I shrugged casually. "There are two hundred guys out here from every penitentiary in the United States and some from Canada" I said. As an afterthought, I told him: "Say, we're having a big party tonight. Most of my best guys will be here. Why don't you come out and bring Al and some of the other boys?"

Rio said he'd relay the invitation. I figured what was going to happen, and it did. Six squads of Chicago police, with a couple of deputy sheriffs from the other end of the county, raided The Arch that night. Remarkable coincidenc, wasn't it? But the raid was a flop.

I had closed down the joint for the night. The prop guns were long gone, and there wasn't an ounce of anything alcoholic on the premises. An 80-year-old Chinese cook, saving money on room rent, had sneaked into the kitchen to sleep, but he—a true blue employee of mine—

couldn't speak a word of English after they disarmed him of a meat cleaver.

Capone next sent two real hotshots—Murray "The Camel" Humphreys and James "Red" Fawcett—to sweet-talk me. I met them at my basement bar. Fawcett and I had bottled beer, while Hump sipped some of the delicious wine my father-in-law made. Murray, who claims to be a college graduate—a diploma-mill man, I would say—made his pitch.

He and Fawcett had a 16-cylinder limousine parked outside. They wanted me to go with them to Cicero and have a talk with Frank Nitti, the killer they called "The Enforcer" —a man who put a bullet in his own brain later when things got too tough. Nitti would resolve all of our differences, Humphreys said, talking with the sincerity of a pimp trying to lead the entire graduating class of Vassar into lives of sin.

I might have been chump enough to go with them, at that—which would have been my death—but the telephone on the wall rang, and I recognized the caller's voice. He was a Capone man for whom I once had done a favor. There was a terrible note of urgency in his voice as he said: "Don't go to Cicero. Don't do it. You won't come back if you do."

No, I told the Hump, I wouldn't go to Cicero. To hell with that. If Nitti wanted to see me, he could come out to my area. I would give him safe conduct. I went over to the wall and fingered a shotgun—a purely ornamental piece, no longer usable—but Humphreys didn't know the difference.

He glanced cautiously around the oak-panelled room. He tried a threat: "You know, Touhy, we can take care of you any time we want to." I grinned at him, and his hand shook when he lifted his wine glass. He was good and scared.

His next remark amazed me: "Touhy, I've got a swell car parked outside. If you drive me back inside the Chicago city limits, I'll give you the car. I want to get home alive."

He pleaded with me, with the courage of a steer field-mouse, to escort him back to Chicago. Fawcett looked on with a smirk contemptuous of his superior. "Go on back to Chicago, both of you," I told them. "You won't get hurt."

They left, but Fawcett came back into the bar alone. "Listen, Touhy," he said, "for $5,000 I'll kill that sonofabitch Humphreys on the way to the city, and for another five grand I'll go to Cicero and knock off Nitti, too." I sent him on his way, along with Humphreys.

The finest belly laugh I had on Al came soon after that, when Capone sent a man named Summers—Tom Summers, as I recall—to see me. Summers gave me the usual waltz-me-around-again-Willie about importing girls, gambling and stills into the suburbs. I danced a few turns with him and introduced him to two friends of mine—no pantywaists, either of them. They were strangers to Chicago from out of town.

I tossed them a couple of $100 bills, after having a few words with them in private, and said: "Take Mr. Summers out and show him the sights. Cicero is a lively place, I hear. I'd go along, but I'm a family man."

Summers got drunk, and very palsy with my friends. They ended up at the Cotton Club, a gambling joint with a floor show which Al had opened up for his brother, Ralph, to run. It had cost $40,000 to remodel and decorate the dump, and it was Capone's biggest money maker.

My lads needled Summers into a fight with Ralph. Then they pitched in, pasted Ralph a few and took a gun away from him. Two other muggs came in on management's side, and they lost their guns, too. My friends took Summers, whooping and hollering happily, into Chicago and dropped him at Al's Metropole Hotel. That's where he wanted to go. He didn't comprehend what the hell he had done, never having seen Ralph before.

When my two friends reported back to me, I sent them right away to their homes in a southwest city and waited for a beef from Al. It came within twelve hours, and he was oily polite, asking for my health and welfare.

"Rog," he said at last, "who were those two guys with Summers at the Cotton Club last night?"

I acted dumb. "What guys?"

"Two big, dark men. Very tough, I hear. I won't hurt them, but I want them to return a couple of guns. It's very important."

Capone was sounding most sincere, and I matched him. "Oh, those fellows. Summers brought them with him when he came to see me. He said they were New York buddies, but I can't recall their names. Sorry I can't help you, Al."

Al said again that it was most important that he contact the two men. He just had to have the guns. "If I see them again, Al," I lied, "I'll get in touch with you. Why don't you ask Summers? They're his friends."

Capone hesitated, said Summers wasn't around just now, and hung up the phone. But he kept calling me and asking me if I had seen anything of "those friends of Summers'." I gave him the same answers. I was sorry about Summers' missing friends and the missing guns, but I couldn't help.

I finally got the level pitch on the thing. The two scrappers who had lost their guns in helping Ralph were federal prohibition agents, drinking incognito in the Cotton Club. If Al didn't return the guns, the feds were going to padlock the Cotton Club—$40,000 investment and all.

They did it, too. Capone couldn't come up with the guns, so the federals raided the club and closed it for liquor law violations. I read about it in the morning paper at breakfast, and laughed so hard I could have split my abdominal wall.

I stopped laughing later when I learned that before his first call to me about the lost guns, Al had had his plug-uglies beat Summers to death with baseball bats and fling him into the Chicago River. This kind of death was a routine matter for Capone associates, whether friends or enemies.

Then I laughed again—out the other side of my face. Capone decided to get back his $40,000 investment loss, with $10,000 interest. His mobsters kidnaped Matt Kolb—all 220 fat pounds of him. I got a telephone call from Capone two days after Matt vanished. He was as apologetic as a waiter caught with both thumbs in a customer's soup. "Rog," he said, "some people have got Matt." It would cost $50,000 in fives, tens and twenties to get him loose.

Capone, the fine, generous character that he was, would be happy to act as intermediary. All I had to do was bring the money to him, and he would make the pay-off. I agreed to do it. What else?

I went to the Proviso State Bank in suburban Maywood, where Matt and I had about $140,000 in a joint account. I explained to the president, Anthony Busher, that my partner and I needed a lot of cash. He sent to downtown Chicago for the small bills. I wrapped the ransom up in a newspaper—it made quite a bundle—and drove downtown to the Metropole Hotel.

I rode up in the elevator to the fifth floor, as Capone had directed. Five or six toughs were sitting around in a foyer and all of them were cleaning and oiling .38s. A warning, I guess. I saw Murray Humphreys and Red Fawcett there.

Capone, wearing a red dressing gown, was behind a big desk in a private room with a half dozen telephones in front of him. Big business executive. Ugh! I dropped my package in front of him. He tore off the newspaper wrapping and riffled through the bills. "Now, Rog, I want you to know I had nothing to do with this," he said, looking at me with his big cow eyes. "I like Matt. I'm trying to help him."

I was mad-to-boiling over the indignity of paying off the fat slob, but I kept under control. I said only two words to him: "Where's Matt?" He told me to drive around the block of the New Southern Hotel, at 13th Street and Michigan Avenue, another syndicate hangout.

I followed directions, and, on my second circle, there was Matt, waddling along the sidewalk. He got into my car, cheerful as a hog in a cool spring wallow on a 100 degree August afternoon. "Now, Roger, my lad," he said. "I know I was careless in getting kidnaped and I'm sorry. Don't scold me."

What can you do with a nice old guy like that?

I never saw Capone again after paying the ransom except, perhaps, from a distance at the races or the fights. Clara, our sons and I spent most of the winters in Florida. Many of my roadhouse customers closed up shop during the cold months, and the bottom would fall out of my business until spring.

Capone was at his fancy estate on Palm Island, in Biscayne Bay, early in 1931. He sent invitations for me and my family to visit him and fish from his yacht, but I stalled. Clara would have slugged me if I suggested taking her and the kids to Palm Island. The Miami area police finally gave Capone to understand that he wasn't welcome. He went back to Chicago, where income tax troubles were piling up for him.

I kept away from all hoodlums and spent considerable time with my labor skate friends from my days of organizing the telegraphers. Eddie McFadden, an old timer with the Teamsters' Union, was one of them. We went fishing together a lot.

One evening Eddie and I were driving through a small town near Miami when a car, coming from a side road like it was jet-propelled, hit my Chrysler. The driver was a U.S. Army major, and he was loop-legged drunk. He begged us not to bring charges against him, or it would mean the end of his military career. We felt sorry for him.

A police car pulled up, and I explained that the accident was all my fault. The major wasn't drunk, I maintained, but only dazed and shocked from the crash. McFadden and I promised the cops to take him to a hospital—but, instead, we drove him home to his wife. The major had little or no money, but he insisted on paying for the damages to my car. He sent me twenty dollars a month for four months, as I recall it.

Years later, after my return to Stateville from my break with Gene O'Connor, Banghart and the others, I sometimes saw the major's name in the World War II dispatches from the Pacific. He had considerable more rank by that time, and he was quite a hero.

Maybe I contributed something to World War II in a backhanded, years-ago way, eh? I thought of Yiddles Miller's "What am I, a stool pigeon?" gag, and I was happy that McFadden and I had fronted for the major in Florida.

That night McFadden had some disquieting news for me. The Capone mob was moving in on my labor union friends in Chicago. A number of union officials had been murdered. The syndicate was out to grab the union treasuries, some of which ran into millions of dollars. The racketeers were stealing the working stiffs' dues and selling them out to certain unscrupulous employers.

That figured, of course, and I had heard many rumbles about it. Everybody knew that Prohibition, the Noble Experiment, as President Herbert Hoover called it, was headed for the drain. The Capone mob had to tap a new source of money. Labor organizations, unprotected by the government and despised by many employers at that time, were vulnerable.

I had no worries about the end of Prohibition. I could dig up a few hundred thousand dollars. My customers in the roadhouses and suburban speakeasies had promised to stick with me when repeal hit. I had trucks to handle deliveries. Matt and I had negotiated to become agents for two legitimate brands of beer after repeal. We probably would do better than we had during Prohibition.

When I got back to Chicago at the opening of the beer-drinking season in the spring of 1931, Matt greeted me a little shamefacedly. Al Capone had shaken him down for $25,000 from our bank account. Matt had paid off.

I wasn't too severe with Matt, but I told him that we never again would give a dime to the Chicago mob. He agreed that I was right, but maybe it turned out that my policy was wrong. On November 18, 1931, Matt was in a speakeasy he owned, the Morton Inn, in suburban Morton Grove, when two gunmen walked into the dump and killed him.

Capone telephoned my brother, Tommy, the next day, and sounded as penitent as all hell.

"I'm terribly sorry," Al said. "There was a drunken caper and Matt got killed. I couldn't feel worse. I always liked Matt. I'm sending a $100 wreath to his funeral."

The pressure from the big Chicago mob really was on now, full force. Any day a machine gun might go chug-chug-chug behind me. The bad thing for me was that I wouldn't hear it. I'd be dead. All I could do was to give

Matt a decent burial—and carry Capone's $100 horseshoe floral piece out behind the funeral home, where I kicked the bejesus out of it on the garbage dump.

The Chicago syndicate had erased Matt Kolb and, I figured, they would be out to eliminate me next.

Chapter 7

The Labor Skates and I

B ack in 1932, I began getting a two-way squeeze. On one side were my friends in labor unionism. On the other was the Chicago mob. The federal government put Capone into prison for income tax cheating, but The Enforcer, Nitti, stepped into his place. And Nitti was looking around hungrily for fresh money.

Repeal was on the way, and the syndicate's big profits from gagging whiskey and watery beer soon would be ended. The great depression was settling down for a long stay. People didn't have the money for gambling. Business in the Capone brothels fell off, even after the price was cut to one buck in some of the dives, with the girl getting forty cents and the house taking the rest.

Banks closed. The Insull utilities empire fell apart. Insurance companies went bust. Brokers jumped out of their skyscraper windows so often that somebody suggested paving Chicago's La Salle Street with rubber.

In the late 20s and early 30s the biggest and most solvent treasuries in the world were in the labor unions. Some of the old-time labor skates didn't trust banks. They socked the unions' cash away in safe deposit boxes or invested in U.S. Government bonds. The top American Federation of Labor unions in the Chicago area had about $10,000,000 in their treasuries.

Chicago gangsters long had been nibbling at the unions around the edges. For years Al Capone was in the business of providing thugs and scabs to break strikes for employers. In breaking a strike, Capone would weaken the union involved and then put his own thieving men into the organization.

Public opinion was against unionism, generally, and the labor men could expect a minimum of protection, if any, from the cops and politicians.

To a union trying to build up its membership, the racketeers had a novel approach. One of them would call on the local officers with a pitch like this: "Let us put one of our men in your office. We'll help you get members. All we want is a job for one of our boys." A union that fell for this sucker bait was through. Once a mobster got any authority, he took over the local, emptied the treasury and stole the monthly dues.

In the late 1920s, my friends from my days of organizing telegraphers came calling on me. They were getting steamroller pressure from the syndicate. Three or four of them wound up murdered or kidnaped. They were afraid to live in Chicago with their families. A couple of their homes were bombed. They wanted to move into my quiet area.

I gave them the okay. What else? They were my friends, and they were safe in the suburbs. The suburban police and town officials wouldn't hold still for any gangster killings or other violence.

Patrick "Paddy" Burrell, a Teamsters' Union International vice president, settled down in Park Ridge and some other union bosses followed him. One of Burrell's business agents, Edward McFadden, was a sort of real estate agent for the labor skates—renting houses for them under assumed names, buying furniture, putting in supplies of groceries and hiring housekeepers.

I had known McFadden, an elderly character with long,

white hair, since my boyhood. He was called "Chicken" because he once had been connected with a union of poultry pluckers in Chicago.

All of the union officials brought their bodyguards with them to the country to live, and it made quite a collection. The bodyguards carried guns, as their profession required, and they represented the alumni groups of about every penitentiary in America. Things were lively around our quiet suburban saloons for a while. I sent word, through McFadden, that the bodyguards were asking for trouble with the local law, and the rowdiness eased off.

In 1929, the syndicate had offered to cut my brother, Tommy, and me in on a multimillion-dollar union racket. Out to Tommy's home in suburban Oak Park came Marcus "Studdy" Looney, a Capone pimp who had graduated into labor muscling. The big dealers of the syndicate had sent Looney. Tommy, who was just out of the Indiana State Penitentiary at the time, telephoned me to join them.

Now, I'm not going to pull any punches in telling about Tommy. I'm his brother, and I'll still do everything I can for him. But he did get into a lot of trouble. He did time for burglary and mail robbery. The sensational newspapers got to calling him "Terrible Tommy" Touhy, and I inherited the nickname after the Factor hoax.

Tommy paid a heavy price for the things he did, and he never complained. He was partly paralyzed back in 1929, and years later he became an almost helpless, hopeless invalid. He finally went to one of the western states to live out his days.

Studdy could hardly read or write, but he was a whiz at arithmetic, particularly at subtracting—subtracting money from people. He brought a list of Chicago area unions with him to Tommy's house with the amounts of money in their treasuries. It added up to about $10,000,000, as I have said.

One top prize to be stolen was the union of Chicago milk wagon drivers, with a bankroll of $1,300,000, and an income of about $250,000 a year in dues. The boss of that local was tough Robert L. "Old Doc" Fitchie, then in about his 65th year. He had been a friend of my father and he had been fighting union racketeers all of his life.

Other labor skates and their unions on Looney's list included Art Wallace of the painters, Johnny Rooney of the circular distributors, Mike Boyle of the electricians, Tom Reynolds of the movie projection booth operators and Mike Norris, a teamsters' man. Many of them were to be murdered or to knuckle under to the syndicate in the years that followed.

Looney brought word that the Teamsters' International, of which Burrell was a vice president, had about $8,000,-000 in strike funds in Indianapolis and Cincinnati. The Chicago mob planned to knock off the teamsters' locals one by one and finally to grab the treasuries. At that time, Jimmy Hoffa was still in knee pants and Dave Beck was slugging it out on strike picket lines.

After dangling the prospect of big money in front of us, Looney made his proposition to Tommy and me: "You guys can each have a union, the boss says. Which ones do you want?"

His meaning was plain. If we would double-cross the labor leaders, some of whom had been our friends for years, we would get rich quick. I could be a lot of help in the swindle, because the labor leaders trusted me. I would be able to persuade them to put some Judases—to be picked by the syndicate, of course—into the locals.

Tommy and I told Studdy that we wanted no part of the scheme. We were polite about refusing, but firm. Looney did some blustering, warned us to keep our mouths shut about the mob's plans, and left. He wasn't a block away before Tommy and I were on the telephone, warning our friends in the labor movement. I was building up a houseful of bad will from the syndicate.

Paddy Burrell called a meeting of unionists in his Park Ridge home and invited us. Tommy went, but I stayed away. After the conference, Tommy and Jerry Horan came to my house. I was working on my fishing tackle in the basement rumpus room.

Horan slapped a cow-choker sheaf of money on the bar and explained: "We union guys have started a war chest to protect ourselves. Burrell put up $75,000 for the teamsters. I kicked in $50,000. We want you to be treasurer. When money is needed, we'll draw it from this bankroll."

I never liked the idea of holding anybody else's money, and I said so. Horan insisted. They didn't want to put the cash in a bank because they wanted it ready at hand, nights or days or holidays. I agreed, at last, but I tacked on a few reverse conditions:

"I'll keep the money for you, but I'm not going to pass it out to any slob who comes asking. You name one man who is eligible to draw from the fund. I'll give the cash to him, and he'll have to sign a receipt for every dollar he takes. Okay?"

Horan said that was all right and we agreed that Burrell's man, Eddie McFadden, would make all withdrawals. I put the money in a fireproof safe behind a sliding panel in the basement. Then we had a bottle or two of my special beer.

The Chicago mobsters learned soon, of course, that I was handling the labor skates' bankroll. The syndicate had stool pigeons everywhere. Another black mark had been checked up against me, and the syndicate never forgot. As the months passed, I began hearing rumbles that my family and I might get hit by a bomb in our home.

I hired two guards, Walter "Buck" Henrichsen, a former county highway cop, and Eddie Schwabauer. Both of them were good shots, and, it developed later, they were even better at lying under oath.

One or another of the guards sat in our back yard playhouse with a shotgun while the kids, Tommy and Roger, were at the swimming pool. Clara drove the youngsters to and from parochial school, about two miles away, or else I did. I kept a man on duty outside the house all night.

We never let the boys know of any possible danger. When we discussed anything like that, we remembered our old Western Union days together. We would hold hands and signal each other with Morse code by pressure of our fingers.

On a sunny spring afternoon, I was in the basement,

making ready for a fishing trip to the Wisconsin lake country. The time came to pick up Roger and Tommy at the school. Clara called down the stairway that she was leaving on the errand.

The telephone rang in fifteen or twenty minutes. It was one of the boys' teachers, and she was screaming with hysteria.

Two men in a car had tried to grab Tommy and Roger as they left school. The boys had jumped into the car with Clara and she had driven away, toward home.

"Mr. Touhy, those men are following," the teacher yelled. "I'm terribly frightened."

I grabbed a deer rifle off the wall and loaded it as I ran to one of our other cars. I rolled along the highway toward the school at ninety miles an hour. I met a couple of cars, but not the one Clara was driving.

A dozen teachers were on the school grounds, some of them crying. They waved frantically and pointed back the way from which I had come. I drove back, slowly this time, but cursing and raging. I thought for sure that the syndicate had snatched my family.

Halfway home, a car I recognized came out of a driveway ahead of me. In it were Clara and the boys. She had stopped off to buy fresh eggs and milk from a farmer, a by-chance thing that had saved them all.

Clara hadn't noticed anything, but the teachers said two men had jumped out of their car as the boys came out of school. They ducked back when Tommy and Roger ran toward Clara's car, parked at the curb in the direction of home. She got away because the men had to make a U-turn to follow her.

I increased the guards around the house and on the kids. I assigned Henrichsen, the former county cop, to watch the school to be certain that the boys didn't get grabbed at recess or lunch time. And I made sure that anybody who tried it wouldn't live long.

A friend loaned me a laundry truck, one of those panel body jobs with a rack to hold bags of wash on the top. I put peepholes in one side of the body and then hinged it so the panel would drop down. I parked the truck—

with myself and three other guys in the back—across the street from the school. All of us had guns.

From inside the truck, we could watch the school through the peepholes. If Murray Humphreys sent his gorillas out again to snatch Tommy and Roger, we would lower the side of the truck. The ex-cops and farmers in the truck with me would start shooting, and so would I.

Things were quiet around Des Plaines and the other suburbs after that, but not in Chicago. Murray Humphreys kidnaped Old Doc Fitchie and collected $50,000 in union money ransom for him. Years later, incidentally, Humphreys was forced to pay income taxes on the ransom, but he never served a day in prison for it. The $50,000 item showed up on a Humphreys tax return made public by a Senate Committee.

Paddy Burrell and his bodyguard, Willie Marks, went to Wisconsin on a vacation. Capone-style gunmen murdered them both. Bill Rooney, of the sheetmetal workers, was cut down by bullets at his Chicago home.

A *Chicago Tribune* reporter, Jake Lingle, was murdered in Chicago as he started for a race track. It caused the biggest stink of all Chicago gang killings, except for the St. Valentine's Day massacre, when the Capone mob lined up five Bugs Moran gangsters, along with two bystanders, and shot them down in a garage.

One of the Chicago newspapers carried an editorial that started out: "Prohibition is ebbing away on a floodtide of human blood."

The union war chest in my basement safe also flowed away. Some of the labor skates gave in to syndicate pressures, but others kept fighting. Fitchie made a steel and bulletproof glass fortress of his headquarters in Chicago— and held out successfully after his kidnaping.

The unionists in the suburbs around me lined up armies of bodyguards. One of the hired gunfighters was Lester Gillis. He built up quite a reputation as "Baby Face Nelson," a John Dillinger torpedo who murdered two FBI agents, only to be killed himself. I never met Gillis, so far as I know.

Charles Connors also was around. He was called "Ice

Wagon," because a getaway car he drove after a bank robbery hit an ice delivery truck. One of Connors' pals, Ludwig "Dutch" Schmidt, a career robber and thief, and Jimmy Tribbles, a stir-crazy ex-convict, were in the area, too, as was Frank "Porky" Dillon, another hale and hearty eye-gouging type.

Now, I never have put myself forward as a candidate for sainthood. I'll admit that I did a lot of things in my life that I shouldn't have done. But I didn't kidnap anybody, including Jake the Barber. I never killed anybody. I never robbed or stole. And I never associated knowingly with Gillis or such killers.

I'll admit that I did accept them around the community as unavoidable evils in connection with my union friends and their fight against the Chicago mob.

Meanwhile, the time drew near for what Judge Barnes called the Factor kidnaping that never happened.

In the election of 1932, Franklin D. Roosevelt whomped the Republican Party with the ease of a bulldozer knocking over a sapling. The massacre of the G.O.P. and the Democrats' victory meant for sure that beer and booze were going to be legalized. I was eager for repeal. It would make me legal. Maybe, the next time they wanted to run me for mayor of Des Plaines, I might accept.

I had been a Republican, mainly because many of the Cook County officials, as well as the suburban and township people with whom I dealt, were Republicans. Tony Cermak, a Democrat, had been president of the Cook County Board, a powerful job, but I managed to get along with him, too.

One of the many Democrats who coasted into office on the Roosevelt landslide was Thomas J. Courtney, as state's attorney for Cook County. Courtney was a handsome, six-foot Irishman with wavy hair, dimples and flashing eyes. As state's attorney, he had one of the most powerful prosecuting offices in America. He was one of the men who was to help put me in prison for 99 years for a kidnaping that never happened.

Courtney, before his Roosevelt-landslide election as state's attorney, was without practical experience in criminal law. During the twelve years that he was state's attorney, he never prosecuted a case.

Courtney had been practically unknown to the voters before his 1932 campaign. The betting odds, almost up to election day, had been against him, but the general public welcomed his victory. He had promised to clean up Chicago and Cook County—and he had a great opportunity to come through

The people had their bellies full of the Capone syndicate. Al had been convicted of income tax cheating, but Nitti, Humphreys, Hunt, Campagna, Paul "The Waiter" Ricca and the rest of the murdering thieves were doing business in the same old way. Murder was commonplace, 100-girl whorehouses were going and the bookie joints were as wide open as the grocery stores. Chicago had the reputation of being the Crime Capital of the World and the people didn't like it.

Courtney had promised to crush organized crime and to crack down on what was then the most popular crime target—kidnaping. The kidnaping of the Lindbergh baby in March, 1932, had inflamed 'the public.

And the flames were going to char me, Roger Touhy. Religious, civic, business and other groups in Cook County were solidly behind Courtney. There were predictions that he could be President of the United States if he brought decency to Chicago. He didn't make it.

The second most important man in the prosecutor's office was the chief investigator, and in that job Courtney put Dan Gilbert, a Chicago police captain.

Gilbert had earlier been an official of a strong, and violent, Teamsters' Union local. The police had questioned him about the shooting and wounding of a rival for power in the union, but he was exonerated. After the shooting, Gilbert was boss of the union. He was always active in politics, and promotions came to him rapidly after he became a policeman.

As chief investigator, Gilbert had charge of gathering evidence for criminal prosecutions of murder, robbery, kidnaping, rape, burglary, arson and other felonies. He had a staff of investigators, mostly policemen on leave from the Chicago force—as was Gilbert himself. He was a strict, harsh disciplinarian.

Gilbert's potential power in that office is easy to see. The man in his job could cinch a case by digging up the proper evidence or he could ruin it by overlooking a few things. And there was no tight, direct supervision to stop the chief investigator, if he saw fit, from manufacturing, faking or planting evidence, either.

The Number-Three man appointed by Courtney was First Assistant State's Attorney Wilbert F. Crowley. He was young, ambitious, vigorous, relentless. He had a mop of reddish hair, a good appearance and fine knowledge of the law. He was one hell of a prosecutor. Believe me, I know.

Crowley, unlike Courtney and Gilbert, was no politician. He had made his reputation as an assistant public defender, handling cases for poor bums who showed up in court without money to hire lawyers. He beat the prosecution so many times that he had to be hired away from the defense. Crowley simply took the cases assigned to him by Courtney and prosecuted on the evidence provided by Chief Investigator Gilbert.

The strong man in the office was, of course, Gilbert. He had years of experience as a policeman. He wasn't a lawyer, but he knew the laws of evidence. Courtney, lacking in criminal law experience and police investigative procedure, had to rely heavily on Gilbert's advice.

And now it is time for a look at Gilbert's record.

During twelve years as chief investigator under Courtney, Gilbert never came up with the evidence to send one Capone mobster—not one!—to jail or prison for so much as one day, as Judge Barnes found. Sure, he put me in the penitentiary, and tried his best to make it the electric chair —but I was an enemy of the syndicate.

The federal government convicted Capone gangsters of extortion, fraud and income-tax violations. The mob hatched a plot in Chicago to bleed $3,000,000 out of the Hollywood movie industry, but local authorities seemed to have been unaware of it. It took Uncle Sam to put Short Pants Campagna, Paul The Waiter Ricca and other Chicago hooligans away for ten-year terms.

True, Gilbert got a mess of Capone plug-uglies indicted for muscling in on the Chicago Bartenders' Union. But when the trial came up, the only real witness—a union skate who had been guarded by a police escort—refused to testify, and the case went out the window. The syndicate won again.

Courtney left office in 1944, but Gilbert stayed on for six years. Did he get the evidence after Courtney's departure to convict any Chicago syndicate mobster? He did not.

During much of the twelve years of Courtney and Gilbert, the Capone outfit—through the operations of two sure-thing characters, Bill Johnson and Bill Skidmore—made a gambling bonanza out of Chicago and parts of Cook County. They had as many as nineteen illegal casinos operating.

My word doesn't have to be taken for it. The court records of the income tax trials of Johnson and Skidmore prove it, as solid as the walls of Stateville. While Gilbert was chief investigator, the state never convicted, or even attempted to prosecute Johnson and Skidmore. Syndicate joints were immune most of the time, except for token raids.

Gilbert was chief investigator for eighteen years. Then, in 1950, he ran for sheriff of Cook County! I was astounded, in Stateville, when I heard that he had the Democratic nomination. He looked like a gutsure winner, too, with the powerful Democratic organization behind him.

But he was far from home free. The *Chicago Sun-Times* pressured the Senate crime investigating committee into calling Gilbert as a witness. Senator Estes Kefauver, of Tennessee, the committee chairman and a loyal Democrat, heard Gilbert's testimony in secret and refused to make it public. The strategy didn't work.

A *Sun-Times* reporter fast-talked the stenographic transcript of Gilbert's testimony out of the committee files. Gilbert's own testimony showed that he had admitted having a fortune of $650,000—built up from a legal income that never passed $10,000 a year, he said.

He said he had made the 650 grand from gambling and market speculation. "I have been a gambler at heart," he testified. He said he made the money against the house odds of professional gamblers and on the grain and stock markets.

The *Sun-Times* printed about twenty columns of Gilbert's testimony. The reporter who took the document spent two years squirming out of going to prison for fraud and impersonation, until the government decided at last there was no criminal intent, freeing him on that ground.

Gilbert, the favorite to win, was clobbered by nearly 400,000 votes when the ballots were counted.

I was happy in Stateville, where Tubbo and Jake the Barber had put me, when I heard of Gilbert's defeat. He had campaigned under the slogan: "I put Roger Touhy in prison." If he had become sheriff, he would have been in a politically powerful position to keep me there. Also, his election would have affirmed, in effect, my conviction as a scummy kidnaper.

Chapter 8

Jake the Barber
Was Kidnaped???

The night of June 30-July 1, of 1933, will remain fresh in my memory forever. It was a warm night. The scent of roses and other flowers around our Des Plaines home was heavy, like in a funeral parlor on the last night of a wake. Crickets—millions of them, it seemed—were chirping in the distance.

I drove to the Oak Park Hospital. My brother, Tommy, was there for treatment and "Chicken" McFadden, the old union character who rented houses for labor skates, was getting over a prostate operation. I had picked up two of Tommy's daughters and taken them along. I gassed with my brother and McFadden for a while and told Chicken:

"Hurry and get out of here, old timer. Clara and the kids and I are going fishing in Wisconsin in a few days. We want you to come along." Eddie said he'd do his best. I left and drove home.

We had a house guest that night. She was Emily Ivins, the girl who had been our chaperon when I first had courted Clara more than fifteen years before. Emily had the blues.

The depression had knocked her out of her job in Chicago, and Clara and I tried to cheer her up.

Legal beer—3.2 percent variety, if you could call it beer—had already returned. Strong beers and wines, ales and liquors could not be far behind. I told Emily about a happening in Touhy-country on the night before 3.2 was legalized. From my breweries and storage places, my trucks had hauled every drop of illegal brew to the speakeasies in the suburbs and along the highways. I had given it away.

Two big, brawny policemen in one of the suburbs had stood drinking the free beer at a bar. They gulped it down from 12-ounce schooners. They agreed maudlinly that Touhy beer was the best beer ever brewed. They said tearfully that the new 3.2 was hogwash. Then they turned and fired their revolvers—shooting holes into twelve barrels of legal Bismarck and Gambrinius beer which I had had delivered in advance.

The pressurized beer shot all over the place and made a lake on the floor. The two cops holstered their weapons and returned to drinking Touhy beer. They had made their protest.

Clara, Emily and I sat on the front porch in semidarkness. The kids were sleeping. A guard—more about him later—was on duty around the grounds. Jim Wagner's saloon, a neighborhood place down the road, seemed to be doing a good business, with cars arriving or leaving now and then.

Emily knew she could stay in our home as long as she wanted. Clara had put her in a spare room. We said we'd be glad to take her with the boys, McFadden and us on the Wisconsin fishing jaunt. But she was anxious to find a job and get working again. She would rest with us for a few days, she said, and then go back to Chicago.

I was hungry and asked about something to eat. There were cold meats in the refrigerator. Clara and Emily nixed me. It was Friday and they wouldn't take meat until after midnight, which would make it Saturday and Roman Catholic legitimate. After the deadline passed, we had sandwiches, salad, sliced pickles and coffee.

During this time, Jake the Barber had been kidnaped,

he later said. Kidnaped by me and my men, he claimed.

Clara, Emily and I sat gabbing until about 4 a.m. What was unusual about that? We were old friends and we had a lot of reminiscing to do. None of us had anything special to occupy us on Saturday.

At seven o'clock on the morning of July first, a knock on the door awakened me. A Chicago police lieutenant was calling. He showed me his badge and said his name was Carroll. I invited him in for coffee. He was a nice-looking open-faced man in a blue suit. What he said surprised me— because I couldn't imagine why he was bringing the problem to me.

Jake the Barber Factor had been kidnaped about one a.m., the lieutenant said, from near The Dells, a Capone syndicate night club and gambling joint near Morton Grove. Factor presumably was being held for ransom. The Dells was a widely-known roadhouse where such headliners as Joe E. Lewis had played. The gambling rooms, presumably as crooked as all other Capone casinos, were on the second floor.

I asked the lieutenant, as I sat in pajamas and sipped my coffee, what the hell this had to do with me. "Go ask the syndicate," I said. "They own the joint. I've never even been in it." He said that, well, I was widely acquainted out in this section of the county and that I might want to help. Factor might be held in one of the suburbs, he said.

The reputation of Jake the Barber didn't smell like any hyacinth to me. I had read in the papers that he was wanted for swindling $7,000,000 out of widows, clergymen and other unfortunate chumps in England. The British Crown was trying its damnedest to extradite Jake back to England. Also, the papers had been full of stories a few weeks before that Jake Factor's son had been snatched by kidnapers.

Still, regardless of what Factor might have been, I detested kidnapers. A dozen or more businessmen, women and children of rich families—including the Lindbergh child—had been snatched for ransom, with some of the victims being mistreated or killed.

There was a national hysteria, and rightly so, against the

crime of kidnaping. Clergymen ranted against it from their pulpits and so did editorial writers in their columns. The noisier politicians in Washington tried to outshout each other in being against a crime that everybody loathed.

A California mob hanged two kidnapers from a bridge and Westbrook Pegler, in his nationally syndicated newspaper column, wrote an article praising the lynching. A lot of people seemed to agree with him.

The FBI set up and trained special crews of experts to fly to any section of the country upon a report of a ransom kidnaping. U. S. Attorney General Homer Cummings appointed a special aide, Joseph B. Keenan, to supervise the prosection of kidnapers. No effort was to be spared, or money either, to put an end to kidnaping.

No kidnaper ever had been captured, prosecuted and convicted during the wave of abductions.

Every police officer and prosecutor in America wanted to solve a kidnaping. Any one of them who put a kidnaper in prison or in the electric chair would be a hero. I, Roger Touhy, and two co-defendants were going to have the murky distinction of being the first men convicted.

I remarked to the police lieutenant in my home that kidnapers seemed to be giving the Factor family an unusually bad time; that the Factor boy had been snatched for ransom just a short time ago. That was right, my caller said, but the son, Jerome, 19 years old, had come home unhurt and without payment of a cent of ransom.

Since I liked kidnapers even less than I did swindlers, I told the lieutenant I'd see what information I could pick up. He left after getting my unlisted phone number and telling me he would call me. I drove around that day, visiting with saloonkeeper friends, seeing how my 3.2 beer was going, taking orders and asking questions.

The beer sales were encouraging and all my customers were staying loyal to me, but rumbles on the Factor snatch were nil. There were a lot of gossip and speculation, but nobody knew anything. I ran into a few of the labor skates' bodyguards, and they knew nothing, either. One of them was Tribbles, the stir-buggy ex-con.

Tribbles was what he himself called "an engaging eccentric." He was stir-crazy from too many trips to the pen, but he was one of the most courteous men I ever knew. He once went into a Chicago combination bookie-saloon and asked a bartender politely: "Please, sir, where is the gentlemen's retiring room?" He liked to use formal, long words.

The barman replied to Tribbles profanely using an uncouth term to designate the john. Jimmy made use of the facilities, pondered over the bartender's coarseness and decided to teach him a lesson. He washed his hands, straightened his tie, returned to the main room, produced a .38 automatic from a shoulder holster and robbed the joint of about $12,000.

"If you had greeted me civilly, instead of outrageously, I would not have felt impelled to commit this depredation," he told the crass employee.

Another ancedote about Tribbles was that he burglarized a department store, strolled into the book department, started reading a dictionary under a night light and still was memorizing long words when the clerks came to work next morning and grabbed him.

Stir-crazy or not, Jimmy gave me some good advice on that first day when I learned of the Factor mess. "Mr. Touhy, sir," he told me, "I think you should not concern yourself about this Barber person. I feel certain that his abduction is a preposterous hoax." Out of the mouths of babes and stir-buggy ex-cons. . . .

That night I went to the neighborhood of The Dells, but I didn't enter the premises. If I did, and something bad happened there as long as five years afterward, the mob would blame me for it, I knew. Instead, I stopped in at Murphy's Roadhouse, across the street from The Dells. I learned there that Buck Henrichsen, the ex-cop I had hired as a guard for my children, had been in the place the evening before with his former wife. I didn't put any importance on that—not until much later.

My next call was Bam's Place. When I asked Bam if he had seen anything unusual around the time of the reported kidnaping, he sneered at me and said: "What are you doing, Touhy, police work?" implying that I was a stool pigeon. I thought of the Yiddles Miller story and of the Judas in the

Last Supper painting of my childhood. I hit Bam on the jaw and knocked him as cold as an alderman's heart.

I didn't learn anything about the possible whereabouts of Jake Factor or the names of anybody who might have embezzled him. But, by reading the papers and checking with some people who knew, I got a pretty straight line on what had happened—presumably.

The Barber had gone to The Dells with his cute, youthful wife, Rella; Jerome, his son by a previous marriage; a friend, Al Epstein; Epstein's wife, and others whose names don't matter right now.

They had dinner and a few drinks, and watched the floor show. After that, Factor shot craps in the gambling room. I heard he lost $20,000, but those things always were exaggerated. Jake gambled on credit, since he didn't like to carry much cash for fear of robbers, and he signed the dinner check. Those things show how chummy he was with the syndicate.

On leaving at about one a.m., the Factor people got into the three cars they were using. Jake, Jerome and Epstein were in one limousine. Factor took charge of seating arrangements, it later developed, and he insisted that the womenfolk ride in the other cars. He presumably didn't want them to be needlessly frightened. They might have interfered with the script by screaming for help or going into hysteria.

Jake's car was the second of the three to pull out of The Dells. On the highway the limousine was curbed, or forced off to the shoulder, by a sedan occupied by men carrying machine guns and other weapons. The machine gunners got rid of Epstein and Jerome; drove off with Jake the Barber.

The papers quoted Jerome and Epstein as saying they had been unable to see any of the gunmen clearly. It had been too dark.

I want to state right here, incidentally, that I have nothing to say against Mrs. Rella Factor, Jerome Factor, Al Epstein or any of the others in the party at The Dells that night. I understand that Jerome Factor became a businessman with a fine family and a reputation for integrity and honesty.

After the hassle at Bam's Place, I went home and did some thinking—and some telephoning. I learned things that made me as skittish as a saloonkeeper with a WCTU delegation on his doorstep.

The man who had introduced himself to me at seven a.m. as "Lieutenant Carroll" was really, I discovered, Lieutenant Leo Carr, on leave of absence from the Chicago Police Department. He was working as a paid bodyguard for Jake the Barber. He therefore had come to me on behalf of Factor, and not the Chicago police. On leave, he presumably had no more police stature than any other civilian.

Things were smelling very, very dead rat, but the aroma got worse. Phew!

I found that Factor had rented the roof bungalow and several suites at the Morrison Hotel in downtown Chicago. His hotel bills came to $1,000 a week. With him much of the time was The Camel Humphreys, the Capone hooligan who had offered me a gift car to guarantee him safe conduct from my home to Chicago.

My reports were that Jake the Barber and Humphreys had been associated previously.

I began wondering a little, right about then, whether the Chicago mob might be setting me up as a patsy for a kidnaping rap. But the idea seemed ridiculous. I put it aside in my mind, which was a mistake, like turning your back on a Capone torpedo.

How could I be clay-pigeoned in the case? I had an alibi from the people in the hospital, including Tommy, his two daughters, McFadden, the doctors, the nurses and others. At the time of the alleged, purported kidnaping, I had been sitting on my porch with Clara and Emily Ivins.

Anyway, why would a man in my situation stoop to what was cursed as the dirtiest crime on the books? Kidnaping, that is. I was a rich man, comparatively speaking. With 3.2 beer back and the complete end of prohibition in sight, I had a future of prosperity. I had standing in my community—even if they never did elect me mayor, which Clara and I used to joke about.

I fell asleep and had a good night of rest, except for a couple of telephone calls from the man who called himself "Lieutenant Carroll." I played along with him, not tipping him that I knew his true connection as a bodyguard for Factor. He rang off after being told by me that I had learned nothing of importance.

On the following morning, July second, we had strawberries and cream for breakfast, with the usual scrambled eggs, bacon and toast, of course. The kids were plenty excited. The Fourth of July was coming up and I had a big box of fireworks—legal at that time—stored in a closet.

Clara got the boys out to the swimming pool and I looked at the papers. There was interesting news of the Factor case. The stories had a between-the-lines, don't-believe-all-you-hear attitude about it. Some of the writers referred pointedly to the fact that Jake was up against the wall on the British extradition matter. It would be most convenient for him to be snatched at that time, since he was in danger of a 22½- to 24-year term in prison for swindling.

A representative of the British Crown in Chicago charged flatly that the kidnaping was a fake, engineered by Factor to beat extradition. Attorney General Cummings' kidnap expert, Keenan, subsequently referred to the hoax as "the *alleged* Factor kidnaping." Jimmy Tribbles, the stirbugs ex-con, seemed to have had a point, I thought.

But, against those anti-Factor angles, there was a disquieting element for me. Tubbo Gilbert, the most powerful law enforcement officer in Cook County, muscled into the picture with a newspaper blast. He announced, flatly and firmly, that the kidnaping was legit and that the "Touhy gang" had kidnaped Jake the Barber. He didn't qualify the accusation. He simply said that Roger Touhy was the man to get for the crime.

Now, wasn't that a remarkable deduction? Gilbert hadn't questioned me. He hadn't asked me whether I had an alibi. So far as I know, he hadn't even inquired about whether I might have been dead or out of the country at the time of the presumed kidnaping. He didn't even know for sure at that time whether there had been a kidnaping, but he blamed me.

I didn't pay a hell of a lot of attention. Some of the Chicago newspapers were pretty irresponsible at that time. Anything for a headline seemed to be the papers' philosophy. I did make up my mind, however, that I would be available at any time the law wanted to question me. I stayed close to home.

I kept up with my paper work in my basement office and saw most of my customers there. I took all of my meals at home. I wasn't away from the place for more than an hour at a time during the time Jake was among the lost, strayed or stolen.

Emily Ivins stayed with us through the Fourth of July and for a couple of days afterward. Mrs. Margaret Morgan, sister of my wife's mother, and her husband, a retired Chicago city fireman, were guests in our house for either five or six days during the period.

Miss Ivins and the Morgans were available to testify that I hadn't been away from home, kidnaping Jake the Barber or guarding him or making ransom arrangements. It was a sensible precaution to take, after Gilbert had blasted me in the papers.

We had our Fourth of July party in the back yard near the swimming pool. Clara served hamburgers and lemonade and homemade ice cream. The place was jumping with kids. One of our boys—Roger, I think—burned his hand on a sparkler. He wasn't hurt badly, but the thing sticks in my mind.

A *Chicago Evening American* reporter came out to interview me. He seemed a mite nervous; probably he expected to find me surrounded by gangsters. I was in my shirt-sleeves beside the pool, with the kids splashing in the shallow end. I was staying at home, so there was no need for a bodyguard.

I tried to make the reporter feel at home, but still he was uneasy, so I told him: "You came out here to ask me if I kidnaped Factor, didn't you? Well, ask it." He did and I told him the answer was no. I told him about having been at the hospital on the night Factor went away and of sitting on the porch with Clara and Emily Ivins until four a.m.. I hadn't been away from my house since the first day, Saturday, for more than a few minutes at a time to take care of urgent business or to do household errands.

The reporter seemed surprised when I told him that no police, except for a lieutenant on leave of absence, had talked to me. I said I was entirely willing to make a statement. I invited the police to search my home and other properties if they had any hope of finding any Factor evidence. Pointing to Roger and Tommy, I told my visitor:

"I want to be cleared of this thing. I don't want those children to grow up with the stink of suspicion of kidnaping on their father. I hope you'll print that in your paper."

I walked with him to his car and he said that, for his money, Factor hadn't been kidnaped at all. There were reports that Jake's relatives and friends were negotiating to pay ransom—$200,000 was one figure mentioned—but that was to be expected in any case. The reporter said he would do the best he could for me in his story. I suppose he did, but most of my quotes got lost somewhere.

The question comes up at this point as to why I didn't give myself up to the law. Well, why should I have? There was no warrant out for my arrest, no charge filed against me. My name had been mentioned in the case by one, and only one, police officer—Tubbo Gilbert. If I went sashaying into a police station to surrender, they probably would have kicked me out on my can. I wasn't wanted for anything.

If the police wanted to find me, they could. Just as easily as the Chicago reporter had. I telephoned my lawyer, William Scott Stewart. Brother Tommy had introduced me to Stewart a couple of years earlier. Stewart told me I was doing the correct thing.

Chapter 9

Nobody Questioned Me

My privately-listed home telephone rang day and night. I couldn't have been more popular if I was the only bookie in Cook County and all the horse race betting chumps had my number.

Lieutenant Carr was pushing me for information, which I didn't have. He wanted to know if I knew certain gangsters whose names meant nothing to me, if there had been any unusual activity in the suburbs. I told him I didn't know a thing and that I didn't expect to hear anything.

The annoyance of those calls was broken when I picked up the phone and heard the voice of a fine friend, Father Joseph Weber, a Roman Catholic priest in Indianapolis. I had first met Father Weber when my brother, Tommy, had been in burglary trouble in Indianapolis. I had gone there, retained a lawyer and did my best to see that Tommy had a fair trial.

Tommy got a two- to 14-year sentence and I remember his telling me after the verdict: "Rog, I'll give you seven to five that I never live to serve it." He was suffering from incurable Parkinson's disease, but he would have lost the bet.

He lived out the term, won a parole and, as this story is written, 34 years later, he is still alive.

Father Weber had done his deeply sympathetic best for me and other members of the family back in 1925. He was a peppery, wiry, white-haired man of about seventy. He was against sin, but, like the Master in whose footsteps he tried to follow, he believed in forgiving the sinner, if properly penitent. I admired him a great deal.

His parish was the poorest in Indianapolis. His people were too poverty-ridden to buy ice during the summer, too poor to supply their big families with milk. I contributed ice and milk funds over the years to his parish. My labor skate friends did the same. He was a convert and his wealthy family—owners of a brewery in Cincinnati—had disowned him when he turned to Catholicism.

The anti-Catholic, anti-Jewish, anti-Negro Ku Klux Klan was active in Indiana when I first had known Father Weber. He was almost rabid against those bigots, who had headquarters in Indianapolis. It was one of his biggest ambitions to get the KKK records, in order to expose some of the business leaders and politicians who were secret members of it.

Somebody broke into the headquarters, blew a safe and stole the records, which wound up in Father Weber's hand. I had nothing to do with it, but I got the blame—or credit. A Klan official offered me $250,000 to give back the documents. I didn't have them, but I wouldn't have taken his money if I had.

I thought upon hearing Father Weber's voice that he was telephoning from Indianapolis. But, no, he was in the La Salle Hotel in Chicago and he wanted to see me. I invited him to come at once and stay as long as he could. He would be able to say his required daily masses in the Des Plaines church. I sent a car into Chicago for him.

When he arrived at my home, I saw that he was deeply worried. He had come to Chicago at the request of Lieutenant Carr, working through an Indianapolis connection, Michael Hanrahan. Hanrahan came into my house with Father Weber. I was curious, and I let them do the talking.

Father Weber wanted to know if I had kidnaped Factor,

and I told him that I hadn't. He asked if I would swear upon the lives of my two sons that I was innocent. I said I would swear, and I did. Then he made an outrageous proposition on behalf of Carr:

Would I take $150,000 in cash, make a deal with the kidnapers, pay the ransom and keep any money that was left over?

I was astounded first upon hearing his words. Then I was deeply hurt. The implication was that Father Weber, my friend, had been talked into believing that I had snatched Jake the Barber. It was horrifying to me.

He was asking me, in effect, to take the money—as Al Capone had taken $50,000 from me for Matt Kolb's release—turn Factor loose and, presumably, live with my conscience thereafter.

Now, I don't mean to imply that Father Weber had any part of such a conspiracy. He was an old man, naive in the ways of politicians and policemen, and he undoubtedly thought he was doing the right thing. I was hurt, more than angry with him. I said:

"Father, when you are ready to go back to Chicago, the car will be outside. I don't want to talk about this matter any more." I went to another room. I heard the car pull away. My visitors were gone.

The old priest and I later became fine friends again. I suspected that $150,000 proposal was a gimmick thought up to frame me, but I was confident that Father Weber had nothing to do with it. Anyway, the risk of being railroaded seemed to be pretty remote at that time. Practically nobody was taking the Factor thing seriously.

Franklin R. Overmeyer, a distinguished lawyer representing the British crown, gave an interview charging flatly that there was no kidnaping; that Jake the Barber again was flimflamming the public. The story was a banner headline in the *Chicago Tribune*. Overmeyer summed up his evidence and gave a step-by-step history of the swindle case.

In May, 1931, more than two years before the reported kidnaping, Factor had been arrested in Chicago on a warrant charging he was guilty in England of "receiving property knowing it to have been fraudulently obtained," which amounted to an accusation of swindling. Overmeyer placed the amount of money taken at $8,000,000. Factor hired the best lawyers and politicians he could find, *including two former United States senators,* to fight the case.

On December 28, 1931, the United States Commissioner in Chicago ruled after a hearing that Factor should be extradited to England, where he faced a prison term of up to 24 years. Jake, as the case dragged along, paid off $1,-300,000 to British investors who claimed he had cheated them of their money. Clergymen, widows, working people and others unable to afford to lose were among the complaining witnesses.

Two office employes who had worked in Factor's London bucket shop were arrested, summarily convicted and sentenced to prison. The prospect for Jake the Barber in London was far from pleasing.

He appealed the Chicago U. S. Commissioner's ruling. His high-priced lawyers said that "receiving property knowing it to have been fraudulently obtained" was not pinpointed as a specific crime under a cloudy Illinois law. Subsequently, he claimed to have settled all the claims, which had him saying, in effect: "I didn't steal the money and, anyway, I paid it back."

Factor's appeal went to Judge George A. Carpenter of United States District Court, who, finding some sort of merit in Jake's pleas, overruled the commissioner and dismissed the extradition case. The government appealed Carpenter's ruling and the U. S. Court of Appeals said Carpenter was wrong.

Such ring-around-the-rosies seem to go on forever in the courts, as I well know. Factor now appealed to the United States Supreme Court to stop his removal to England. He had been free for most of the time on $50,000 bond. He lived like a multimillionaire, which he was, and he hobnobbed with The Camel Humphreys and other Capone mobsters.

On April 18, 1933, Attorney Overmeyer was in Washington, D. C., waiting to argue before the Supreme Court. The newspapers carried stories stating that Jerome Factor had been kidnaped. Jake the Barber had skipped his Supreme Court appointment in Washington, which he had a good reason for doing. If he had appeared in the District of Columbia, he would have been in federal jurisdiction—without the protection of the foggy Illinois law which was keeping him in the United States.

In Washington, he might have been arrested and summarily shipped to Merrie Olde England.

With his son reported kidnaped, he had an excellent alibi for failing to appear in Washington, of course. Nobody would expect a father to leave home in the midst of such an emergency.

On May 29th, 1933, after Jerome had returned home, the Supreme Court again assigned the Factor extradition case for a hearing. John Bull once more was jangling the handcuffs eagerly in anticipation of snapping them on Jake's wrists.

But The Barber wasn't going to be had easily. Just about seven weeks after Jerome had been reported snatched, his father vanished, presumably into kidnapdom. What a coincidence! Or, as Jimmy Tribbles might say after a session with a stolen dictionary: How propitious!

And what a hell of a mess it was going to leave Roger Touhy in!

During the days while Jake the Barber was reported missing, and while I was being interviewed by Lieutenant Carr, Father Weber and the *Chicago Evening American* reporter, I did some research on the Jerome Factor incident. It was pretty engrossing stuff.

Now I don't say there was anything kinky about the case. And if it was a frame-up, I honestly don't believe Jerome had any part of such a conspiracy. I'll just tell the facts—or such facts as were made public—and let the reader judge.

Young Factor was a brilliant but quiet student at Northwestern University's School of Speech. He stood five feet four inches tall and weighed only 110 pounds. He was living at the home of his mother, Mrs. Leonard Marcus, married again after being divorced from Factor, at 1215 Lunt Avenue, on Chicago's North Side.

The Barber's current wife, Rella, was in California with

their six-year-old son, Alvin. Their expensive apartment in Chicago's Pearson Hotel was unoccupied, as were Jake's roof bungalow and suites at the Morrison—except probably for The Camel Humphreys and some of his pals.

Jerome was reported to have been kidnaped from in front of his mother's home at about 11 p.m. on April 12. He had been out with a friend in his father's fancy Deusenberg car. Mrs. Marcus thought she heard a call for help, looked out a window, saw nobody and concluded she had been mistaken.

Jake the Barber came up with more heroics than Alan Ladd, Errol Flynn and other Hollywood bravados could have put on film in a lifetime. With a voice of righteous wrath, he said he was going to rescue his boy from the filthy kidnapers. He talked with the police—and then he darted over to his friends in the Capone mob for help. He acted the role of a mystery man, as well as that of an outraged father.

The mobster he picked to dicker with the kidnapers was The Camel Humphreys, which might have been considered to be an unusual choice. After all, Humphreys was himself a kidnaper. He had snatched Old Doc Fitchie, the aging boss of the milk wagon drivers. Humphrey's name was high on every public enemy list put out by Chicago authorities.

Chicago police hadn't been overjoyed at being dealt out of the investigation by Jake. They raided a suite in the Congress Hotel and arrested Humphreys, Golf Bag Sam Hunt, Frank Rio and Tony Accardo, Al Capone's eventual successor. Humphreys stated that he and the other mobsters were working to get Jerome Factor freed.

Jake announced that he had received a ransom note demanding $50,000, with a threat that if he didn't pay his son would be sent home to him "in pieces." Jake later admitted, with amazing candor, that he had written the note to himself. His explanation went like this:

"The kidnapers were asking for $200,000. I released the $50,000 note to the press for a good reason. It got the kidnapers to thinking some one of them was double-cross-ing the others. Dissension arose among them and I got my boy back without paying anything."

The Barber added, with modesty befitting a hero, that he and a carload of armed men—presumably Capone gangsters—all but captured the kidnapers on Chicago's West Side. "We had them spotted in their car," he said, "but some policemen came along in a squad car and the criminals sped away."

Jerome came home safe and sound, eight days after his disappearance. He said he had been kept blindfolded all the time, and that he would be unable to identify any of the people who held him.

I don't know what was behind the kidnaping of Jerome. It may have been a real kidnaping—but, if so, the kidnapers seemed to have been bunglers or amateurs.

Whatever the circumstances, however, the incident gave Factor a gratifying respite in his fight against being removed to England. No democratic government could be so cruel as to send a man away to prison in a foreign land when his son was in the hands of vile kidnapers.

If Jake could keep on stalling, the statute of limitations would run out on the extradition effort. He then would be able to thumb his nose at the British Government for the rest of his life. The case would be dead forever, and Factor could live happily with his swindled millions.

On the night of July 12, twelve days after he vanished from the Dells, Jake came back into public view. He showed up in the suburb of LaGrange, walking along Burlington Avenue. A car was parked at the curb. Jake went to it, identified himself and asked to be taken to a telephone.

In the car was a policeman, Bernard F. Gerard, from nearby River Forest. He took Factor to the LaGrange police station. Gerard was a shrewd, observing policeman. He noticed a great many things for which, later, I was to be thankful.

Jake's black hair was long, but neatly combed. He had grown a full beard. He wore a clean white suit which appeared to have been freshly pressed except for a slight wrinkling at the knees and elbows. His white shirt was unwrinkled and unsoiled, and his necktie was neatly in place. He had a manicure, his face and hands were clean and his shoes had a high gloss polish. There were no bruises or other marks in sight.

All of these things Policeman Gerard noted and filed away in his memory, as a good investigator should. He was to relate them later under oath—and damn near lose his job, as a result, at the instigation of Tubbo Gilbert.

Within an hour, the police station was mobbed with policemen, newspaper reporters and photographers. Gilbert was there, and he took charge. Jake gave a brief interview before Gilbert hurried him away to the Factor apartment in the Pearson Hotel.

Factor said that he had, indeed, been kidnaped. He had been held for 12 days in a basement of a house within an hour's drive of Chicago, and he had suffered terribly. The kidnapers had refused to let him bathe, change his clothing, shave or take off his shoes. He had been blindfolded constantly except for a very few minutes when the kidnapers had him write a ransom note.

Policeman Gerard duly noted those statements. He also managed to stand close to Jake the Barber and sniff delicately. If a person in the heat of a Chicago summer goes without a bath or a change of clothing for 12 days, anybody with a nose will know it. But Gerard could detect no noisome aroma.

The important, burning question of the interview was whether Jake had recognized any of the kidnapers. The Barber answered fully and decisively. He said he hadn't so much as glimpsed any of his captors. He would be unable to tell any one of them from a load of hay. He had been blindfolded all of the time, except for the note-writing interval.

A reporter mentioned that Tubbo Gilbert had blamed Roger Touhy for the kidnaping and asked for comment. "I never have seen Roger Touhy in my life, so far as I know," Factor replied. "Anyway, if he was one of the kidnapers, I wouldn't know it. As I have told you, I didn't see any of them."

Jake was to repeat those statements again and again and

again. A story, under Factor's name as author, appeared in the *Chicago Evening American*. In the story he said that about 20 men were in the kidnap gang, and that he hadn't seen any of them.

His beautiful wife, Rella, had dug up $70,000 ransom for him, Jake told the reporters. A family friend had delivered the payoff on a lonely country road. The friend, it developed later, could identify nobody.

In answer to final questions, Factor said his blindfold had been taken off and he had been pushed into the darkness out of the kidnapers' car only a few minutes before he had encountered policeman Gerard. With that, he headed for Chicago, saying he wanted to be with his family.

Policeman Gerard had some questions in mind. Nobody else seemed to be interested, but he wondered about such things as:

1. If Factor had slept, eaten and lived in the same clothing for 12 days in a basement, how come his suit, shirt and tie were unsoiled, unstained by perspiration and virtually unwrinkled?

2. If his blindfold had been removed so recently, why hadn't he been blinded by the bright lights in the police station?

3. If he had been blindfolded all the time, how had he managed to manicure his nails? Or had, perhaps, the kidnap gang included a manicurist?

4. Factor claimed that his shoes hadn't been off for 12 days. If so, his feet should have been so swollen and sore that he would hardly be able to step on them. But he wasn't even limping.

5. If he hadn't bathed for nearly two weeks, why didn't he have a gamey attar about him?

6. Who had polished Jake's shoes?

All of those significant points went unnoticed, except by Gerard, during the hysteria over Factor's return. Newspapers printed columns of material, with dozen of pictures—including one of Factor with necktie askew, as posed by one of the Cecil B. DeMilles among the news cameramen. Everybody concerned, including Factor's wife, was interviewed. Factor retold his story, adding a few horrendous details, such as being threatened with a blowtorch unless he wrote the ransom note. Jake the Barber, swindler, became a hero to the press and public.

Newspaper editorial writers raised an outcry for the capture of the kidnapers. The FBI already was in on the case, with Melvin Purvis, who later became a headliner by directing the killing of John Dillinger, in charge. Factor kept on saying that he saw none of the so-called kidnapers and that he could identify nobody.

I read the newspapers carefully about the Factor case, although I usually started at the back and stopped after the comics and the sports pages. My name cropped up in the stories, with mentions that Tubbo had put the blame on me. But there were no fresh blasts against me by Gilbert or anyone else.

A few sane voices were raised. The British Crown lawyer, Overmeyer, repeated his accusation that Factor had faked the kidnaping. Attorney General Cummings' expert, Keenan, kept referring to Jake the Barber's case as an *"alleged kidnaping."*

A significant thing brought out was a point that no record was made of serial numbers of the bills withdrawn from a bank by Mrs. Factor to pay the $70,000 ransom. Not even that precaution had been taken. Whoever had the money was free to spend it.

I loafed around my home for two days after Factor's return. Nobody came to see me; not Tubbo Gilbert or Melvin Purvis or anybody else. The law seemed to be uninterested in me. I did get a phone call from Father Weber, and we made up our differences. He was at the Morrison Hotel, headquarters for Factor, Lieutenant Carr and The Camel Humphreys.

"Mr. Factor and Lieutenant Carr would like to meet you, Roger," the priest said. I said that would be okay with me, but that I would have to know the meeting place in advance and give my approval of it. I figured that Humphreys might have some idea of drygulching me, and I was taking no chances. The Chicago mob still had reasons to want me out of the way.

Father Weber left the telephone for a minute or two, returned and said to forget about the meeting. That was fine with me; I was sick unto death of the Factor nonsense. I wanted to forget it.

Chapter 10

Gone Fishing

A ll that spring and early summer, I had been itching to go fishing with my family in the Wisconsin north woods. Business matters had held me up for a while, and then it was brother Tommy's hospitalization. After Gilbert accused me of kidnaping Jake the Barber, I had to stick around, or, probably, be accused of taking a runout powder.

With Factor back with his Schweppes-man beard and saying he couldn't identify anybody, I figured I was free to be on my way. I telephoned my lawyer, Stewart, and he said he didn't see why not, so long as the law wasn't showing any interest in me.

Clara had planned on going with me and taking the boys, but now she had misgivings. The weather had turned hot, and it would be a long, uncomfortable drive. There was a great danger of polio in those pre-Salk shot days. Roger and Tommy might be better off paddling in the pool at home.

Old "Chicken" McFadden made up Clara's mind for her. He had been staying in our home after getting out of the

115

Oak Park Hospital, where he had been on the night of the Factor happening at The Dells. He wanted me to make good on my invitation for fishing, and he had some friends who would like to go along. Clara dealt herself and the boys out of the trip.

McFadden and I got in my big Chrysler and headed north. With us were two of the labor movement's divided-septum bodyguards.

One of them was a lanky redhead out of California, using the name of Gus Schafer. He celled next to me at Stateville for a lot of years as Peter Stevens, but that wasn't his name, either. I'll call him Stevens for the purposes of this book. He had a record for armed robbery, I later learned.

Stevens was a serious, seldom-smiling guy. A big guffaw or belly laugh for him was a slight twitch at the corners of the lips. But he had a terrific sense of humor and his dead-pan jokes were fine. The newspapers later hung the tag of "Gloomy Gus" on him. He never had a rap against him while at Stateville, and Warden Ragen called him the best behaved con in the joint. Everybody was happy for him when he was paroled in 1959.

Another of McFadden's pals was Willie Sharkey, a short, dark man with a pot-belly. Willie had two talents—getting into jail and buying clothes that didn't fit him. He drank too much and he wasn't too smart, but he had a good heart and I liked him.

All of my companions had guns under their coats or in their luggage, I assumed. What professional bodyguard travels without a gun? I took along a .22 target pistol for banging away at tin cans in the woods, or, maybe, shooting a muskie in the head.

I didn't suspect it at the time, but Stevens and Sharkey knew a whole lot more about the fake Factor snatch than I did. I only suspected that the kidnaping was a hoax; but they *knew* it was. I would have blown my stack if I had known what they had been doing.

They were, unintentionally, helping along the kidnap frame that was building up against me—and them.

We went to Rhorbacker's Resort, one of my favorite vacation spots, in the Lake Flambeau Indian Reservation, and the fishing was terrific. It was a secluded place, with no newspapers and not even a radio or telephone in our quarters. I would be out in a boat soon after dawn and spend most of the day fishing for big, fighting muskies, the greatest of fresh-water game fish.

McFadden and Stevens went fishing a couple of times, but Sharkey stayed ashore, saying that boats made him seasick. The three of them spent most of their time carousing in local taverns.

Willie got a supply of bootleg booze and seemed to be trying to get every Indian in Wisconsin loop-legged drunk. He organized, and led, war dances all over the place. It was against federal law to give liquor to an Indian, but Sharkey was casual about all laws.

He also had an eye on a coppery Indian maiden with a shape to fit a 38 bra, only she didn't have a bra, and he was trying to get into her tepee out in the woods. Her regular sweetie was a six-foot brave, and I didn't want to see Willie's scalp dangling from the brave's belt. I decided it would be smart to head for home. And we did.

At the little town of Elkhorn, Wisconsin, a light mist was falling and I skidded off the road. I hit a wooden telephone pole with a solid thump. My heavy car was undamaged and nobody was hurt, but the pole broke off at the base and crashed to the ground. From the back seat, Sharkey hollered: "T-i-m-b-e-r!"

I waited until a policeman, or maybe it was a deputy sheriff, came along. He said it would cost $22.50 to replace the pole and I said I was willing to pay. I went with him to settle up. McFadden, Stevens and Sharkey spotted a tavern down the street and went there to wait for me.

While we were away, another cop searched the car, recognized the name of Roger Touhy on some papers, saw my target pistol and the bodyguards' guns, and raised a rumpus.

Into jail went McFadden, Stevens, Sharkey and I. Nobody would explain why we had been sneezed. I had plenty of money and offered to put up bond, but blank stares were all I got from the law. What I didn't know was that while I was in the north woods, Tubbo Gilbert had issued a statement to the press saying that he had the evidence to prove me guilty beyond doubt of kidnaping Factor. I had been without news or a phone at the lodge.

The Elkhorn jail was belly-deep with cops before dawn. Gilbert was there, and so was FBI-man Purvis. Newspaper reporters and photographers were on hand by the dozens, it seemed. The guns from my car, along with a partly used roll of adhesive tape from a first aid kit and a tow rope, were laid out on a table. The camera men made pictures and the photographs showed up in the Chicago papers as "the Touhy gang's arsenal."

The rope, it was presumed, had been used for binding kidnap victims and the tape for fastening blindfolds in place.

(It was the first time I had heard that Jake claimed to have had his blindfold pasted on with adhesive. If that had been true, wouldn't the removal of the tape have pulled out some of his eyebrows or hair? Or wouldn't the gummy stuff from the tape have been left in his hair or beard on his unwashed skin? As anyone knows, a piece of tape over the flesh for any length of time leaves a clearly defined marking. The pictures made of Jake in the LaGrange police station showed no such traces.)

FBI Agent Melvin Purvis finally got around to telling me that I was being held for the Hamm kidnaping. I was perplexed. Having limited my newspaper reading mostly to the comics and the sports pages up until the time of the Factor case, I didn't know what he was talking about. I tried a feeble joke: "What do you mean by ham, Mr. Purvis—a ham sandwich? Or did I kidnap a ham steak?"

Purvis looked pained at the pun—for which I don't blame him. He gave me a brief rundown. William Hamm, Jr., a millionaire brewer of St. Paul, Minnesota, had been kidnaped from outside his place of business on June 15. That had been 15 days before Factor's reported snatch. Hamm had been released four days later after $100,000 ransom had been paid. The rap now was being charged up to McFadden, Stevens, Sharkey and me.

That was, indeed, a doozie. I knew no more than Little Lord Fauntleroy about Hamm. I recalled that I had a solid alibi for June 15. I told Purvis so, adding that I was innocent of the Cock Robin killing, too. He looked at me with the tight-lipped, gimlet-eyed way that FBI men had—and which detective-actors on television have plagiarized.

"Mr. Purvis, I know you are very, very anxious to convict a kidnaper, and I don't blame you," I said. "I don't like kidnapers any better than you do. But you're making a big mistake in accusing me of the Hamm crime. I haven't been in Minnesota in two years."

He didn't answer me, but within a few hours, I had handcuffs on my wrists for the first time. The cuffs were attached to an escape-proof safety belt around my waist, and a policeman held me on a chain like a dog on a leash. McFadden, Stevens, Sharkey and I went to Chicago that way.

The removal was an absolute violation of our constitutional rights. We were taken across a state line without a court appearance, without an extradition warrant, without our consent and without a charge against us. We were not taken before a judge or magistrate within a reasonable time, as the law provides. I demanded to see a lawyer, but I was ignored.

All of those privileges, the rights of any person under the U.S. Constitution and the Bill of Rights, were thrown in the ash can. A suspected kidnaper, no matter how false or skimpy the evidence against him might be, had no rights in those times.

In Chicago, McFadden, Stevens, Sharkey and I were fingerprinted and photographed in the Bankers' Building FBI offices. Each of us stood in turn before a door with a full length, one-way vision glass in it. A person on the other side of the glass panel could see us, but we couldn't see him.

Among those who looked at me and the others through the Judas glass was Jake the Barber. But I never saw him. I asked many times to use a telephone to call a lawyer, and the FBI agents gave me those vague, 2,000-yards-in-the-distance stares.

They brought us bottles of ice cold beer—delicious!—and I noticed that the glass was smeared with some sort of sticky stuff. I guessed that the stickum would hold fingerprints and that the bottles might be planted in a house where Hamm had been held by kidnapers. That would be evidence against us. I whispered an explanation to the others, and we wiped off the bottles with our handkerchiefs—except for Sharkey: he had no handkerchief, so he used his shirt tail.

From the FBI offices, we were taken to Chicago Police Headquarters. In charge of the detective bureau there were two tough, but almost unbelievably honest police officers. They were Chief of Detectives William Schoemaker and his second in command, Lieutenant William V. Blaul.

Schoemaker, called "Shoes," spent his nights off kicking in the doors of whorehouses and booting pimps around. He and Blaul had so much integrity that a good many policemen didn't want to work with them.

"We're going to give you a square show-up," Schoemaker said. McFadden, Stevens, Sharkey and I stood handcuffed to each other on a raised platform with bright white lights shining down. Out in front of us in a darkened auditorium were victims of various crimes. They could see us, but we couldn't see them.

A police officer with a microphone had us turn this way and that to show us both in profile and full face. We answered questions so the witnesses could try to recognize our voices. It was a spooky experience. When it was over, Chief Schoemaker told me: "You men are clean so far as we're concerned. Nobody fingered you at the show-up." He added that Factor had been in the audience.

They chained us up again, put us in cars and took us back to Elkhorn. Stevens remarked glumly: "They're going to a lot of trouble to get $22.50 for that telephone pole."

In Elkhorn, FBI Agent Purvis read us warrants charging us with kidnaping Hamm. It was a federal offense, he said, because the evidence was that Hamm had been taken across a state line from Minnesota to Wisconsin. We were liable to life terms in prison under the Lindbergh antikidnap law, if we could be convicted in St. Paul.

It was nonsense to accuse us of the Hamm job. We knew no more about it than our grandmothers did. I had a solid alibi for the time of the snatch. There was absolutely no honest evidence against us. Our innocence was to be proved beyond doubt two years later—when the real kidnapers were caught and convicted, with guilty pleas by some of them.

Against that situation, Purvis said in Chicago that there was an "iron-clad case" against us. Special Attorney General Keenan predicted that all of us would be given life. Still, after thinking things over, I figured we weren't in such bad shape.

I hadn't been anywhere near Minnesota during the Hamm crime. There was no possible evidence against me. McFadden, Stevens and Sharkey said that the same held true for them. Hamm was a legitimate businessman, and a prominent citizen. He certainly wouldn't swear us falsely into prison.

Also it appeared that Gilbert's original big balloon of talk about my guilt in the Factor mess had been punctured. There were these angles to be considered:

1. Jake the Barber had viewed us in the FBI offices and at the police showup in Chicago. Chief Schoemaker had told us that we were clean; that nobody had fingered us.

2. If Factor had identified us, would Gilbert and Courtney have allowed us to be taken away to another state on the Hamm case? Certainly they would not. Gilbert and Courtney were just as eager to get the honor and glory of a kidnap conviction as was every other police officer and prosecutor in America.

3. Would Factor, if he really had recognized any of us, have stayed mum and allowed us to be taken out of Illlinois? Hardly! considering the zeal with which he lied against us later.

I reasoned that we were home safe on the Factor fake and soon would be cleared in St. Paul. In a few months— even weeks—our troubles would be ended. An optimist, eh? I was going to get 298 years of trouble!

The government took us in chains from Elkhorn to the County Jail at Milwaukee. Weeks of hell followed. We were maximum-security prisioners, in separate cells. No visitors; no consultations with lawyers; no visits by families; no radio broadcasts; no newspapers.

I went into the jail in excellent physical shape. When I came out, I was 25 pounds lighter, three vertebrae in my upper spine were fractured and seven of my teeth had been knocked out. Part of the FBI's rehabilitation-of-prisoners system, I supposed. All of the men who gave me the treatment were strangers to me.

They questioned me day and night, abused me, beat me up and demanded that I confess the Hamm kidnaping. Never was I allowed to rest for more than half an hour. If I was asleep when a team of interrogators arrived at my cell, they would slug me around and bang me against the wall. I trained myself to sleep for 20 minutes, and be on my feet for the questioners.

I couldn't have confessed if I had wanted to. I didn't know what Hamm looked like, how the ransom was paid, where he was held, or anything else. Neither did McFadden, Stevens or Sharkey. But that seemingly made no difference.

On August 13, a federal grand jury in St. Paul indicted all of us for kidnaping.

Jangle, jangle, jangle, we went in our chains to the Ramsey County Jail in St. Paul. The beatings stopped, but not the maximum security. We were allowed no visitors, including lawyers. Our trial date was approaching, and we were totally unprepared.

Chapter 11

Fiasco at St. Paul

Poor Willie Sharkey all but fell apart during those weeks of horror. He never was a strong-willed fellow and he couldn't endure being beaten. He had a childish fear of solitude, too. His mind was gone by the time we reached St. Paul. I was shocked when I saw him.

There were times when Willie didn't seem to know where he was. He mumbled about our fishing trip to Wisconsin, the last freedom he ever was to know on this earth, and about the Indian maiden on the reservation. His mind seemed to refuse to accept the fact that he was up against a kidnaping rap, and maybe two. He screamed in his sleep at night and sometimes he tried to fight the guards.

I had lost track of time, in jail, and then I had a visitor. He was a round-faced, pleasant man—Thomas McMeekin, former Ramsey County prosecutor at St. Paul, and an able lawyer. He explained that Stevens' family had retained him about a California matter. That was why he happened to be in the jail.

After offering me a cigarette, he said: "Stevens asked me to see you, so I'm here. He says you and your codefendants need a lawyer in the Hamm case. Well, I'm not applying for the job—in fact I wouldn't take it if you offered it to me—but I'll get word to the lawyer of your choice, if you like."

McMeekin impressed me right from the first minute. He was quiet, with none of the dramatic ham of some shysters. He wasn't looking for a fee; only trying to help a prisoner who needed it. I asked him to get in touch with William Scott Stewart in Chicago, and he said: "Sure, I'll do that. Stewart is a good man."

As he turned away, I appealed to him. I knew we would need a local lawyer, in addition to Stewart. I had a feeling that McMeekin was the man. He inspired confidence. But when I asked him to come into the defense, he shook his head and said: "Sorry, Touhy. Bill Hamm is a good friend of mine."

I begged him. I swore I was innocent. I said I had an alibi that couldn't be beaten. I spoke of my family and background. He seemed a little surprised when he heard that I had no previous criminal record. He leaned against a wall, puffed a cigarette and looked at me sidewise now and then as I spieled like an auctioneer.

At last he said: "I'm not convinced, but you've got me thinking. I'll look around a little and then we'll see what Stewart says. I promise you nothing." He handed me the rest of his pack of cigarettes, walked away and left me feeling better than I had in weeks.

Stewart came to see McFadden, Stevens, Sharkey and me. McMeekin paved the way for the visit with the authorities, I believe. I asked Stewart to take in McMeekin as co-defense lawyer, and he agreed. Stewart wanted me to give him my alibi defense and the alibis of McFadden, Stevens and Sharkey. I didn't do it—for an excellent reason.

Two FBI men stood in the room, listening to every word and making notes. I didn't want them to hear the names of my witnesses. Why tip off the prosecution in advance? Especially when you know that you're being framed. I had an inspiration, and I brushed away Stewart's questions.

"Send my wife up here to see me," I said. "I have some

very important things to tell her about this case. She'll understand what to do. I don't recall the names of some of my witnesses, but she will remember." Stewart said he would try to arrange a visit by my wife.

Well, sir, Clara didn't have a bit of trouble getting to see me in the jail. They brought her in and sat her down across a table from me. Two FBI men, each with pencil poised above a pad of paper sat at the ends of the table. I smiled at them apologetically and said that I hadn't seen my wife for a long time and did they mind very much if I held her hand.

They nodded agreeably. Clara and I clasped hands and began telegraphing to each other. A short pressure of a finger was a dot and a long pressure a dash. We had practiced it often when talking secretly in front of our sons. Vocally, I talked inanely about our neighbors and such, at the same time telegraphing instructions to her. She pressured back: "O.K. Papa, I understand." I rambled along about nothing much at all in conversation, and our listeners looked at me as if I might be in as bad shape as Willie Sharkey.

In Morse code, I told her to get in touch with Edward J. Meany, a suburban real estate dealer, a man I had known for most of my life. I had recalled that Meany had come to our home on June 15th and invited me to his daughter's graduation exercises that evening, the date of the Hamm kidnaping.

I also telegraphed Clara a reminder that I had gone by chartered airplane from Chicago to Indianapolis on about June 18, during the time when brewer Hamm was missing. I asked her to check with the pilot and with the Claypool Hotel in Indianapolis, where I had stayed overnight. Father Weber, too, I thought, probably would remember seeing me on that date.

At the end of our conversation, we coded each other the messages of "30" and "73," which meant "that's all" and "best regards". The listening FBI men gaped at us. They hadn't heard enough to merit putting pencil to paper. But my wife and I had done a lot of communicating.

The St. Paul trial was a farce, a fiasco, but the government tried its damnedest. Special Assistant U. S. Attorney General Keenan, the government's antikidnap specialist, bossed the prosecution. With him was U. S. District Attorney George F. Sullivan, of St. Paul.

On the opening trial day, newsboys were peddling the St. Paul and Minneapolis newspapers in front of the courthouse. The banner headlines said that McFadden, Stevens, Sharkey and I had been indicted in Chicago for kidnaping Jake the Barber Factor. The prospective jurors, reporting for duty at the trial, couldn't help but see the headlines.

The stories said that we were mobsters, murderers, bank robbers and thieves. The people on the jury panel undoubtedly had read those articles at breakfast.

(We had been indicted in state court in Illinois because, unlike the Hamm case, there was no evidence of the victim having been taken across a state line.)

There were mobs of spectators in the streets around the courthouse. We were manacled and chained when taken from jail to court. Police with riot guns and machine guns were everywhere. Observers, including the jurors, must have been mightily impressed—and prejudiced. Selection of a jury, with U. S. District Judge M. M. Joyce presiding, began.

Stevens nudged me and whispered: "Take a look over your shoulder, Rog. You got friends in court." I sneaked a glance. There, in front row seats, were Tubbo Gilbert and Jake the Barber, side by side. I knew Gilbert, of course, but I had never seen Factor before. I recognized him from newspaper photos. He was a small, perfectly-groomed man with an olive complexion and a round face. His hair was dark and it glistened with oil. His eyes met mine for a fraction of a second and then darted away.

Now, why in the world were Factor and Gilbert in St. Paul? They could have no part in the Hamm prosecution, because they knew nothing about it. They could not testify. They were present because their pictures were in the Twin City papers and they were a constant reminder to the jurors that another kidnap indictment was pending against us in Chicago. The prosecution was ignoring no bets.

The Barber gave an interview to St. Paul and Minneapolis newsmen. It was the most prejudicial piece of vicious propaganda I ever read. Factor can't repudiate this, because it was carried by the Associated Press and printed in newspapers from coast to coast and abroad. He never denied it. What he said was:

"I wouldn't hurt a fly, but I could take that guy's [Roger Touhy's] throat and twist it until the blood came out. And I could drink the blood, the way they tortured me."

The Hamm trial had a sort of let's-pretend-we're-all-nuts tone.

Hamm told of being kidnaped from in front of his brewery in broad daylight. He was trying to tell the absolute truth, I am sure, but he conceded that he had been under a great deal of pressure from the police and the FBI. A business associate told of dumping a $100,000 ransom payment on a highway near Wyoming, a Minnesota town.

Hamm said a man resembling Chicken McFadden had taken him by the hand and led him into the kidnap car. Our lawyers got him to admit that he once had identified a photograph of Verne Sankey, a notorious bank robber, as the man who had him by the hand. Under cross-examination, Hamm, an honorable man, said that he didn't know whether McFadden was among the kidnapers. He added that he never had seen Stevens, Sharkey or me, so far as he knew.

That ended Hamm's testimony. It proved nothing.

A farmer from near Wyoming testified that he saw some men in a big black car near his place on the day Hamm was turned loose. His testimony was pretty vague.

Special Assistant U. S. Attorney General Keenan next sprang a surprise witness on us. He was a printer from Chicago, and he gave all of us a gasp at the defense table. The witness said he was in St. Paul looking for a job on June 15, hadn't found one and had gone out to the Hamm Brewery. He always was interested in breweries, he said.

After hanging around the brewery for a while, the witness swore, he went to a store, bought a package of cigarettes and returned in time to see Hamm kidnaped. He identified McFadden, Stevens and Sharkey as being among the kidnapers and, by implication, that meant I was the fourth one. "I thought they were just drunks, and I paid little attention," he said.

The printer said he had gone to Chicago that night, read of the Hamm kidnaping, written a letter to the U. S. Attorney in St. Paul and carried it around in his pocket for three or four weeks without mailing it. After having read of our arrest at Elkhorn, he went on, he had sent a telegram to the authorities at St. Paul. Who could believe that story?

I told Attorneys McMeekin and Stewart to get in touch with the Dannenberg Detective Agency in Chicago for a check. Within 48 hours, the answer came through. The witness had been working as a printer in Chicago at the time he claimed to have witnessed the kidnaping in St. Paul. The payroll records proved beyond question that he was a liar.

Was he ever charged with perjury? He was not.

Clara had a private detective check the Indianapolis hotel where I had stayed. An assistant manager told the gumshoe that a man with a federal badge of some kind had taken my registration card, so there was no proof that I had been at the hotel. It looked like destruction of defense evidence, but I couldn't prove anything.

The pilot who had flown me from Chicago to Indianapolis was reported to be on vacation. I wondered who paid his holiday expenses. We thought about calling Father Weber, but it didn't seem worth while.

My real estate dealer friend, Meany, did get to the stand. He swore that on June 15 he had invited me at my home to attend his daughter's graduation exercise. The prosecution gave him a savage cross-examination, but he wouldn't budge an inch.

He testified that a Chicago FBI man came to him with this warning: "If you go to St. Paul to testify for Touhy, you'll be sorry, and maybe you won't come back."

The St. Paul jurors returned a not-guilty verdict for the four of us. There was nothing else they could do.

But the people of St. Paul didn't understand. They had been indoctrinated too well by the press. They seemed to regard the phony witness as a hero. There was a howling mob in the streets around the jail that night. I figured we were going to be lynched, all of us. Attorney McMeekin appealed for police protection at his home when a mob formed there.

We, the acquitted defendants, sat in our cells through that long night. Our next trial would be in Chicago, for the Factor case. I figured that Jake the Barber now would identify us for sure, although he had said repeatedly that he didn't recognize any of his supposed kidnapers.

The mob's howls ring in my memory today. I wonder how those self-appointed vigilantes felt, two years later, when Arthur "Doc" Barker, Alvin "Creepy" Karpis and other Dillinger mobsters were convicted of—or pleaded guilty to—the Hamm kidnaping. Were they relieved then, that they hadn't lynched Roger Touhy and his innocent co-defendants?

Of one thing I had convinced myself during the Hamm trial. I wasn't going to let Willie Sharkey go through any more of his personal hell. I had had to hold him down in his seat during some of the Hamm case. He wasn't responsible, I knew, although I couldn't get a mental expert to examine him. Willie should be committed to an institution, I felt, and I was going to do something about it.

I was too late. Willie hanged himself with his necktie in the Ramsey County Jail. I wept. Willie's life might not have amounted to much, but he shouldn't have been driven to ending it.

I thanked McMeekin for all he had done. He gave me a rueful smile, and I understood. Right at that time, he was as popular in St. Paul as an acute case of leprosy. He was paying for having defended a gang of dirty kidnapers.

McFadden, Stevens and I went back to Chicago, jangling our chains. In the Cook County Jail, things were a little better. We had newspapers and radio programs and we could send out for some decent food now and then. The prosecution ran in a substitute for Sharkey—Albert Kator, who had driven a beer truck for me.

"I don't know why I was grabbed," Kator told me. "But I think Factor might have fingered me." I figured that theory was right. If Factor hadn't falsely identified all of us, we wouldn't have been indicted. I was a little worried, but our attorney, Stewart, reassured me.

He said that no jury in the world would believe Factor, because of his bad reputation. "You'll never go on trial," Steward said. "The case surely will be dropped." I believed him.

I couldn't understand why Chicken McFadden had been indicted with us. He had been in the Oak Park Hospital during the entire period that Jake the Barber claimed to have been in the hands of kidnapers. Chicken couldn't possibly have had anything to do with the Factor snatch—which hadn't happened, anyway.

I didn't remember, which I should have, that I had given the use of my name as a reference when Chicken had rented a house at Fir and Elm Streets in the suburb of Glenview, about five miles from my home.

The stories in the Chicago papers irked me a little. The news stories now were calling me "Black Roger" and "Terrible Touhy." I discovered that I was a machine gunner, a bomber, a probable murderer, and a few other things I hadn't known about myself.

My co-defendants had brand new nicknames, too. Chicken McFadden had become "Father Tom." It was certain to make readers and prospective jurors think of the St. Valentine's Day massacre, when a couple of Capone's killers masqueraded in black gowns and round collars as Roman Catholic priests. A nice touch of poisoning the public mind, that was.

Kator was called "Polly Nose" in the press. He happened to be of the Jewish faith, and an appeal to anti-Semites was in the nickname. Stevens, indicted under a phony name, was called "Gloomy Gus," but it fit his appearance so well that I couldn't complain, and neither could he, really. Stevens never was one to let his real wit shine forth.

But the thing that really astounded me was the plush, red-carpet treatment now being given to Factor in the Chicago press.

At the time of Jake's extradition troubles and during the time of the so-called kidnaping, reporters had written of him freely as "Jake the Barber, International swindler."

But now, with our trial coming up, he wasn't Jake the Barber, swindler, any more. He became "John Factor, international speculator," in the press. It was comical, in a way, that every Chicago paper used exactly the same wording—"international speculator"—in describing Jake.

The top editors of the papers and the bosses at the Associated Press, United Press and International News Service apparently felt that, for the first time, there was a chance in America to convict a vicious kidnap gang. At any rate, Factor got a whitewash, presumably in the interest of real justice, and to end the kidnap evil.

Courtney may have believed at the time that McFadden, Stevens, Kator and I really were guilty. He was a political office holder, almost totally inexperienced in prosecuting and investigative work. In his position, he had to rely on what Gilbert told him.

And the editors probably can't be criticized too severely for giving the prosecutor's office a slanted assist, either. Courtney was publicly committed to a conviction, and the glitter and glamour hadn't worn off the handsome, boyish, dimpled state's attorney. To hundreds of thousands of Chicagoans, he was the shining knight who was going to cleanse their city of the Capone stink. It was the popular thing, as well, to be against kidnapers.

Modern Chicago newspapers would never play mumble-de-peg with records in such a way, I am sure. In fact, if Jake the Barber or one of his ilk tried to fake a kidnaping in Chicago today, the dirty work undoubtedly would be exposed within 24 hours. If the police missed, the newspapers, with their staffs of reporter-investigators, would do the job.

In the late years of my imprisonment, as doubt increased about my guilt, the Chicago papers were almost solidly behind me all the way.

But, in 1933, the publicity against us was as staggering as a right to the jaw by Joe Louis. We were mad dogs, and Factor was being almost beatified, considering his past. I remember recoiling a little in jail when I picked up a newspaper with a big, black headline:

"STATE TO SEEK DEATH FOR TOUHY GANGSTERS!"

Stevens saw it, too. He gave me what passed for a smile and said: "Well, Rog, maybe you can get Tubbo to hold your hand when you sit down on the chair and they turn on the juice. That would be nice." Stevens' sense of mirth had a touch of Edgar Allen Poe at times.

They took us from the jail to the Criminal Courts building through an underground passage that has been called "the tunnel of hopeless men." We rode up a special elevator that landed us in a bullpen, or cage, at the rear of a courtroom. Photographers took our pictures, and we looked like public enemies number-one through -four, with our stubble of jail beard and wrinkled clothing. More pictorial propaganda for the prosecution.

We pleaded not guilty. On that day, or subsequently, the trial was assigned to Judge Michael Feinberg.

We went back to jail, and attorney Stewart said farewell for a while. He was going to Cuba for a vacation. He sent me a box of cigars for Christmas. I didn't smoke cigars, but it was a nice thought.

On that joyous Yuletide, the papers announced, every jail inmate would be served a turkey dinner. On that basis, I told Clara not to send us any special food for the holiday, since we would be feasting on drumsticks and white meat, with cranberry sauce, sage dressing, giblet gravy, two kinds of potatoes, hot rolls, celery and mincemeat pie. That's what the menu in the papers said.

About 20 years later, in Stateville, we got an inmate who had been an Air Force pilot. He used to sing a song that went:

"I wanted wings

"Until I got the goddam things,

"And now I don't want them any more."

Wings! Turkey wings! That's what we got for Christmas dinner in the jail. The luxury hotels didn't serve wings to their guests, so the poultry merchants lopped them off and sold them to the politicians who bought the food for the jail.

Stevens poked a fork at his wing, floating on a sea of grease, and said: "If I had this many feathers, I'd fly over the wall."

It was an unmerry Christmas, and the prosecution was preparing an unhappy New Year for us.

Chapter 12

Washington Gets
into the Act

In December, 1933, the United States Supreme Court ruled, as had been expected generally, that Jake the Barber had to go back to London. England's extradition case against him was bonafide, the justices ruled. The decision meant curtains for Factor. He could appeal for a re-hearing, but his lawyers told him that he wouldn't get it. The Supreme Court seldom changes its mind.

Off to Washington went State's Attorney Courtney. He had a conference with President Roosevelt, telling him that Jake was needed in America to convict a gang of the nation's most vicious kidnapers, including Roger Touhy. Courtney has conceded under oath that he did so.

Special Assistant Attorney General Keenan backed up Courtney. Keenan, after failing to convict me for the St. Paul frame-up, no longer was referring to the Factor fake as "an *alleged* kidnaping." He had thrown in with Courtney in an endeavor to put me in the electric chair in Chicago.

F.D.R. undoubtedly did what he did in good faith. He had no way of hearing my side of the story. Anyway, he telephoned Secretary of State Cordell Hull and asked him to tell the British Embassy that Factor's removal to England was being held up indefinitely. Hull agreed.

Factor now had put over the biggest flimflam of his life. He had hoodwinked the President of the United States. He had tweaked the British Lion's tail and managed to let go in time.

Courtney announced that his prize witness would remain in the United States until such time as the kidnap charges against me and my codefendants were settled finally. Upon receiving the news, Jake put on a victory celebration, with champagne. Whoopee! As for McFadden, Stevens, Kator and I, we didn't feel so good in our jail cells.

Over the years, I have become a student of Factor. I have listened to him testify for hours, I have read about him and I have talked to many people who knew him, including his cell mates in prison.

He has given his birthplace, at various times, as Dunzska, Russia; Lodz, Poland; Hull, England, and Chicago. He reported the year of his birth variously as 1890 and 1892, which would make him either 41 or 43 when he said he was kidnaped in 1933.

His father, an itinerant rabbi, brought him to the United States at about the turn of the century. Jake took out his first papers, but he did not become a United States citizen. The records show that he registered for the World War I draft in 1917 but never spent a day in service. He was married by that time, and a father.

Jake first had appeared in Chicago as a boy bootblack, shining shoes in a West Side barbershop. The price of a shine was two cents, but, the story goes, Jake made a good thing out of it. Many of his customers were unwary farmers, called "greenhorns," in the city to sell vegetables at the produce markets.

To one of them, Jake would say: "You want a steamboat shine, Mister? Only one cent." If the chump agreed, young Factor would shine one shoe until it glowed like one of the big diamonds in the pawnshop window down the street. The lad then would step back and say: "There's your steamboat shine, Mister. For a dime, I'll shine the other shoe."

If the customer beefed, Jake would pass it off as a joke and finish the shine. But, more often than not, the out-witted patron gave him the dime. He also worked as a hat-check boy and men's washroom attendant in Chicago restaurants.

Jake graduated from clipping shoeshine customers to clipping hair. He became a barber. A shave was a dime and a haircut 15 cents, but he found a way to keep on ' fleecing the greenhorns. When one of them got into his chair he would get a sales talk like this: "Mister, we have a special today. I'd like to have you try it. You just relax and I'll do the work."

Factor then would go into a routine of funny stories and fast patter. The chump, diverted, would get a shave, hair-cut, facial massage, sure-thing mange cure, hair singe, blackhead eradication, scalp rejuvenation, dandruff treat-ment, eyebrow trim, removal of wax from the ears and a closing essay on his greatly improved appearance.

When the conversation-bewildered customer stepped out of the chair, he would get a big smile from Factor and a bill for $4.50. If the complaint was noisy, Factor would settle for half, and still be money ahead. Sometimes he got the full price.

Stock-market craziness was sweeping the country, with politicians and financial page columnists feeding the pub-lic such slogans as "Don't Sell America Short" and "Big Business Is Your Best Bet." Illegal bucket shops, and legit-imate brokerages, too, sold stocks on the installment plan. The U.S.A. was a con man's paradise.

Factor got into the stock-market through the back door. He became a collector of monthly installments on sold-on-time shares. He had gone to school only three months in all his life, but he trained himself to speak well. He could figure the odds of horse-race betting and dice; and stock market percentages were just another step in the same direction.

He switched from collecting to selling stocks on com-mission, and soon he was the wonder boy of the brokerages.

He could sell anything—probably including home heating plants for summer use in Havana, Cuba. Sales commissions on the stocks peddled in those days ran as high as 75 percent, and the shares made lovely wallpaper.

Jake's pockets bulged with money, and he spent it as if the stuff were going out of style. The gambling joints got a lot of his cash and he lived like a teller with a key to the bank's night lock. He would be broke at breakfast time some days and rich before sundown.

When the Florida land boom was raging, Jake got in on it and became a multimillionaire. He was indicted in one of the Florida deals, but the case was dropped.

Factor has been required to testify at various times that he went to England and set himself up, under at least three names, as the Broadstreet Press, Ltd., and other enterprises. He became what the British called a "stock pusher." Jake stayed in the back room, mostly, and hired stooges to stick their necks out.

Britishers—mostly pensioners, widows with a bit of insurance money, clergymen, keepers of small shops and tram conductors with a few pounds tucked away in post office savings—began getting copies of a weekly stock-market information newspaper.

The paper advised the free-list subscribers to buy certain legitimate, conservative-type stocks listed on the London Exchange. The shares went up in price. Factor made sure they did by investing heavily in them with his own money. Everybody made profits—on paper.

The thing snowballed, as Jake knew it would. The people who made profits talked their friends into investing. The demand for the stocks increased and the prices spiraled ever upward.

The Barber nursed his chumps along for two years. Some of them mortgaged their homes or borrowed from loan sharks to buy more stocks. Jake wrote a weekly column of stock market advice for the paper under the alias of Norman D. Spencer. The stocks recommended in the column always went up in price. The investors wrote letters of glowing praise to the paper.

Factor spent nearly $1,000,000 on his bait. He published the newspaper at considerable expense and he operated brokerage offices where the customers could buy their stocks. Everything was legal.

And then came the switcheroo. Norman D. Spencer advised his followers to sell their blue-chip shares and invest their every shilling in new securities. The profits were certain to be big and quick, wrote the infallible Norman D. The newly recommended stocks were not listed on the exchange, but soon would be, Spencer promised.

The suckers all but broke down the doors of Jake's bucket shops to buy shares in such never-were companies as Asbestos & Holding Trust, Ltd., Vulcan Copper Mines and Rhodesia Border Mining Corp., Ltd. Jake was printing the stock certificates on the same presses that put out his newspaper.

In seven months, from March to October of 1930, Factor rooked his trusting boobs of 1,619,726 pounds, or more than $7,000,000 in American money at the rate of exchange of the time. It was one of the biggest swindles of its kind in history.

The individual losses were mostly small. Some of the chumps lost only a few hundred dollars, but there were thousands of them—practically all victims who could not afford to lose. Factor had bled them white. The London press reported a number of suicides at the time.

In October, 1930, the investors in Jake the Barber's fake stocks got printed notices in the mail. Good old Norman D., the infallible, had a touch of the pip. He was going to the country for a rest and the paper was suspending temporarily. But Norman D. would be back of course, to guide his dearly beloved friends into even bigger profits.

Factor's offices were flooded with sympathy letters and "get well soon" messages. An 82-year-old widow, with her husband's life insurance money trustingly invested in Vulcan Copper, called at Factor's Broadstreet Press offices with a noggin of calf's-foot jelly for the invalid Norman D. The door was locked and the blinds were drawn.

Jake had most of his $7,000,000 cabled, mailed or sent by courier back to the United States. He sailed to France and went on a gambling jamboree that made headlines in the French press. He beat one of Europe's Royalty big-wigs out of $625,000 in one night at *chemin de fer,* according to the press reports.

The squawks from the British chumps, meanwhile, were all but deafening. Factor, in the manner to which he was accustomed, said in France that he would pay them off—at 20 cents on the dollar, approximately. Many of the victims accepted—but not the Reverend Arthur Travis Faber, an Anglican clergyman in the city of Leeds, England.

The Reverend Faber didn't aim to accept 20 per cent. Or 90 per cent, either. He had invested his daughter's dowry with Factor, and he wanted every farthing repaid, with compound interest. Factor, annoyed at what he deemed impertinence, had one of his stooges deliver a crude message to the parson. "Tell him," Jake said, "that I will see him in hell before I ever give him a penny."

That was a bad, bad mistake. Jake should have known better than to consign a righteous man of the cloth to fire and brimstone. The Reverend Faber journeyed from Leeds to London, saw a lawyer, plunked down 100 pounds and said: "This American bounder, Factor, should be brought back to England and prosecuted. Please arrange to do so."

In Chicago, Attorney Thomas C. McConnell's law firm received a letter from the London solicitors, explaining that Jake the Barber had barbered Britons for more than $7,000,000. Would McConnell be interested in undertaking a legal action to recover, on a percentage basis? There was a 100 pound retainer available.

McConnell read the letter with no enthusiastic cries of joy. The retainer was skimpy. It was probable that Factor, in common with all swindlers, had hidden away his loot so carefully that it could never be found, so recovery would be next to impossible. Still, a fat percentage of $7,000,000 would be a lovely thing.

McConnell was dummy at a bridge game a few nights later, but he wasn't dumb. He overheard a banker say that Factor had deposited $1,000,000 in each of two Chi-

THE
STOLEN
YEARS

This was a familiar sign just before
curfew fell on alcohol—and my heyday as
a Beer Baron (slightly illegal) began.

BONE DRY IN JUNE!
PREPARE NOW!
Lay in a Stock of our
WHISKEY at the OLD PRICE
Before the NEW TAX is added.

PROHIBITION SURE!
with another Tax due any day
BE WISE & BUY NOW!
To-Morrow may be too late!
Our Whiskey at $6.00 per gal. Unsurpassed.

Prohibition agents are shown busting up one
of Al Capone's breweries, which didn't
make me feel a bit bad. After a lot of
Capone's breweries had been raided, he
bought beer from me—and tried to cheat
me on the price.

AL CAPONE fishes from his yacht at
the dock of his palatial, walled
estate on Biscayne Bay at Miami
Beach, Florida. Capone's mob
kidnaped my partner, Matt Kolb,
and I paid him $50,000 ransom.

"The Crime of 1920", somebody called in
when prohibition agents sent 130,000
quarts of hard liquor down the sewer in
Waukegan, Illinois.

MURRAY "THE CAMEL" HUMPHREYS, Capone hoodlum, once
was terrified that I would have him killed. I
peddled illegal beer, but I never killed anybody.

The government nailed AL CAPONE for income
taxes in 1931, just before my troubles began.
He went to Alcatraz Penitentiary and came
out with his mind a wreck.

AL CAPONE loved to hobnob with politicians in pubic.
Here he is at a 1931 Notre Dame—Northwestern
University football game. Man at left is Albert J.
Prignano, former Chicago alderman. Prignano later was
murdered, a not-unusual fate of Capone associates.

Relic of prohibition gang warfare is this 1928
Cadillac, owned by Al Capone. It is armor
plated, with bullet proof glass. A gun turret
is at the rear. A collector bought it at
auction for $580 in 1958.

When George "Bugs" Moran, old Chicago gangster, saw
this photo in a newspaper,he said: "Only Al Capone's
mob kills like that." I agree. The picture is of
the St. Valentine's Day Massacre of 1929 when
Capone killers lined up seven men in one of Moran's
alcohol depots and killed them.

United Press International Photo

Wide World Photo

THOMAS J. COURTNEY who was prosecuting attorney in my two Factor trials.

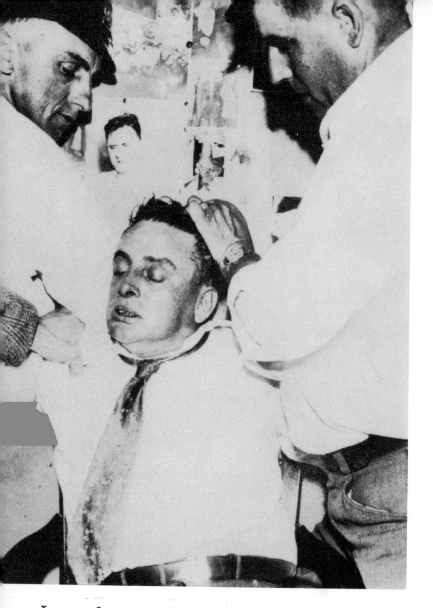

Law enforcement officers manhandled me so that news photographers could shoot my picture after the arrest in Wisconsin. My three companions and I were beaten and abused for days thereafter.

Chicago's DANIEL A. GILBERT was
Prosecutor Courtney's chief investigator.

On trial at St. Paul, McFadden, myself,
Stevens and Sharkey are shown with
Major C. J. Shuttleworth, Chief Jailer at
left, and Sheriff G. H. Moeller, fourth
from left.

I look pretty skeptical here, listening
to evidence at my second trial in what
has been called the "never-happened"
Factor kidnaping. I was!

BASIL "THE OWL" BANGHART was a prison
escape artist. He was sent to Alcatraz
after being captured following his escape
from Stateville.

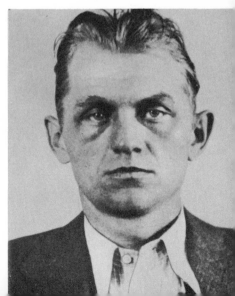

Here I am, on trial in Chicago in January, 1934
for the Factor "kidnaping" which was declared 2
years later by a federal judge as a hoax.

My wife, Clara, looks tired and drawn in this
picture, made at my trial in St. Paul for the
Hamm kidnaping. With her is my Chicago lawyer,
William Scott Stewart. I was acquitted in the
Hamm case—and the real kidnapers later confessed
or were convicted.

ALBERT KATOR, nicknamed "Polly Nose" by the
prosecution, is shown on trial in the Factor case.
Seated beside Kator at right is an armed guard,
while William Scott Stewart, our defense lawyer,
leans over the chair.

Courtroom scene during the William Hamm, Jr.,
kidnaping trial at St. Paul, Minnesota. From
left to right, front row, Attorney William
Scott Stewart, myself and a deputy; second row,
Attorney Thomas McMeekin, Willie Sharkey and
a deputy; rear row, Peter Stevens, a deputy
and Edward McFadden, with only the top of his
head showing.

PETER STEVENS, who seldom smiled, was
another Factor case defendant. He was
sentenced to 99 years, along with mysel
and two others.

FBI Agents trapped Basil "The Owl" Banghart,
Edward Darlak and me in this building on Dec.
29th, 1942. We lived in the second floor
apartment at right, with drawn shades.

Illinois police lock the barn door—too late—
at Stateville Penitentiary after the 1942
prison break.

On New Year's Eve, 1942, I'm being taken fr
Chicago FBI office for a trip back to
Stateville Penitentiary.

FEDERAL BUREAU OF INV
UNITED STATES DEPARTMEN

Wide World Photo

My co-defendants and I, at left, had a sad
Yuletide in jail in Chicago in 1934. Edward
McFadden stands next to me, then Peter
Steven, closest to bench, and at far right,
Albert Kator, partly obscured by desk lamp.

ROBERT B. JOHNSTONE (right),
Chicago lawyer, wrecked his law
practice and suffered a physical
breakdown while fighting for my
freedom.

The late JOHN P. BARNES, distinguished federal court judge, who
ruled that Jake the Barber Factor
faked a "kidnaping" and that I was
guilty of nothing.

Gene O'Connor's body is carried from a Chicago apartment building after FBI men killed him and another escapee, St. Clair McInerney.

Manacled and chained, I'm on my way to court at Joliet, Illinois, to be sentenced to 199 years for "aiding and abetting" one of my escape buddies.

WARDEN JOSEPH E. RAGEN, of Stateville
Penitentiary, and a guard returning me to
prison in January, 1943, after one of my
many court petitions had been denied.

The manacles go on and freedom ends after 47
hours. Here I am surrendering to Sheriff
John Babb (left) and U.S. Marshal William
Kipp, Jr.

I'm being led, handcuffed, into Judge John P.
Barnes' court in Chicago for hearing that
brought me temporary freedom.

Victory at last! ATTORNEY ROBERT B.
JOHNSTONE and I leave Judge John P. Barnes'
Chicago courtroom after hearing ruling that
I was innocent.

A glum shot of me behind Stateville Penitentiary
bars after my brief period of freedom.

Ray Brennan, who helped me write
THE STOLEN YEARS, shown here at a recent
visit to Stateville.

WARDEN JOSEPH E. RAGEN, foreground, has just
given me the news that I would be eligible for
parole in October, 1959. The picture was made
early in 1958.

Reporters talk to me as I receive word
early in 1958 that I will be eligible for
parole in 18 months.

Candid camera studies of me at a press
conference early in 1958.

Wide World Photo

Wide World Photo

Wide World Photo

Following are some recent shots of myself and my cubicle-home
for the past quarter century — at Stateville Penitentiary.

Arthur Shay Photo

Arthur Shay Photo

Ray Brennan, who helped me write
THE STOLEN YEARS.

cago banks. The news was music for any shrewd lawyer. McConnell's firm snapped up the 100 pounds and set out ambitiously to collect the percentage. Now that some of Factor's boodle had been located, recovery was far from impossible.

The Chicago lawyer and his associates got back $1,800,-000 for rooked Britishers who joined with the Reverend Faber in a suit. What percentage the Chicago law firm received was not revealed, but it certainly was not small. The Reverend Faber, incidentally, got back his every shilling with interest.

Back home in Chicago, Factor left a trail of $100 bills wherever he went. A star sapphire twinkled from a ring on his finger. His lovely wife, Rella, was with him in Paris gowns at the Chez Paree, the Empire Room, the Marine Dining Room and other fancy spots of Chicago night life.

He hit The Dells and other Capone gambling joints, where he had a credit of $50,000 at the tables. His Deusenberg car, with liveried chauffeur, was known everywhere in Chicago. In suburban Des Plaines, I heard gossip about him as the biggest spender since Diamond Jim Brady.

With Factor at the finest Chicago restaurants and night clubs were politicians, Capone mobsters and police captains. Jake was drunk with money.

The British government didn't like this vulgar display. Jake was indicted in London and an extradition warrant was sent to the State Department in Washington. Two of Factor's stooges, Harry Geen and Arthur J. Klein, were convicted in London and imprisoned. Jake, as the brains of the swindle, could expect no mercy in the British courts.

While his underlings took his raps for him, Factor opposed extradition with the best lawyers that money could retain. Then came what seemed to be a series of remarkable coincidences.

Son Jerome was reported kidnaped—and once again I want to state in all fairness that I have no reason to believe that Jerome was involved in any fakery in the matter. Nevertheless, the alleged abduction came at a crucial time in his father's extradition fight. Coincidental, wasn't it?

After that came Jake's own vanishing act, his reappearance, his statements that he had seen none of his purported kidnapers, his grandstanding with Tubbo Gilbert in court at my trial in St. Paul, his appearance before a county grand jury in Chicago that indicted Stevens, McFadden, Kator and me.

(Incidentally, Factor must have been relieved—as were Sharkey, McFadden, Stevens and I—when we were found not guilty in St. Paul. If we had been convicted and sentenced to life for the Hamm job, there would have been no excuse to keep Jake in the United States. He would have been on his way to England.)

After State's Attorney Courtney went to President Roosevelt in December, 1933, Factor could feel fairly secure. He could remain in the United States indefinitely.

He testified against me and my codefendants—and subsequent chapters of this book will show that he lied, again and again. His lies show up, without dispute, in his sworn testimony. Factor has admitted that he lied, and that Dan Gilbert, at least, knew he lied.

After Factor had perjured me and my codefendants into prison for 99 years each, he beat the extradition rap for all time. The government locked him up in the county jail at Sycamore, Illinois, for 60 days. During that time, the State Department made no move to honor the British government's extradition warrant.

When the 60 days were up, Factor went free, under the law. The cheated British chumps didn't even have a chance to testify against him. He never could be prosecuted for the London swindle—unless he made the mistake of stepping on British soil, from which no extradition would be needed to put him on trial. He was smart enough to remain in the United States, of course, but he didn't stay out of crime.

He pleaded guilty at Cedar Rapids, Iowa, in 1943, in connection with a plot to swindle $1,000,000 from Roman Catholic priests and other victims in a fake deal involving whiskey warehouse receipts. He served from August, 1943, to February, 1948, in the Federal Penitentiary at Sandstone, Minnesota.

Also, Jake tried to go into the whiskey business in Chicago. He had a federal Alcohol Tax Commission hearing on an application for a permit to deal in alcoholic beverages. A hearing commissioner turned him down, with the comment: "John Factor is a person who can not be believed under oath."

So, Jake was too big a liar to get a legal permit to peddle booze. But he was believed so trustingly in the Cook County Criminal Court that he was able to lie me and my codefendants into 99-year prison terms. Could there be any greater mockery of justice?

Courtney and Gilbert since have claimed that they had witnesses to back up Factor's testimony. Judge Barnes later agreed with them, and so do I. The fact is, however, that the corroborative witnesses were as big liars as Factor was. The sworn stenographic record will bear me out.

Chapter 13

What Jake the Barber Said

Our lawyer, Stewart, came back from his tropical vacation early in January, 1934, and things didn't look too rosy. The Factor case was assigned to Judge Michael J. Feinberg and he wanted a trial right now—or sooner, if possible. There would be no delays, which left us little time to locate witnesses or prepare a defense.

An emissary came to me in the jail with a proposition. A message had been sent to him that McFadden, Stevens, Kator and I would go free for a pay-off of $25,000 to a politician. I said to hell with it. I was innocent, and no politician was going to get fat off me. We would beat them in court, just as we had beat the Hamm frame-up.

My wife, Clara, visited me and begged me to pay the $25,000 bribe. We had plenty of money. Legal expenses had eaten at my bankroll and my business, without my attention, had gone to pot. But still I could have made the pay-off without scrimping myself, if I wanted to. I wouldn't do it.

There was danger in going to trial, and I knew it. Jake the Barber had had more than five months to manufacture evidence, buy off witnesses and weave a pattern of lies. If he convicted us, he was a cinch to stay in the United States for two or three years while we appealed to the higher courts. By that time the case against him in England probably would be dead. He had reason to want a guilty verdict desperately.

Clara, one visiting day, brought me the front pages of the two Chicago morning papers of the previous July 8th. Factor had been reported to be in the hands of kidnapers at that time.

The headlines of the two newspapers were almost identical. The *Chicago Tribune* read: "FACTOR CASE BRANDED HOAX." The *Herald and Examiner*: "BRAND FACTOR CASE HOAX". The *Tribune's* story began:

"Convinced that the kidnaping of John 'Jake the Barber' Factor was a hoax arranged by connivance of the millionaire speculator and his friends to enable him to escape extradition to England, Lewis Bernays, British consul here, served a demand yesterday on federal authorities to capture Factor and jail him."

My wife looked at me warningly and said: "The papers have changed their attitude in the last few months, Rog. They believe Factor now. Maybe the people on the jury will believe him, too." She was right. Jake the Barber had a "Mr. Factor" standing in the papers now and I was "Black Roger" or "Terrible Touhy." The bad publicity had me in a box.

Judge Feinberg banged his gavel for order at 10 a.m. on January 11, and away we went. Every seat in the courtroom was filled, and spectators were standing around the walls. People lined up for hours for a glimpse of "Terrible Touhy" and his arch-criminals. It was the Hamm trial all over again, but Assistant State's Attorney Crowley added a gimmick by asking a new question of a prospective juror being qualified for duty:

"Have you any religious or conscientious scruples against the infliction of the death penalty in a proper case?"

He made it sound like a commonplace inquiry as: "How do you like your eggs for breakfast?" or "Milk or lemon with your tea?" Over and over, day after day, I heard that question asked as the jury was being picked. It haunted me, and it still does.

It gives you a lousy feeling, believe me, to hear yourself referred to as a miserable, lowlife, vicious criminal—good only for meat to be fried in the electric chair. I realized for the first time the bottomless shame of being so low as to be sent to your death by your fellow men. I hoped that, if they sent me, my sons never would know.

When 12 men—no women, at that time—were in the jury box and sworn to be good and true, Crowley scorched them with a fiery opening address. He stressed the fiendishness of the crime of kidnaping. He promised to prove beyond a reasonable doubt that we were guilty. Stewart replied that the case against us was a frame-up by Factor and the Capone mob. During a recess, Stevens pointed out to me that two Roman Catholics were on the jury. He didn't like it.

Stevens told me to take note that Crowley and his trial assistant, Marshall Kearney, both were wearing insignia pins of the Catholic order of the Knights of Columbus in in their lapels. I asked Stewart about it and he explained that he had accepted the two jurors as good strategy. "Don't forget that your friend Father Weber is going to be an important witness for us," Stewart said.

After giving me that message Stewart said: "Rog, there's an old Chinese saying that goes: 'Man who tries to be own lawyer has fool for a client'." I knew what Stewart meant. He was running the law suit and I was to keep my mouth zippered up. I did—for a while.

It is impossible to use in this book all the testimony given at the trial and at subsequent proceedings. To do so would fill 100 books twice as long as *Gone with the Wind*. This book will, however, cover all testimony that had any lasting effect on my case.

A half dozen witnesses told of being at the "kidnap scene" near The Dells. They related that a band of men with machine guns and other weapons took Jake the Barber away in a car. A couple of them identified a photograph of dead Willie Sharkey as that of one of the gunmen.

Those people told the truth—as they saw it. They had no way of knowing the real situation—the fact that Factor had hired the men to fake a kidnaping so realistically that they would have no suspicions.

Factor's wife, Rella, testified that she rounded up $70,-000, as directed in Jake's note, and Dr. Soloway told of delivering a package to a gang of strangers on a dark, lonely country road. The doctor said he assumed the packet was money, but that he didn't know how much. "It could have been old calendars for all I know," he said.

And then Factor went to the witness chair. I braced myself, sensing that the lies were going to start. Prosecutor Crowley led him along skilfully through his life story, building him up as a "self-made broker."

Jake's answers came in a clear, firm voice. I listened, and I soon realized why Jake had been such a successful operator. His manner was bland and his big, dark eyes were trusting. He had a sincere, little-boy look of utmost confidence in being believed.

Factor was a great actor. He was embarked on the most important swindle of his life—the swindling of a judge and 12 jurors.

When he reached the incident near The Dells, Jake identified the photo of Willie Sharkey as that of one of the men with guns. Also, the witness said he got a good look at another man who had walked in front of the glare of a car's headlights.

That man was Stevens, Factor said. He fingered Stevens in court.

After being put in the "kidnapers" car, Factor said, he was driven for about 20 minutes. During that time, he went on, one of the kidnapers asked him: "How soon can you get $500,000?" Factor said that he pleaded poverty, saying he didn't have that kind of money.

Soon after being snatched, Jake testified, he was blindfolded with his own handkerchief. At the end of a short ride, he continued, the car turned into a driveway and stopped. He said that he was taken down a flight of seven steps and that one of his captors told him: "This is what we call putting them into the basement, Jack." (Factor generally referred to himself as Jack rather than Jake.)

The prosecution then brought into court a big diagram, or plat, of the basement of a house. The place was identified as the cellar of a house at Fir and Elm Streets in Glenview. Something like an electric shock ran through me. I had given my name as a reference when Chicken McFadden had rented that house.

I looked over my shoulder at McFadden, sitting at the counsel table behind me. He shook his head slightly, indicating that he didn't know what this was all about. What the hell, he had been hospitalized all the time that Factor claimed he had been kidnaped.

Jake the Barber went on to say that he had visited the basement on July 28, 1933, at a time when I was in jail in Milwaukee.

Factor said he went to the house with an F.B.I. man and a private detective guard. He swore that he had no advance knowledge that McFadden had any connection with the place or that I had been a reference for the rental.

Crowley interrogated Jake closely about the July 28 visit to the Glenview place. Almost every material reply made by Factor was a lie. It has been proved that Factor lied. He has admitted it. Judge Barnes affirmed it.

"I opened the door and I went down to this basement and I immediately recognized that that was the basement where I was held," Factor testified.

(Factor lied when he gave that answer. He never was in the basement—or anywhere else in the Glenview house—at any time during his pretended kidnaping.)

Crowley continued with the interrogation:

Q. How many stairs did you walk down, approximately, on the night you were taken, July 1?

A. Six or seven.

Q. And how many stairs did you walk down the day you were out there [July 28] with the government men?

A. Six or seven.

Factor identified the basement diagram, saying it was clear to him. He pointed out the john, a stairway, the location of a place where he said he sat, a supporting post shown on a photo of the basement and other incidentals.

Q. All right, on the night that you were taken down to the basement, did you have occasion to use the lavatory?

A. Yes, sir.

Q. The plat is clear in your mind now?

A. Yes, it is. I went this way and sort of over to the right and then to the left.

Q. And how many times while you were in that basement did you go to the lavatory?

A. Very often, that night.

Crowley paused for effect and McFadden interpreted the technique later when he said: "The prosecution was trying to get across the idea that Jake had the shit scared out of him."

Crowley continued his questioning:

Q. Is there anything else by which you can recognize that basement?

A. The sound of the stairs.

Q. Will you describe the sound of the stairs in the basement in which you were held the first time, on July 1?

A. There are two different sounds to these stairs. As you go up, I couldn't understand the sound. But as I was out there I had one of the men walk down and walk up again and as you get up to the top of the first floor, in order to go up from the basement, there is two different stairs and one of them is very thin wood and the other one is heavy, so the sound is quite different.

Jake the Barber's lies went on and on:

Q. Do you remember anything about any shrubbery?

A. Coming out, as you open the door, I remember when I was brought in there there was shrubberies sort of brushing me. I was brushing them or they were brushing me when I was going in and out, and those same shrubs were there over the door or very close to the door. . . .

Q. Did you hear anything else?

A. I heard train whistles, lots of trains going by.

Q. When you were out there on July 1?

A. On July 1, yes, sir.

Q. And when you were out there on July 28?

A. The same whistles.

The whistling trains were a deft touch. Glenview is served by suburban trains to and from Chicago. Those trains do have signal whistles of distinctive sound.

The reason for McFadden's being on trial now was obvious. Because of his hospitalization at the time, he could no more have been convicted of kidnaping Factor than could Shirley Temple. Chicken was a defendant because, through him, I could be connected with the Glenview house.

His kidnapers asked him that night for the names of ransom contacts, Factor testified, and he suggested Sam Hare, known as part-owner of The Dells, and a couple of other persons. Nothing was settled, Jake said. He was left with two men, later to be known as the "good man" and the "bad man."

The bad man searched his pockets, found only $10 or $11, Factor said, and told him angrily: "I'm going to cut off your ear and send it to your wife as a souvenir." The fellow then got a pair of scissors and clacked them near his ears, Factor said. A couple of the jurors gazed at him sympathetically.

Throughout, Factor had the attitude as he lied of a humble—but dignified and brave—citizen, doing his duty. He smiled apologetically at the jury when he quoted his captors as using swear words. It was a great performance.

The good man was kind to him through the long, frightening night, talking to him to help pass the hours, Factor said. When he complained of pain from the handkerchief blindfold, tied tightly about his head, the man removed the binding, tore it into strips and pasted it back over his eyes with adhesive tape, the witness said.

While his eyes were uncovered, Factor testified, he looked up briefly and saw a man. Could he identify that man? Crowley asked. Yes, replied Jake, and fingered Kator. Kator was the bad man, Factor said.

The good man brought him toast and coffee in the morning, Factor testified, and three or four of the snatchers came to the basement. They wanted $200,000, so Jake said he told them he could raise money only by writing a letter to his wife. He quoted one of the kidnapers as replying: "That is out. We will have nothing to do with the

G." apparently meaning that they were afraid of using the mails.

There was steak with mashed potatoes for supper, Factor went on, after which the bad man put handcuffs on his wrists and told him: "You are going for a ride." The words, in gangster talk, meant that he was going to be murdered, and Jake testified, with a sympathy-begging quaver in his voice, that he had wept.

Instead of being killed, however, he said he was driven in a car for 40 or 50 minutes and ended up in a second-floor bedroom of a house. Jake said he had no idea of the location of the house. That was another lie.

The good man read the newspapers to him on Sunday, including the stories of his disappearance, Jake said, and another kidnaper told him ransom negotiations had begun. Jake said he suggested Dr. Soloway as a contact and gave the man his watch, a Ten Commandment token and a ring as identification.

At one time, the witness testified almost tearfully, he was kicked in the stomach and, another time, a kidnaper told him: "If there is any monkey business . . . we are going to bring out a torch tomorrow and burn your feet." When he was terrified for his life, Factor said, he began to pray, only to be told by a callous kidnaper: "Why are you praying to God? Your life belongs to me."

As the negotiations dragged, Factor said, he told the kidnapers: "Maybe they [his family and friends] think I am dead. Let me write a letter. You can throw it into a friend of mine's office and my wife would get it. You would not be using the mails." The kidnapers agreed, Factor said.

The letter, introduced as evidence, showed that he had instructed Rella to get $55,000 from his broker, along with other money.

The kidnapers lifted the blindfold to allow him to write the letter, Jake said, and as they did so he looked up and saw—guess who? Roger Touhy, of course. He said another man and I were standing before him and holding a blanket up to the level of our chins.

The story couldn't have been true. The defense later proved by scientific testimony that it was a lie. The letter writing took place on Thursday—after Jake, by his own sworn testimony, had been blindfolded constantly for five days and nights. An eye doctor testified that he couldn't have seen anything when the bandage was first removed. The light would have blinded him just as fully as the blindfold had.

A man he could not see stood behind him with a machine-gun muzzle pressed against the back of his neck, ordering him to keep his head down as he wrote, Factor said. How Jake the Barber knew it was a machine gun, and not a revolver, rifle or shotgun, was a puzzle to me, since I could observe no eyes in the back of his head.

After Jake fingered me in court, he testified that he also had identified me and recognized my voice in a Chicago show-up soon after the Wisconsin telephone pole incident.

On Tuesday, July 11, Factor swore, a voice he recognized as mine told him: "Well, Jack, how much money can you raise if we let you out of here? . . . We spoke [by telephone] to your wife today. You have got a good wife. . . . She has raised $70,000. How soon could you raise $50,000 if we let you go?"

Factor said he replied that he probably would need a week or so for this delayed-action ransom payoff. He testified that the kind kidnaper then spoke up, saying he would come to Jake's office and get the additional money. The good man was quoted as saying that he would telephone Jake telling him: "I will say, 'This is the coffee man—the man who brought you coffee.' "

After that conversation in the kidnap house, Jake testified, the good man removed the blindfold by soaking the adhesive tape with alcohol. The blindfold was replaced by a handkerchief and the kidnapers drove him in a car for an hour and a half, dumping him at LaGrange, Factor said.

The kidnap tale was ended.

Chapter 14

Alice in Factorland

T he atmosphere of the trial, for me, was saturated with
    an *Alice in Wonderland* feeling. I had heard so
many lies that I couldn't keep track of them all. If the Mad
Hatter and the March Hare had jumped up on the judge's
bench and started talking jabberwocky, I would have taken
it almost as a matter of course.

After Jake the Barber had identified Stevens, Kator and
me in court, the newspaper reporters battered him with
questions in the corridor. Why, they wanted to know, had
he lied to them? Why had he told them—hundreds of
times—that he had seen none of his kidnapers? Factor had
a ready answer, as might be expected: Tubbo Gilbert and
the F.B.I. people had instructed him to lie to the newsmen,
Jake said.

The explanation was ridiculous, of course. The reader
need not take my word for it. Here are the words used years
later by Judge Barnes:

"Captain Gilbert and Factor have sought to explain
Factor's many statements . . . by saying that the F.B.I.
agents and Captain Gilbert instructed him to lie.

"So far as the F.B.I. agents are concerned, this statement is impossible to be believed.

"The F.B.I. agents are thoroughly trained investigators. . . . It is difficult to believe that any one of them would ever tell a prospective witness . . . to deny ability to identify . . . and thereby to lay himself open to successful impeachment.

"So far as Captain Gilbert is concerned the statement is so difficult to believe that it seems highly improbable . . . .

"Lawyers and investigators almost invariably advise witnesses not to talk, but good lawyers and good investigators *never* advise witnesses to lie."

After his time out for newspaper interviews, Factor resumed his story at the trial.

On July 24, twelve days after he showed up at LaGrange, he said, he got a telephone call from the good kidnaper—the "coffee man." Factor said the caller wanted to know when he would be ready to pay off the added ransom.

Jake testified that he told the "coffee man" he needed more time, and that another man called him back on August 11. Jake said he stalled some more. Gilbert and Purvis now were in on the thing, according to the witness, and an F.B.I. secretary made notes at an extension telephone.

There were more phone calls and Jake said he finally agreed to send $15,000 by Western Union messenger in a Checker taxicab out into the country. A dummy package of $500, padded out with paper, was sent to the meeting place. One police officer was driving the cab and another rode along, wearing a messenger's suit.

One of the nutty things about it was that the cops put their weapons, including a machine gun, under a seat cushion of the taxi! After they delivered the dummy bundle, they had to get out of the cab, remove the cushion and get the guns. Airplanes were flying overhead with F.B.I. agents in them and the area swarmed with policemen, but the ransom collectors got away clean.

One of them ran to a farmhouse, said he had been caught with a married woman by her husband in a secluded picnic area and paid $10 for a ride to Oak Park.

Another Adventure in Wonderland was ended.

Now, isn't it silly to believe that any kidnaper would try to collect more money from Factor after he had been released? Factor had been in close contact with the F.B.I., the Chicago police and Gilbert. The newspapers had reported that Factor and members of his family were closely guarded against harm.

Under those circumstances, why should a kidnaper believe that Jake would come up with another $50,000—or $15,000, or even 15 cents? He wouldn't, of course.

A much more sensible theory—later upheld by Judge Barnes—is that Jake was afraid his original kidnap story wouldn't be well enough believed to stop his extradition to England. He had, therefore, dreamed up the idea of the added-ransom story in a desperate effort to bolster his flimsy case.

Stewart tried to take Factor through a blistering, whip-lashing cross-examination. He wanted to show that the kidnaping had been faked for a double motive:

1. To keep Factor safe in the United States.

2. To get me out of the way so the Capone mob could take over the labor unions.

It also was important to the defense to show that Jake the Barber was someone who couldn't be believed under oath.

Prosecutors Crowley and Kearney objected to every question asked of Factor except those directly concerned with the kidnaping charges. Judge Feinberg upheld the prosecution most of the time.

Stewart did manage to get across, however, that Factor was wanted in England for swindling and that he had been an associate of Humphreys and other Capone mobsters.

In spite of the judge's limitations on the questioning, Stewart had Jake sweating and faltering at times. I was fairly confident that the jurors would have some doubts about Factor. My codefendants agreed with me.

Two other prosecution witnesses of importance were Eddie Schwabauer, a character who drank too much and never held a job for long, and his mother, Mrs. Clara Sczech, a poor, middle-aged, bedeviled, bewildered woman who had toiled at cooking and scrubbing all of her life.

They told so many different stories as time went on that I had trouble keeping them straight.

Schwabauer was a former employee of mine. I fired him in June, about three weeks before Factor "disappeared" through Alice's Looking Glass. I had hired Eddie to guard my home nights after the attempted kidnaping of my boys. I wasn't taking any chances on a bomb being tossed through one of my windows.

Eddie said he had gone on duty at my home between 9 and 10 p.m. on June 30, which was his first untruth. He was no longer in my employ. I had replaced him with another guard.

Except for about 20 minutes when he went to Wagner's saloon down the road for a drink or two, Schwabauer said, he was on my property until 2:30 a.m. Nope, Eddie went on, he hadn't seen a living soul around my home all night —no lights were on in the house and nobody was on the front porch.

He said that he never went back to work for me and that he never got his final pay. The implication to the jury was that he had taken a runout after learning that I had kidnaped the Barber.

Mrs. Sczech was an unwilling witness, but Crowley got testimony from her that she worked at the Glenview place, which McFadden had rented, for 14 days, from June 17 to June 30. Buck Henrichsen, who worked days on my property as a guard, got her the job, she said. A "Mr. Burns" was her employer, and she fingered McFadden as the same Mr. Burns.

She saw a lot of men around the Glenview house, she said, but mostly she didn't know their names. She identified a police photograph of a character she knew as "Larry Green" or "Larry the Aviator." That was Basil "The Owl" Banghart.

Mrs. Sczech said she sort of thought I had been in the Glenview house. She semi-fingered me, saying: "I am not sure whether I seen him there or not. This here fellow [me] looks quite a lot like him, still there is not quite so much resemblance." That was the way she testified. I had never been in the house, and haven't been to this day.

In questioning Mrs. Sczech, Crowley revealed that she made two contradictory statements to him, in writing, before the trial. I don't believe that even Crowley could have known when she was telling the truth and when she wasn't.

At the trial, she testified that she finished her duties in the Glenview house about 6:30 p.m. on Saturday, July 1st, had a talk with Eddie and decided not to return to work at the place again.

The implication from the mother-and-son testimony was that they had read of the Factor vanishing act in the newspapers, that they suspected he was being held in the Glenview basement and that they dumped their jobs to keep out of possible trouble. Jobs were too scarce to be quit without good reason in those depression times.

Oh, well, Schwabauer and his mother were to change their stories again and again.

But I didn't expect Buck Henrichsen to shove a knife between my ribs and twist it. I had never done anything but good for him. When he was broke and out of work, I gave him a job. In February, 1933, he came crying to me that a credit company was going to repossess his household furniture for nonpayment of installments. I gave him $200 or $300 and I paid his grocery bills. His wife, Helen, had sent me a thank-you note.

Weeks before we went on trial in Chicago, my friends told me they believed Buck had sold out to the state's attorney's office. He was living at the Oak Park Arms Hotel and the Palmer House, eating steaks at the prosecution's expense. I couldn't believe it.

"What the hell," I told Stevens in the jail, "Buck would be lost in any hotel that cost more than $1.25 a night." I was wrong. Gilbert had given Buck expensive tastes.

Henrichsen couldn't meet my eyes when Crowley called him to the witness stand. He was ashamed, but he went right along with the play to put me, Stevens and Kator in the electric chair for a crime that never was committed.

Buck testified that I had instructed him to look up a house to be rented in McFadden's name. That was the

Glenview place, of course, but Buck's claim was news to me. Except when I signed as a rental reference, I had never heard of the damn house before the trial.

On June 30, the evening before Jake the Barber had had himself snatched, Henrichsen was in Jim Wagner's saloon during the early evening, he said. He told of seeing me there, along with Stevens, Banghart, Sharkey, Kator, Tribbles and other divided septums.

Following that, Buck said, he hadn't seen me until I sent word to him to meet me at Porky Dillon's home on July 5. He testified that he did and that he found me with Dillon, Stevens, Kator, Sharkey and, probably, Ice Wagon Connors.

Q. [By Crowley] And what was the conversation you had between you and Roger?

A. [By Henrichsen] I was told to go to The Dells to pick up a man there at 9 o'clock.

Q. Who told you to do that?

A. Roger.

Q. And did you go to The Dells?

A. Yes.

Q. Whom did you pick up?

A. Joe Silvers.

Silvers was one of the managers of The Dells and, the evidence showed, he was in the place on the night Factor disappeared. Silvers' name was brought into the trial, obviously, to indicate that he had put the finger on Factor for me to kidnap.

We never were able to find Silvers to use as a defense witness, incidentally. He went to Florida and vanished— vanished like a guy who was murdered, put in a concrete shroud, taken out in a Capone-mob yacht and dumped into the Atlantic Ocean. That was what happened to him, according to the rumbles I later got in prison.

Another of the managers at The Dells was named Silversmith. He also figured in Henrichsen's testimony.

After picking up Silvers at The Dells on July 5, Buck testified, he took him to the Commercial Club at Golf Road and Milwaukee Avenue, where I was waiting with Stevens, Kator and Sharkey. Buck said I had talked with

Silvers for an hour.

Two days later, Buck went on, he picked up both Silvers and Silversmith at The Dells and took them to the Commercial Club for another hour-long conference with me.

Q. Did you carry a gun with you?

A. There was a machine gun in my car.

Q. Whose gun was that?

A. Roger's.

In about mid-July, Buck testified, I gave him $1,000 and told him to buy a car. The innuendo to the jury was that the money came from Jake the Barber ransom.

That just about wound up the prosecution's case. There had been positive identification of Stevens, Kator and me by Factor, but he wasn't a person to be readily believed, to put it kindly.

Schwabauer, Mrs. Sczech and, especially, Henrichsen had dirtied us up, but nobody except Jake had accused us directly of kidnaping.

Why did Henrichsen lie against me? It will be shown later that he was rewarded by the Capone mob. As for Schwabauer and his mother, Judge Barnes was to rule on the evidence that they were impressed by Factor's money and awed by Gilbert's power.

Chapter 15

```
                          A Hung Jury
               —and Hope for Me
```

When the prosecution rested its case, Prosecutor Crowley asked the court to dismiss all charges against McFadden. Judge Feinberg granted the motion. Old Chicken jumped out of his chair and went out of the courtroom with the speed of a cannonball. He'd had a bellyful of being tried for kidnapings about which he knew nothing.

Stevens said in the jail that night, with the trace of a grin: "Chicken really left us with a burst of speed. His coattails were sticking out so far behind him that four people could have played pinochle on them."

McFadden no longer was needed by Gilbert, Courtney and Crowley. His presence as a defendant had served its purpose. He had been used to tie me up with the Glenview house. His usefulness was ended.

The defense now went to bat.

Our witnesses were good, I thought. Anyway, they told the truth and the jurors certainly seemed to pay close attention to them.

Emily Ivins testified to sitting on the front porch with

Clara and me until shortly before dawn on July 1. She was positive, explicit and unshaken by Crowley's cross-examination.

We had a couple of surprise witnesses, too. One of them was Policeman Gerard, of River Forest, of whom bearded Jake had asked help on the night of July 12 in LaGrange. Gerard was a real, honest-to-God, stand-up witness.

Gerard testified that Factor hadn't blinked at the police station lights as might be expected of a man who had been blindfolded almost constantly for 12 days. He described Jake's shined shoes, his clean hands and face, his manicured nails, his almost-immaculate suit, his seemingly-freshly-laundered shirt, his neatly combed hair.

A couple of jurors smiled, I noticed, when Gerard testified that a news photographer in the LaGrange station had pulled Jake's necktie askew, for purposes of kidnap realism, before shooting pictures.

Policeman Gerard, on cross-examination by Crowley, went through an ordeal that might have driven the usual man into an insane rage. Crowley hinted that Gerard lied and that he wasn't fit to be a police officer.

When Gerard left the courtroom, Gilbert's policemen grabbed him outside the door. They took him to Tubbo's headquarters on the second floor of the Criminal Courts building where, sworn testimony showed later, Gilbert called him a liar, told him he would be fired and said he had no right to testify as a defense witness without notifying the state's attorney's office in advance.

While he was being denounced and berated by Gilbert, Policeman Gerard later testified, Jake the Barber walked into the room and told him in effect: "I will break you if it is the last thing I ever do and if it takes every cent I have."

For months thereafter, Gerard's life was made a hell. He was tried before the River Forest Civil Service Commission—on charges most probably pushed by Gilbert. Efforts were made to fire him from his job. He said that he had told only the truth, and the commission exonerated him.

Gerard later became chief of police in River Forest, one of Chicago's finest suburbs.

Stewart bore down hard on Jake the Barber's testimony that he saw me standing behind the blanket immediately when his blindfold was lifted for writing of the ransom note. One of our witnesses was an eye specialist who said it couldn't have happened the way Jake said it had.

The human eye takes at least four or five minutes to adjust itself to the point of being able to see a face under such circumstances, the specialist said, and the prosecution couldn't budge him on cross-examination. Crowley seemed to me a little worried at that point.

Probably the best of my witnesses was Father Weber, a testy, peppery, white-haired, skinny, somewhat shrunken old man. As he testified, I glanced at the two Roman Catholic men Stewart had welcomed to the jury. They were as full of belief of Father Weber, I thought, as a couple of devouts approaching the rail for Holy Communion.

Father Weber testified that he had been with me in my home on July 8 and that he was convinced I had nothing to do with Jake the Barber's vanishing act. He said he believed I was being framed.

Father Weber came back with a cutie when Crowley asked him with a Christ-like air whether he didn't realize that Roger Touhy was a law-violater, a bootlegger. Father took a long, meaningful look at the jury box and at the crowded courtroom and then replied along this line: "I knew that Roger Touhy sold beer, and I also knew a lot of good people who drank it."

The good father got across the idea, discreetly, that he sometimes enjoyed a tall and frosty glass himself.

If I had had the Twelve Aspostles to testify for me, they couldn't have given better evidence than Father Weber. He reported, truthfully, that I had knelt in prayer with him for the safety of Jake Factor and that I had sworn on the lives of my two boys that I had nothing to do with any kidnaping.

Another witness I had wanted to testify was Clara's aunt, Mrs. Margaret Morgan, who had visited with us during the time Factor claimed to have been snatched. Mrs. Morgan was available, but Stewart didn't call her. I don't know why.

As the trial moved toward a close, I was fed up to the Adam's apple with our lawyer. So were Kator and Stevens. Stewart wasn't any too happy with us, either.

Somebody told me that Stewart had gone to lunch with Crowley and that he chatted with Tubbo during court recesses. I asked Stewart about it and he advised me, again, to act like like a defendant and not like a fool trying to be his own lawyer, as the Chinese saying went.

I wanted to go to the witness stand, tell my story and deny guilt. Stewart strongly advised me against such a move.

If I testified, Stewart said, he would have to call Stevens and Kator as witnesses because he represented them as well as me. They had records for felony convictions, of course, and he couldn't take a chance of subjecting them to cross-examination, which would bring out their pasts and dirty up everybody concerned.

I talked over the situation with Kator and Stevens in the jail. They said for me to go ahead and testify. Their idea was that if I—maligned as "Black Roger" and "Terrible Touhy"—could prove my innocence by testifying, they wouldn't be convicted either. I was the Number One defendant, and if the jury acquitted me, Kator and Stevens certainly would go free with me.

Stewart, although he knew I was innocent, wouldn't listen to me. His record in defending criminal cases shows that he seldom put a defendant in the witness chair. I threatened to stand up in court and demand of the judge that I be heard. If I did that, Stewart said, he would walk out of the court. The squabbling between us was endless.

When the last word by the last witness, including those called to rebut other witnesses, had gone into the record, it was time for the oratory. Stewart and Crowley spoke for hours—wheedling, pleading, cajoling.

Stewart concentrated in his summation on showing that Jake was a liar and a swindler, impossible of belief. He pointed out that Factor had lied to the press and he hammered at the eye specialist's testimony to show that Jake had lied in court. He challenged the jury to believe

Schwabauer's testimony against Miss Ivins' sworn statements that she had been with me and Clara through the crucial hours on the front porch.

The testimony by Father Weber and Policeman Gerard got a thorough review. Stewart screamed frame-up by Jake the Barber and the Capone outfit. He went over my protection of the labor skates from the mob, the effort to kidnap my children and everything else he had been able to get on the record through direct testimony or cross-examination.

Stewart told a couple of feeble jokes, too, and that gave Crowley the cue for his opening remarks.

The prosecutor bounded to his feet, slapped fist against open palm and began: "Men, this is serious business— m-i-g-h-t-y- s-e-r-i-o-u-s business." That set the tone for Crowley's finale to the jury. He went through every form of oratory from a muted whisper to a mighty roar.

Kidnaping, he said, was the dirtiest crime on the books. He talked about motherhood and the sanctity of the home. Crowley closed with the recommendation that the jury send all of us to the electric chair.

Came now the time for Judge Feinberg's instructions to the jury on the law in the case. He expounded at great length. He went over some of the testimony. He explained to the jurors that if they had a *reasonable* doubt— but not a silly, ridiculous or dubious doubt—as to the defendants' guilt, then the verdict should be "not guilty." If there was no reasonable doubt, then a conviction was in order.

He explained that in Illinois a jury, in addition to deciding guilt or innocence, sets the penalty in a capital case— a case in which the death penalty is a possibility. The judge pronounces the sentence, but the jury decides it. Judge Feinberg explained that, in case of a guilty verdict, the jury could sentence us to:

1. Life in prison (Under such a term, we would be eligible to apply for parole after 20 years, under an Illinois Supreme Court decision.)

2. Any number of years in prison, from five to 199. (We would be eligible to ask for parole after serving one-

third of the set term—after 10 years on a 30-year term, for example.)

3. Death.

The jurors returned to their room to deliberate. Stevens, Kator and I sat around in the prisoners' bullpen off a corridor at the rear of the courtroom for a few hours. Then they took us back to the jail, offered us food, which none of us could eat, and locked us in our cells.

The big danger, as the hours dragged, was that the Factor jurors had found us guilty but were unable to agree on the penalty. Maybe they were 11 to 1 for the death penalty, with the lone holdout demanding 199 years instead of the chair. On the other hand, they might be 11 to 1 for acquittal, with one character holding out for the five-year minimum.

After 24 hours, the guards and bailiffs handcuffed us and took us back to court. We asked if there was a verdict and one of the guards tipped us off: "Naw, the jury seems to be deadlocked. The judge is calling them in to inquire. Keep calm."

The jurors filed into the box and I gazed at the all-too-familiar faces. I had looked at them a lot in more than three weeks. The trial had started on January 11 and it now was February 2. Several of them looked at me sympathetically as they now returned to the box, and I felt heartened.

Maybe, just maybe, the jurors believed us by 11 to 1 and we would be free in a few hours after the twelfth was won over.

Judge Feinberg inquired of the jurors if they had selected a foreman. They had. The foreman stood up. The judge asked if a verdict had been reached. "Not yet," the foreman replied. The answer seemed to me to mean that there was hope for agreement and that the jury would be sent back to deliberate some more. I was quite hopeful there—for a second or two.

Bang! Down came Feinberg's gavel. He discharged the jury. Stewart tried to protest, but he got no attention. His Honor had spoken. The trial was ended. But there would be a new, long, expensive trial.

I looked around the courtroom and saw my two worst enemies. Tubbo Gilbert was rubbing his undershot chin. Jake the Barber was showing his big, white teeth in a beaming smile. Judge Feinberg's ruling meant that he could remain a fugitive from England for the duration of the second trial, *and* for our appeals, in case we were convicted.

Immediately after the first trial, I fired Stewart, in a nice way. "Scott, we're not getting along, and I want a new lawyer," I said. Well, maybe I didn't exactly fire him. He quit at the same time. He didn't want any more part of me, either. I was an uncooperative client: I had made up my mind, come fire or disaster, I was going to testify at the second trial and Stewart wouldn't hold still for that.

I signed a sworn affidavit in the Cook County Jail saying that I didn't want to be represented by Stewart any more. Stewart signed an affidavit saying he was through with me, too. It was mutual.

Now, one of the firm principles of criminal jurisprudence is that a defendant must have a lawyer of his own choice. He cannot be required to go on trial with a lawyer he does not want. Hundreds of court decisions have affirmed that proposition.

Clara visited me, and I told her to get a new lawyer. I gave her the names of two Chicago attorneys and of Thomas McMeekin, the St. Paul lawyer who had been with our defense at the Hamm fiasco. Any one of the three would be okay with Stevens, Kator and me.

As she left the jail, Clara collapsed and was hospitalized. She underwent major surgery, but she managed to get word to McMeekin and the other two lawyers that I wanted to see them. They came to the jail—but they didn't get in. The warden had orders from the Criminal Court that I could be visited only by the lawyer listed as representing me—Stewart, that was.

When Stewart went to Judge Feinberg and tried to pull out of the case, the judge refused. Furthermore, Feinberg threatened to put Stewart in jail unless he continued to represent us. The judge also ordered Stewart to be ready for the re-trial on February 13, only 11 days after the first jury had been discharged. Stewart then asked for a change of venue, for a transfer to another judge. Feinberg refused. He also ignored my demand for a new lawyer.

Stewart, disgusted, decided he wouldn't show up in court. That didn't work either. Judge Feinberg had his personal bailiff deliver a letter by hand to Stewart telling him to handle the defense—or else. He had to obey.

Away we went again. For the upcoming trial, I had a lawyer I didn't want before a judge who, I believed, hadn't given me a fair trial in the first place. It was unconstitutional. My codefendants, Stevens and Kator agreed with me. So did Stewart. But, anyway, we went on trial for the second time on February 13, 1934.

The lies against us at the second trial were astronomical. Witnesses—including Factor—changed their stories at will. Judge Feinberg didn't question the obvious perjury.

And Factor and Gilbert had the biggest liar of all stashed away for Round Two.

Chapter 16

The Witness Who
Wasn't There

Nobody gave a hoot, this time, how many Roman Catholics were on the jury, and there was a reason why. Father Weber had sent word to us that he would be unable to testify. His superiors had told him that he would be shipped off to a monastery if he attempted to speak up for us again.

Jake the Barber went to the witness stand and told the same, now somewhat frayed-at-the-edges, story of how he said he was kidnaped against his will from the Dells. When he reached the proper point in going through his testimony again, I expected the bailiffs to trundle out the plat, or diagram, of the Glenview house basement. They didn't.

In fact, the house vanished from Jake's second-trial testimony. Crowley didn't bring it up and Factor didn't once mention it on direct examination.

He said nothing about the train whistles, nothing about the stairway with the tread that resounded strangely to a footfall, nothing about the six or seven steps, nothing about the shrubbery near the door, nothing about the location of the bathroom which he had told earlier of visiting so often during his travail.

When Jake came to the part about having identified me behind the blanket, he hedged cagily. He now indicated that his blindfold hadn't been too tight, after all; that some light came through to his eyes. And, it now appeared, he may not have seen me *immediately* after the bandage was removed from his eyes.

Jake ducked away from a glaring error which the defense had caught in the first trial. There was no sense in Stewart calling our eye specialist again. His testimony would have been pointless. Jake's switch took an important time-at-bat away from the defense.

On cross-examination, Stewart asked him if he hadn't positively identified the Glenview basement at the first trial. "Yes," Factor replied blandly. On the matter of identifying me, he insisted that he was telling the same tale about the lifting of the blindfold that he had told at the first trial. Judge Feinberg listened and didn't so much as reprimand him.

Under a screwball Illinois law, since changed, Jake was practically immune from conviction for perjury, no matter what he said. The law stated that a witness could testify at one time and later tell an exactly opposite, completely contradictory story under oath. Unless the state could prove which time he lied—and that often was impossible—he couldn't be convicted.

I had been warning my codefendants to watch out for another phony witness to come prevaricating along, à la the Hamm trial in St. Paul. Factor and Gilbert came through as I had expected. It happened when our trial was well under way. But first, a little background is necessary.

On November 15, 1933, a mail truck had been robbed of $105,000 at Charlotte, North Carolina. Blamed for the job—and guilty as a bank cashier with a credit rating in a gambling house—were Isaac "Ike" Costner, a Tennessee mountain whiskey moonshiner, and Basil "The Owl" Banghart, mentioned at the first trial as Larry Green or Larry the Aviator.

Ice Wagon Connors probably was in on the Charlotte

deal, too, but somebody tied him up with baling wire, shot him as full of holes as a Swiss cheese and deposited him in a muddy ditch outside of Chicago before anything could be proved. Some day, in that Great Beyond they talk about, I hope to sit down for a quiet talk with Ice Wagon. I think I know who had him drygulched and I sure as hell would like to be sure.

Anyway, as the February winds blew into the Windy City of Chicago, Banghart and Costner got themselves arrested in Baltimore. They practically were asking for it, by boozing with women in their Baltimore apartment. The neighbors complained, the police moved in and the place was sprinkled like confetti with bank wrappers from the stolen money.

Banghart and Costner had been stupid, as are all thieves. Even the smart ones, like Willie Sutton was supposed to be, spend most of their lives in prison. I knew hundreds of them in Stateville and few of them could make an honest living at anything more intellectual than digging ditches or cleaning out cesspools.

Organized gangsters with million-dollar bankrolls, the best lawyers and political power—such as the Capone mobsters—are the only ones who get away with crime consistently. And even they get nailed now and then by the federal government for income-tax dodges or deportable offenses.

Upon learning of the arrests in Baltimore, Tubbo Gilbert hastened there, taking Jake the Barber along. Joining them was Joe Keenan, the special assistant U.S. attorney general who had been appointed to bring an end to the scourge of kidnaping in the United States. It must have been a jolly gathering, with reminiscences about the Hamm fiasco at St. Paul.

Banghart had no reason for any interest in turning state's evidence against Stevens, Kator and me. He was under charges of robbery more times than most people go to the grocery store during a lifetime. He had escaped from the County Jail at South Bend, Indiana, after throwing pepper in a turnkey's eyes and he had beaten the wall of the federal pen at Atlanta, Georgia.

No matter what he said or did, the law was going to throw the key away on Banghart. Costner, on the other hand, was vulnerable to a proposition from Factor. Only the North Carolina postal-truck thing and a moonshine rap were hanging over Ike. He might be able to squeak by with only a few years behind bars if he made a deal.

Jake the Barber and Gilbert spent two days with Banghart and Costner in Baltimore. Keenan got into the spirit of the thing. He allowed Tubbo to take Costner and Banghart back to Chicago—rather than send them to North Carolina for the postal-truck robbery! It was highly unusual for the government to relinquish custody of prisoners to a state when a federal conviction was a cinch.

Evidence later developed that Ike Costner was promised he would be let off with five years for the robbery and freed of prosecution in the Factor case if he would testify against Stevens, Kator, Banghart and me. It was a questionable deal—but anything went to nail a kidnaper in those times.

After their tête-à-tête with the prisoners in Baltimore, Factor and Gilbert rode back by train with Costner and Banghart to Chicago. Tubbo boasted of that ride in an interview with the late Elgar Brown, famous *Chicago American* writer and war correspondent.

Gilbert said in the interview that he sat on the train most of the time with Banghart. Jake the Barber concentrated on Costner. How would you expect a guy, smart enough to swindle $7,000,000 out of British investors, to make out against a Tennessee moonshiner?

Factor could be expected to win, of course. And apparently he did.

On the day that Factor and Gilbert brought the two witnesses back from Baltimore, or the day after, I was walking in the corridor leading from Judge Feinberg's courtroom to the prisoners' elevator during a recess. Ahead of me, I spotted Dan Gilbert and a man I never had seen before.

I figured it might be another fake finger, so I hunched down my head, and hid my face with my coat collar. I heard

Tubbo say—*sotto voce*, as the British write in those long, frequently boring novels in the Stateville library: "The guy in the light suit—that's Touhy." Gilbert was fingering me, I found later, for Ike Costner.

In my cell, I got the hell out of the light suit and put on a dark blue one. When I got back to court, Costner was the first witness. I didn't know what he was going to say, but my blue serge felt real snug and comfortable on me. After some preliminary questions, Prosecutor Crowley asked Ike if he could identify Roger Touhy anywhere in the courtroom.

Costner stared wildly around the room. He looked at the spectators, the bailiffs, the jurors and even the judge. He was searching, apparently, for a man in a light suit. I wanted to laugh, but I kept a straight face. Ike seemed to be bewildered.

The charm was broken suddenly. Our lawyer tapped me on the shoulder and said: "Stand up, Roger." There was nothing I could do but obey. I stood, and Costner fingered me, blue suit and all. I figured right then that Stevens, Kator and I were ticketed to sit down on 22,000 volts or else to go into dry rot in prison.

I always have been bitter and always will be about Stewart's making me a clay pigeon for Costner to shoot down. It wouldn't have happened, probably, if I had been on speaking terms with my lawyer. But I wasn't. I hadn't told Stewart about the fingering, and my switch from the light suit to the dark blue.

Stewart said he regarded it as psychologically important with the jury to have a defendant admit his identity at once, rather than wait to be pointed out. Maybe so, but I don't believe Costner could have identified me without my own lawyer's help.

Ike testified he had known Banghart for four or five years and that Basil The Own had visited him in Knoxville, Tennessee, during mid-June. My brother, Tommy, Kator. Ice Wagon Connors, Willie Sharkey, Jimmy Tribbles and others also came a-calling, Costner testified. That must have been a jolly group, too.

Now, the rules of evidence provide that a witness at a

trial may not repeat any conversations which took place outside the presence of the defendants. The prosecution didn't dare try to put Stevens and me in Tennessee because we were supposed to have been in St. Paul, kidnaping William Hamm, at the time.

Therefore, Costner couldn't come right out and say that my brother, Kator, Banghart and the others had recruited him to help snatch Jake the Barber. Crowley, by adroit questioning of Ike, got the idea across to the jury, however.

Costner said he drove to the Chicago area alone between June 25 and 28, went to Park Ridge and stayed at The Owl's apartment. He knew why he was in Illinois and what was going to be done, Costner indicated.

Why a tough Chicago-area gang should take the trouble to go all the way to Tennessee to persuade a hillbilly to join in kidnaping Factor was material for a comedy skit. Costner was a moonshiner and chicken thief, with no hot-shot reputation for crime up until the Charlotte mail job. He conceded that he was a stranger to all of the purported kidnapers except Banghart. Why would they trust or want him? His story was ridiculous.

Ike said he was introduced to Stevens and me in Jim Wagner's bar. He said he slept at various houses, but that he couldn't identify the Glenview house, which had been so important for the prosecution at the first trial. He didn't even know the names of the towns out there, the witness said, and he was always getting lost on the streets and highways. As stupid a kidnaper as could have been recruited: that was Ike.

At about 11 o'clock on the night of June 30, he was sleeping in one of the houses and somebody—maybe Ice Connors—awakened him, Costner went on. He told of seeing Stevens, Kator, Banghart and me, adding that Banghart said—in our presence—"We are going to grab Factor." Ike said he got dressed and joined the group. I was driving his car, he said.

There was a wait of an hour or two by the kidnapers in several cars near The Dells, according to Ike. He said that a man presumed to be Silvers, one of the managers, twice came out of The Dells, and talked with the kidnapers.

describing Factor's Deusenberg and his clothing. Silvers was the character who reportedly ended up in the Atlantic Ocean in a concrete coffin.

Costner's story of the alleged kidnaping was about the same as Factor's. Ike said he had carried a shotgun and that he saw machine guns and other weapons. He testified that Factor was taken in his car and that I, Roger Touhy, was in the back seat with Jake.

He drove for quite some distance, Ike said, following directions from me, and stopped at a house into which Jake the Barber was hustled. No, Ike said, he didn't know the location of the house, he couldn't recognize it again because of the darkness and he hadn't gone inside the house that night.

Ike spoke in a low voice, with a deep southern accent. The jury of twelve Yankees had trouble understanding him. He tried to be a believable, straightforward witness, but he had handicaps. His biggest stumbling block was his ignorance of Cook County geography. He didn't know the names or locations of towns, railroads, landmarks or houses. When such points came up, he said in a whining voice, over and over again: "Ah cain't remember." As a liar, Ike was lacking in Jake's finesse.

Throughout his testimony, Costner tried to set himself up as the kidnaper described by Jake as "the good man" or "the coffee man." If was obvious at this point of Ike's story that somebody was lying.

Factor had testified that the good kidnaper sat with him all of that first night, comforted him with conversation, brought him toast and coffee in the morning. But Ike said under oath that he hadn't been with Jake at all that night. Costner said, instead, that he stayed at another house, the location of which he couldn't remember, with people whose names he couldn't recall.

He went back to the purported kidnap house the following night, Ike said, and drove in a motorcade that took Jake to a farmhouse about 50 or 60 miles away. No, no, he didn't remember where the new place was. Maybe he might recognize it if he saw it again.

Ike said he stayed in the place during all the time Jake

the Barber reputedly was held captive there, or for 11 days. He said he went out on the lawn now and then but that he couldn't recall anything about the surroundings. He said—and stuck to it—*that he didn't even know what color the house was painted.* "Ah cain't remember," he said.

The witness's tricky memory, or lack of rehearsal, tripped him on a number of points.

Jake said that he saw me and another man partly hidden by a blanket when he wrote the ransom note. Ike testified that there was a blanket in the room—over a window. It seemed apparent that he was not aware of the significance of the questions about the blanket. Jake had sworn that there was a lamp on the table on which he wrote the note. Ike said the light came from a ceiling fixture. Also, Costner said he never had seen Factor look up at me, or anybody else, while writing his note.

Those items, taken separately, may seem insignificant, but there were hundreds of other contradicted prosecution points throughout the trial. Added up, they became important in a monstrous pattern of perjury.

When asked about Factor's physical condition, Ike said that it had been bad, very bad. He testified that Jake had been very sick, very weak, unable to eat heartily, very nervous, "shaking like a leaf" as he reclined on a bed in the second house. It was tear-jerking stuff, but it didn't fit well with Policeman Gerard's description of Jake when he showed up at LaGrange.

On the night of July 12, Costner said, he soaked the adhesive away from Jake's face with alcohol, put a new blindfold on him and drove the car that took the victim to LaGrange. Stevens and Banghart were with him, Ike testified.

I noticed that Basil The Owl was being dirtied up wherever possible. He had refused to turn state's evidence. He was a bad man. Costner, conversely, was being presented as "the good kidnaper," an approach that might make him more acceptable to the jury. It had audience appeal.

On the day after delivering Jake the Barber to freedom, Ike said, he went to Banghart's Park Ridge apartment and Banghart gave him $2,400. "I understood the money was my share of the ransom," Ike stated, adding that he carried the cash, in $20 bills, for a week and then put it in a bank.

The truth was that Ike hadn't been within several hundred miles of Chicago on the date Factor claimed to have been kidnaped, or during the following 12 days or at the time Jake told of being released. Costner was in Tennessee during all of that period.

Ike went on in his testimony with the silliness story of making telephone calls to Jake, as "the coffee man," to collect another $50,000. He made all the arrangements, Ike said, but went to New York by plane on August 14, the day before the comedy over the phony bundle of boodle in the country.

As we defendants went back to jail in our handcuffs and chains after hearing Costner's lies, Stevens had a comment. "Magnificent," he said. "Magnificent." I asked him what the hell he was talking about, and he replied: "A magnificent frame-up, of course."

I yammered to Stewart to send some investigators down to Tennessee and check up on Costner. It was a fine idea, but there wasn't time. Ike had been a surprise witness, and there had been no opportunity for defense to investigate him in advance.

It would take days, or weeks, to run down Costner's story in Tennessee. By that time the verdict would be in— and it would be a bad one, I felt certain.

Chapter 17

I Get 99 Years

Steward slammed at Costner on cross-examination like a mad-at-the-world workman attacking a paved street with an air hammer in a "quiet please" zone. He showed that Ike was a worthless bum, a faker, a thief, a mail robber and a stool pigeon.

The effort accomplished little. The prosecution already had conceded that Ike was seven different kinds of a scoundrel. Costner insisted that this time—just this once—he was telling the honest-to-God truth.

Stewart demanded to know whether Ike hadn't made a deal with Factor in Baltimore and on the train, whether he didn't hope to get a pass in North Carolina in exchange for lying against Stevens, Kator, Banghart, me and others. "W-a-a-l," the Tennessean drawled, he sure hoped he would get a break.

On his story of taking part in the fake kidnaping, Ike stumbled a few times, but he never fell down completely. His "Ah cain't remember" got him out of many a tricky spot and he didn't contradict himself too badly. Stewart couldn't break him. I sneaked a look at the jurors now and then, and I sensed that they were believing Ike. Maybe they thought his story was too fantastic for anybody to have made up.

As Costner left the witness stand, I recalled a favorite saying of my father: "The rabbit turned around and shot the hunter." Ike had won. He had been a powerful witness.

Buck Henrichsen repeated his fabrications of bringing Silvers and Silversmith to see me at my request while Factor was away growing his beard. But, at the second trial, he added that he went along on the collection of $70,000 "ransom" from Dr. Soloway.

He was in a car with Willie Sharkey and Jimmy Tribbles when the payoff was made on the highway, Henrichsen said. They took the money in a suitcase to the Glenview house, Buck went on, and there he saw Stevens, Kator, Banghart, Connors and Porky Dillon.

Stewart got Buck to concede that he hadn't mentioned the ransom collection trip at the first trial. "I was trying to protect myself," he said.

Jake's testimony was only about one-fourth as long as at the original prosecution. The big gun at the second go-around had been the moonshiner, not the swindler.

The absence of Father Weber from the second trial was a deep loss to us. He wrote to my wife that he was praying for us. But the lies of Factor, Costner, Henrichsen and others were getting through to the jury better than were the Hail Marys of the good priest. Sin was winning again.

Policeman Gerard came back and repeated his testimony that the bearded Factor had looked well and smelled not badly at the LaGrange police station. Emily Ivins returned, too, and so did the other faithful.

It wasn't enough, and I told Stewart so. Stevens, Kator and I were going to be convicted, and probably put in the electric chair, unless we did something. I demanded that I be allowed to testify. Stevens and Kator wanted to take the stand, too. It was our only chance.

Our lawyer haggled with us. He wouldn't gamble on Crowley's cross-examination of my codefendants with their past records in crime. Crowley would tear them apart, he said. And if he called me as a witness, he would have to call Stevens and Kator, or leave them as sitting ducks alone, he said.

That was our lawyer's logic. It didn't make sense to me. Costner had identified all three of us positively as his accomplices in the kidnaping. Were we such gutless wonders that we wouldn't get on the stand and call him a liar? Factor's testimony had been bad enough, but Costner's was damning.

I told Stewart that I was going to stand up and demand of the judge that I be heard. "You can walk out of court if you want to," I said to Stewart. "I don't care three howls in hell what you do. I didn't want you at the start of the trial, and I don't want you now."

Stewart stalled a while, and then he had a brainstorm. He would call Basil The Owl Banghart as a witness. It sounded idiotic to me.

Banghart was, in a sense, as much a defendant in the Factor case as were Stevens, Kator and I. He hadn't been indicted, but he had been accused by both Jake and Ike. Banghart had a worse, longer criminal record than either Stevens or Kator.

If The Owl had the courage to testify for the defense, what about us? Wouldn't the jury regard our silence as a sure sign of guilt? What were we—100 per cent cowards?

Stewart mollified us. He had talked with Banghart and he promised us that The Owl's testimony would wreck Costner as a witness.

We consented to go along with the plan, since Stewart was a lawyer, and we didn't know a tort from a tart.

Banghart went to the witness chair and swore to tell no lies. With his widow's peak hairline, his bony beak and his slowly blinking eyes beneath highly arched brows, his resemblance to an owl was remarkable. His manner was assured, his answers glib, his expression serious. He was an experienced witness.

He testified that he had known Costner for about six years and that Ike came to his Park Ridge home on July 19, the date I was jailed at Elkhorn, by a coincidence.

The Owl denied that he had any part in kidnaping Jake the Barber or in collecting $70,000 ransom. After that,

Stewart, with a triumphant expression, turned Banghart over to the prosecution for examination.

Chaos followed. If we had had the chance of a snowflake at a bonfire before, Banghart ruined it. It wasn't his fault. He was trying to help us, but he wasn't equal to it.

Crowley got him to admit that he had given the state's attorney's office a statement saying he didn't know Kator, Stevens and me. Banghart now reversed himself and said he knew all three of us. He thus was established as a liar at the outset.

Part of Basil's testimony seemed almost comical as I read over the transcript years later. Crowley brought out that Banghart hadn't worked for a living in 1932, '33 or '34. The Owl said with a trace of pride that he had a steady job in '31, however.

Q. Where did you work in the year 1931?

A. In the cotton-duck mill in the U.S. Penitentiary at Atlanta, Georgia.

The Owl said that he "left the prison without permission," or escaped, and was at large for more than eight months. Crowley brought out that Banghart currently also was wanted for breaking jail after blinding a guard with pepper at South Bend, Indiana.

Stewart asked Banghart to give his current occupation, and he got a silly answer.

"I am a fugitive," the witness replied solemnly.

Q. Fugitive from where?

A. From justice.

Q. From what kind of justice?

A. The courts of Indiana, South Bend.

Q. They wanted you for what?

A. Automobile banditry.

Q. Anything else?

A. No—well, you might say breaking jail.

Q. At the time you broke jail, what did you do? Did you have a machine gun when you broke jail?

A. Yes.

Q. Did it go off?

A. Yes.

Q. Did anyone get hurt?

A. An officer.

"Too bad," said Crowley, glancing at the jury. He now had set up our witness as a prison escaper and a desperado who shot down a law enforcement officer. Basil wasn't doing well.

Crowley tried to get him to confess the $105,000 North Carolina mail heist. Banghart dodged the issue, saying it had no connection with the Factor case.

The dialogue got ludicrous again when Crowley asked him if he knew Ludwig "Dutch" Schmidt, later convicted for the mail robbery. Banghart said he did, having been in stir with Schmidt.

Q. You were down in Charlotte with him, weren't you?

A. No.

Q. [Incredulously] What?

A. That has not got anything to do with this [case].

Q. You mean Charlotte has not?

A. Yes.

Judge Feinberg [alertly]: Are you talking about a girl or a town?

Crowley: Charlotte, South Carolina.

Stewart: North Carolina.

Crowley: I just got the states mixed up.

Amid such Abbott and Costello badinage, The Owl told the story which Stewart had said would wreck Costner. Ouch, what a boomerang!

Banghart said he had met me about a dozen times and that he believed I was with him in Wagner's place on the night of June 30. That was a lie. It hurt my case. I hadn't known The Owl from a truck load of jack-o'lanterns.

After his falsehood about knowing me, Banghart gave testimony which since has been shown to be the absolute truth, although the jury didn't believe it.

The Owl said that Costner came to him with a proposition for getting some money from Jake the Barber. The newspapers had carried stories quoting Jake as saying that he had agreed to pay an additional $50,000. Banghart testified that he told Costner the deal looked too dangerous, but that Ike urged him for a week. He said that the Tennessean finally told him:

"Now, this fellow Factor is willing to pay off and there won't be any trouble at all. Would you be convinced if I had you talk to him?" Factor and Costner already had discussed the deal, apparently.

On August 9, The Owl went on, he and Costner met Factor on 12th Street in the Chicago suburb of Maywood. He was introduced to Jake by Ike, and Jake said his kidnaping story was doubted by certain Federal people and by lawyers for the British government, Banghart recalled.

Jake said he was willing to pay $50,000 to make the snatch look completely legitimate, according to Banghart. The proposition would seem reasonable, of course, in that $50,000 would be pennies as against Factor's $7,000,000 British swindle—and nothing as against the prospect of many years in prison if the kidnap hoax collapsed.

Q. What else was said out there [in Maywood]?

A. Well, he [Factor] said there was a lot of fellows he could get for a lot less money, but he couldn't depend on them, and he explained to me what he wanted done.

Q. What did he want done?

A. He wanted us to call him and build up a story. He said the wire would be tapped and so on and that he had a couple of friends to deliver this money to us, that would not be armed.

Q. What else was said?

A. I objected. I said: "Well, I don't want to. . .get shot in the head," and I said: "I don't want to harm any of those fellows who have been arrested with Touhy. You know and I know that they did not kidnap you."

[At the time of this conversation in Maywood, Stevens, McFadden and I were under arrest in Milwaukee, charged with the Hamm kidnaping.]

Banghart continued with his story of the conference with Jake Factor:

"Well, I told him I wouldn't do it if it was going to harm these men that had been arrested and he said: 'Why, I never will identify anybody. . .' I told him: 'You know, I don't know if you were ever kidnaped or if you was not' and he didn't want to talk about it at all. He said: 'That has not got anything to do with our transaction.' "

Banghart said he assumed the $50,000 would be delivered by law enforcement officers, presumably government men.

Q. [Crowley] And you, a fugitive from justice, were going to accept money from government men?

A. Yes.

Q. Go ahead.

A. But he assured me that there would be no guns. . . and there wouldn't be any shooting. Of course, there would be a little chase and an effort of some kind made.

Q. It was going to be an act?

A. That is it.

On the street in Maywood, Banghart testified, Jake the Barber slipped a roll of $5,000 cash to Costner as a down payment.

The remaining $45,000 was to be split equally between himself, Costner and Ice Wagon Connors, The Owl said. He told of joining with Costner in making telephone calls to Jake. He knew that law enforcement officials were listening in on the calls, Banghart said. It was part of the act.

Q. So that you were fooling Captain Gilbert and all the rest of us. This was all in fun?

A. I think Mr. Factor was the one who was fooling him [Captain Gilbert].

Crowley said he was curious as to why Factor selected Banghart to be one of the persons to take part in the $50,-000 ransom collection, and The Owl gave a reasonable answer: "Well, the reason he said [in Maywood] that he preferred me is that Costner had told him I was a fugitive."

That made sense. Banghart, a wanted jail breaker, was in no position to squeal on Factor. Factor could put a hammerlock on Basil any time he wanted to apply it. It was a criminal's way of doing things—of taking out insurance against a double-cross.

The Owl said that he and Ice Wagon Connors tried to

make the collection on August 15, after Costner had gone to New York. The Owl didn't get the $500 in the fake parcel, he said, and he didn't know whether Ice Wagon managed to retrieve it.

I watched the jurors while Banghart was testifying. All of them smiled and a couple of them laughed aloud. The judge held a handkerchief over his mouth, obviously to conceal mirth. The Owl had done his best—but it was no good.

Banghart's testimony was anticlimactic. It seemed to be contrived—a last, desperate effort by the defense to make a bum out of Costner. The humor in the situation was unfortunate for Stevens, Kator and me. I had a sinking feeling that the jurors believed we had put a comedian on the stand to amuse and divert them—to sidetrack them from the real issues.

Stevens, Kator and I were hooked. We couldn't beat Factor and Costner. Not with the added burden of Banghart's testimony on our backs. We gave up any idea of testifying on our own behalf. It was too late.

We listened to the usual roars of oratory by the lawyers. Crowley called Banghart a liar. Stewart said that Factor, Costner and Henrichsen were liars. It didn't mean a damn thing. The jurors already had made up their minds.

In his closing remarks, Stewart pounded at the fact that no record was kept of the serial numbers of denominations of the ransom bills.

He also talked scornfully about the fact that no statement in writing by Factor, after he showed up at LaGrange, was produced at the trial. Such a statement must have been taken. It was police routine in all such cases.

My theory was that Jake signed a statement saying that he recognized no kidnapers. If so, it would have been powerful defense evidence.

Crowley's final words were a dramatic demand for the death penalty.

The jury reached a quick decision. The verdict: Guilty. The sentence: 99 years in prison for each of us. Some of the people in the audience cheered. I didn't get a look at

Tubbo or Jake the Barber, but they must have been smiling.

As the bailiffs led us out of court into the corridor leading to the bullpen and the County Jail elevators, I threw up. Kay Hall, a girl reporter for the *Chicago Times*, was near me. I'm sorry that I messed up her shoes. I couldn't help it.

Chapter 18

My Stolen Years
in Prison

A prison, no matter how modern and progressive, strips the last shred of dignity from a man. I learned that when they had me take off my clothing in the prison diagnostic depot at Joliet. They gave me a short haircut, clipped the hair from the rest of my body and put me through delousing.

An inmate in a maximum-security prison is always under a gun. There is a gun ready to drill him dead if he makes a wrong move as he walks across the prison yard, as he sits in his cell, as he hunches in silence over his plate of food on a stone-topped table in the dining room at Stateville.

The cells are six feet wide, 12 feet long and 14 feet high. In most of those tiny cubicles are caged two or three men. An open toilet bowl, without screen, stands in one corner. I've often thought during my quarter century of confinement that having a bowel movement in private would be the world's finest luxury.

Maximum security requires that every man be in his cell from before dusk until after dawn. In Stateville, that meant at least 14 hours every day. Fourteen hours with the same man, or men. It is a marvel that they don't kill each other.

A man is nobody, a number. I became 8711. After I went over the wall and came back, they added an "E", for escapee, to it. Also, the color of the identification shingle above my cell door was changed from white to red—red for danger.

I'm not meaning to beef about Stateville, in particular. I have no basis for comparison, since I was never in any other prison. Convicts who have made the circuit of pens told me Stateville isn't a bad place, comparatively.

Many convicts learn to do what is called "easy time" in prison. The day comes, after months or years, when they lose their mental anguish, get rid of their bitter resentments, shrug off the daily indignities. They learn to live placidly behind bars, to make use of the advantages that modern penology offers.

It never happened to me. I never made a good adjustment. I tried to obey the rules and I did my work as long as I had a job assignment. But the thought nagged me constantly that I was innocent, that I had been framed. My souvenirs from the F.B.I. boys—spinal injuries—gave me hell. The prison doctors made X rays and sent the plates to Chicago to be read by experts.

Back came the word. Medical science could do nothing for me but "a warm, dry climate might help the patient's condition." A joke, eh? I had 99 years—stolen years—ahead of me in Stateville.

Because of my physical condition, I was taken off all

work details. I listened to radio news broadcasts and I read the newspapers, but I didn't have the energy or ambition to go to prison school. It seemed that I couldn't focus on anything. There were no more than a dozen inmates with whom I was friendly during all of my prison time.

There is humor in prison, and I got to appreciate it. Gambling—without money—is one of the funniest things. One convict will say to another, "I'll bet you 16 glasses" on a prize-fight or a ball game.

The loser must drink 16 brim-full glasses of water within a time limit of, say, 20 minutes. Or the pay-off may be touching the toes with the fingers 100 times without bending the knees. I heard of a pickpocket who paid a bet by using his left hand only in the dining hall for six months.

When the guy left stir, he could pick pockets equally well with either hand, they said.

Nights are the worst time in prison. Cons yell in their sleep. Some of them weep and call out for their mothers. The sense of shame for the present and remorse for the past rides them constantly.

My point is that any prison is hell. Stool pigeons are everywhere and homosexuality festers. Boredom and regimentation are constant. Men go no place in prison; they are herded. Herded at meal times, herded at recreation, herded at work, even herded at chapel.

The next time you read of convicts being babied or mollycoddled in prison, don't believe it—at least so far as Illinois is concerned. Torture chambers aren't needed to make penitentiary life a constant punishment. Confinement —the segregation that means you are unfit to associate with your fellow men in the free world—is enough.

Warden Joseph E. Ragen of Stateville never was a buddy of mine. He has no pals among inmates. But he has one idea with which I heartily agree. Every inmate should be celed alone in prison. Decency demands it.

Soon after I was outfitted "convict-style," the psychologists examined me—"bugged" is the verb used by cons— at the diagnostic center. I kept telling everybody I was innocent, which is what every incoming con says. One of the head-shrinkers told me: "Settle down, Touhy. Learn to do your time the easy way, a day at a time. Don't throw your money away on legal appeals."

The chief shrinker asked me if I would take a lie test, and I jumped at the chance. Leonarde Keeler, the perfector of the polygraph, came to see me from Chicago and said the test would be made the following Friday. He said it would be okay if I had an outside observer present and I picked Tom Reynolds, the labor skate with the movie operators' union.

Full of hope, I wrote to my sister, Ethel, and arranged for her to bring Reynolds to the diagnostic depot on the designated date. It didn't work out. On the day before the scheduled interview I was shipped from the depot to Stateville, about 10 miles away. I beefed about being beaten out of the chance to show my innocence under the polygraph and one of the shrinkers told me: "You're too anxious, Touhy."

At Stateville, I was confused, bewildered for days. I tried to figure out what the hell had jinxed me. Under Illinois laws, it would be 33 years, or a third of my 99-year term, before I could even ask for a parole. I tried to think out what had happened to me and I finally hit on a reasonable theory. It turned out to be exactly right.

Jake had gone to the Capone mob for help in faking a kidnaping in order to beat extradition. He was close to Murray Humphreys, Sam Hunt and the others. The syndicate big-shots would have no part of actually pulling a kidnap job not even a hoax. Jake was advised to talk things over with Sam Hare or Joe Silvers or Louis Silversmith, or all three, who ran the Dells.

Buck Henrichsen formerly had hung out at the Dells. He once was chauffeur for a politician who gambled at the place. Buck was an ideal man to set up the hoax. He had rented houses for the labor skates, and he would have no trouble providing hideouts for Factor. Also, he could provide men with guns who would make the kidnaping look legit.

Henrichsen had brought in Sharkey, Stevens, Kator,

Tribbles, Connors and some of the other deviated septums. They carefully kept the stunt secret from me because I would have put a stop to it.

Factor had paid the $70,000 to vanish for 12 days. After appearing with his beard at LaGrange, he told the story of the demand for another $50,000—as an ace in the hole if he needed it. He did need it, when the British bulldog kept nipping at his heels. He used the $50,000 gimmick to build up his story.

Through Henrichsen, probably, Ike Costner and The Owl Banghart were engaged to collect the belated pay-off. They hadn't been in on the kidnap fake and, if caught, they would be unable to expose the details of the hoax, such as Jake's hiding places. Ike and The Owl were former prison pals of Ice Wagon Connors. They had brought Connors in on the deal, probably without Factor's knowledge. Jake had crossed them up by sending a dummy package of $500, instead of the big pay-off.

I can't say for sure whether the original conspiracy included a frame-up for me. It is possible that I was an added starter in the thing. It must be remembered, however, that within a few hours after Jake the Barber vanished, Gilbert accused the "Touhy gang" of responsibility.

The only loose end left hanging around was Ice Wagon Connors, and he had been murdered. I certainly am looking forward to that chat on a cloud with Connors.

The ridiculous spectacle of my trial at St. Paul for the Hamm snatch had allowed plenty of time for Jake's identifications to be arranged. The testimony of Henrichsen, Eddie Schwabauer and Mrs. Sczech—all later proven to be liars—was obtained in advance. The Glenview house became an added tidbit to entrap me.

Stevens, Kator and I became the patsies. Banghart was thrown into the pot after he refused to "cooperate" in giving false evidence.

All of that theorizing made sense, but I couldn't substantiate it. Stevens and Kator never had admitted a word to me about helping fake the Factor snatch. I couldn't communicate with them after I reached Stateville because

Stevens was sent to the old prison in Joliet and Kator to the downstate Menard penitentiary at Chester.

Attorney Stewart came to visit me with my two sisters. He said he was filing an appeal with the Illinois Supreme Court. I tried not to be bitter toward him, but I said: "No, you're not, Scott. We're through. I want no part of you."

He made the appeal anyway, basing it on the fact that my constitutional rights were violated because I was denied a lawyer of my choice at the second trial, and on other grounds. The appeal was turned down after a brief hearing —and it was the last time that the merits of the case were heard for nearly 20 years. After that, my petitions invariably were denied without a hearing.

That phrase—"denied without a hearing"—was to become poison to me. No court in Illinois would listen to me after the original turn-down. Neither would the United States Supreme Court.

Banghart went on trial before Judge Walter P. Steffen in Chicago on charges of kidnaping Factor. Costner's sister, Ella, came up from Tennessee and testified that Ike and The Owl had been in and around Knoxville and Gatlinburg during all of the so-called Factor kidnap period.

She had affidavits from 15 other Tennessee people saying the same thing and the defense offered to bring all of them as witnesses. The judge refused to allow a delay in the trial to round up the 15. The Owl was found guilty and sentenced to 99 years. Then they took him to Charlotte and tacked on 36 years for the North Carolina mail heist. He wound up at Menard with Kator.

Costner got the dirty end of the stick from the federal government, and I couldn't feel too sorry for him. A judge at Charlotte socked him with 30 years. Ike screamed in protest that the Department of Justice had promised to let him off with five years in a trade for his testimony in the Factor case. The judge wouldn't listen and the D. O. J., as far as I know, didn't lift a finger to help Ike.

Dutch Schmidt, another of the Charlotte heisters, got 32 years. He and Costner went to the federal pen at Leavenworth, Kansas. Dutch was to become important to me years later.

What about Jake the Barber? A-a-a-h, he wound up with a sweet deal.

Even after the convictions of Stevens, Kator, Banghart and me, the Cook County authorities claimed they still needed to keep Factor in Illinois. It might be necessary for him to testify against us on appeal, it was explained.

The government sent Jake to the county jail at Sycamore, Illinois. He stayed there for two months, technically in custody. Buck Henrichsen went to visit him and got "loans". Eddie Schwabauer was a visitor, too. Those two characters weren't letting loose of a good thing.

At the end of 60 days, the government had not honored England's extradition warrant for Factor. Jake went free. Under the law, he never could be collared again for return to the British Isles. He had it beat for all time. He was free to go forth and swindle people again—which he did, and for which he later went to prison.

Another incident in Jake's strange life took place in 1940 when he applied in Chicago for a permit as a whiskey distributor. Among his character witnesses—to put him on a pedestal as a lovely, honest, patriotic, sweet-smelling citizen—was listed Tubbo Gilbert. The hearing commissioner turned Factor down on grounds that he could not be believed under oath.

Ironic, wasn't it? Jake the Barber was too big a liar to be allowed to peddle booze, but he was believable enough to swear four men—Stevens, Kator, Banghart and me—into prison for a total of 396 years!

As the months and years trudged by in Stateville, I became, as many long-termers do, a cell-house lawyer. I studied law books. I got transcripts of the testimony at my trials. I became a sort of expert on the writ of habeas corpus, one of the most precious rights Americans have, although few understand it.

It is the citizens' protection against unlawful detention—against a person being held by police for days of third-degree questioning, against an illegally convicted defendant being buried in prison for life without recourse to justice. On a writ of habeas corpus, a person in custody can obtain a hearing before a court of law.

That was what I needed—a hearing. On every appeal I made, the answer was the same . . . denied without a hearing . . . denied without a hearing . . . denied without a hearing. How could I get justice if no court would listen to me? I was nailed in a box and I had no hammer to batter my way out. Thousands of Illinois convicts were in the same fix.

Ella Costner's testimony at the trial of The Owl was terrifically important for Stevens, Kator, Banghart and me. If she, and 15 other witnesses, would testify that Costner and Banghart had been in Tennessee from June 30 to July 12, 1933, it meant that Ike Costner, star witness, had lied in the second Factor trial.

My trouble was that I couldn't get into court to have such evidence heard.

In 1935, Banghart tried a brand new escape caper at Menard. He got into a big, heavy truck on the prison grounds, aimed it at an iron gate that led to freedom and stepped on the gas. Wham! Bang! Crash!

The truck was ruined when it hit the iron gate. The Owl damn near killed himself. But the gate won. It wasn't even dented badly. They put Basil back together again in the prison hospital and sent him to Stateville. The maximum security at Menard wasn't maximum enough for Banghart. It wasn't maximum enough at Stateville, either, as things turned out.

I met him for the first time in the yard at Stateville. The only time I had seen him before was when he had given that well-meaning—but gawd-awful—testimony at the second trial in Chicago. I asked him why he had said those things, and he replied:

"I understood you guys needed an alibi. I had never seen you before but I tried to help you. I had nothing to lose."

That was why he had testified that he knew me and had seen me on the night of June 30 at Wagner's bar. He had thought the testimony would alibi me for the Jake the Barber snatch.

The Owl said it was true that he and Costner had been together in Tennessee during the time Factor had been growing his beard. He told of going to wrestling matches, of celebrating the Fourth of July and of dating Tennessee belles while Ike was along.

At about that time, my wife, Clara, got a long distance call from a Knoxville lawyer, Homer Atkins. He wanted her to meet him in Washington, D. C., and she went there, taking Tommy and Roger, Jr., with her. They stayed at the Ambassador Hotel, and the kids were entranced. Clara and I had taken them to the same hotel on a Washington sightseeing trip and they remembered it.

They didn't know I was in prison, and they kept asking such questions as: "When will we see Daddy again, Mommy? Will Daddy come here? Will he take us to Hall's and the Occidental to eat? Will we see the Capitol and the Supreme Court and the White House again?" If Clara's heart hadn't been broken already, it would have been then. She had to tell the boys that they wouldn't be seeing me in Washington.

Attorney Atkins said he had absolute proof that Ike Costner had been in Tennessee at the time of the alleged kidnaping. Atkins and my wife went to Attorney General Cummings and told him of the new evidence. Cummings said he would look into the matter. But he never did, so far as the record shows.

Atkins came to see me in Stateville. "Touhy, you'll be out of here in a few months," the Tennessee lawyer said. He thought he was telling me the truth, and I believed him. That was before I had been completely disillusioned by the "denied without a hearing" responses to my appeals to the courts.

When stories of my appeals showed up in the papers, I was called "Black Roger" or "Terrible Touhy" or referred to as a notorious gangster. No judge would stick his neck out to do anything for me under those circumstances. The collective mind of America had been poisoned against me.

In about 1936, Clara retained Thomas Marshall, a fine Chicago lawyer. He was convinced from the start that I was innocent, but we needed to convince another person —a judge. I told Marshall that I thought it was senseless to go to bat on another appeal until we had put a mass of evidence together.

"We need to have a solid, substantial case of innocence," I said. "The evidence has to be somewhere, if only it can be found."

Marshall agreed, but he was a busy lawyer with a top-drawer list of clients. It wasn't his job to go digging up evidence. So he got approval from the prison authorities for Morris Green, a private detective who once had been a lawyer, to visit me. Green turned out to be a jewel, a really rich prize.

Morris seemed a bit cynical when he first came to see me. He sat across the visitors' table from me in the long, narrow room where 50 or more convicts can talk with their lawyers or with their relatives on approved visiting days. I could see that Green wasn't impressed with his mission. He knew—and so did I—that convicts always are screaming "bum rap."

"Okay, Touhy," he said. "What do you want me to do? Get you out of here the day before yesterday, I suppose." I explained quietly that I didn't expect any miracles. What I wanted was a thorough, painstaking investigation.

I told him about Ella Costner's testimony and of the word from the Knoxville lawyer, Homer Atkins. Morris eyed me narrowly and I was glad that he did. If I could convince him of my innocence, it should be a cinch to persuade a judge. I suggested that he get in touch with Stevens, Kator, Buck Henrichsen, Mrs. Sczech and her son, Eddie Schwabauer.

Green jotted down the names, grunted, said goodby and left. He didn't seem to have been impressed, but in two weeks or so he was back. This time his attitude was different. He had a smile. He was almost jubilant as he sat across the table from me.

"Hi, Touhy," he said. "Hi! Say, you really are innocent, aren't you? I've been talking to some of those people you told me to see. This case was a stinking frame-up. I have the facts to prove it."

My blood temperature went up a few degrees, I guess, when I heard those words. I figured now—at last—that I had Factor, Gilbert, Courtney, Costner, Henrichsen, Schwabauer, Mrs. Sczech and all the rest of them beat. I was happy. I had convinced a private eye, and they are among the most doubting of all people.

Morrie turned out not to be really a cynic. He was a kind, considerate, conscientious man with a deep hatred of injustice. There had been bitter disappointments in his life, and he had understanding for unfortunates like me.

People expect to be bled white by private detectives and I was in no position to object to being gypped. Although my legal expenses had been enormous, I still had about $50,000 which my family had salvaged from my ruined beer business. But Green charged only reasonable fees and he didn't pad his expense accounts.

One of the people Morrie had interviewed was Buck Henrichsen, at Bill Skidmore's Chicago junkyard near 26th Street and Kedzie Avenue. The junkyard later was shown in federal court testimony to be a pay-off spot for pimps, bookies and other gambling racketeers, receivers of stolen property and assorted thieves.

Buck had a soft job at the Bon Aire Country Club, a fancy gambling joint with swimming pool and golf course near the Chicago suburb of Wheeling. It was one of the mob casinos that Gilbert never raided during his 18 years as chief investigator. Wasn't that a coincidence?

Henrichsen died in 1942, but his widow, Helen, signed a sworn statement on my behalf. She said Buck gave her to understand that Gilbert interceded to get him the job.

Why would Gilbert do a favor for Henrichsen and why would the mob find a pay-roll spot for Buck? Judge Barnes decided that it was a pay-off for Buck's testimony against me.

Green said he told Henrichsen that they both knew I was innocent and that Henrichsen ought to do the decent thing by telling the truth. Green continued in sworn testimony before Judge Barnes:

"He [Henrichsen] told me that he has got a wife and three or four kids—I don't remember [which]—and that he has got a job, that he owes a duty to his wife and family, and he couldn't jeopardize his job or antagonize Gilbert."

Green, under interrogation by one of my lawyers, Frank

Ferlic, also quoted Buck as saying some other interesting things:

Q. Did he [Buck] at any time tell you about having gone down to the Sycamore jail to see Factor?

A. He says he used to go there and get money and he used to meet him [Factor] on the stairway.

Q. Did he say anything about anyone else going down there with him?

A. Yes, Eddie Schwabauer.

Q. Schwabauer got money, too?

A. That I couldn't say.

Q. Did you ever have any conversation with Henrichsen about his testimony in the Touhy case?

A. He said he had to testify the way he did.

Q. You wanted to get a sworn affidavit from him, didn't you?

A. That is right. He said he had the choice of being a defendant or testify the way he did and eat steaks.

[Buck was referring to his luxury life in the Palmer House and the Oak Park Arms Hotel while in "protective custody" as a prosecution witness.]

Q. Did he [Henrichsen] tell you who gave him that advice?

A. Gilbert and Wilbert Crowley.

Q. He [Henrichsen] made it clear, did he, that they were the ones who gave him this advice?

A. They told him he would be indicted for the same crime and be a defendant right along with . . . Roger Touhy and the other fellows.

Gilbert and Crowley denied Henrichsen's statements, as quoted by Green. Nevertheless, Green's testimony had a powerful effect on Judge Barnes' decision that I was innocent. The judge said so.

Anyway, what Morrie Green learned from Henrichsen was only a tiny part of the private eye's contribution to my case. The job he did on Schwabauer and Mrs. Sczech was truly remarkable. Morrie was a great detective, a truth-seeker who would not be denied.

Chapter 19

Enter Johnstone
—and Hope Again

Morris was extra-jubilant when he told me of having interviewed the mother and son. He was grinning like a lifer with a full pardon in his pocket. Both Mrs. Sczech and Schwabauer had admitted to Green that they had lied at my trials. They had told the truth at last.

"I didn't have much trouble with them," Morrie said. "I told them that I had the proof of your innocence. They admitted almost right away that they were perjurers."

Within an hour after the kidnap fakery at the Dells, Mrs. Sczech said, Factor had arrived as a voluntary guest at her Des Plaines home. Two or three of the divided septums had been with Jake, she recalled, and he hadn't been blindfolded or bound.

Factor had remained in the house from about 2 a.m. until after evening darkness of that day, Saturday, July 1, 1933. He had been free to come and go and to use the telephone. Nobody had restrained him in any way, the mother and son said.

Green now had positive proof that Jake the Barber had

not been kidnaped. He hurried to Attorney Marshall with the new data.

Mrs. Sczech and her son were willing to sign sworn statements, they said, but they were edgy, for obvious reasons, about doing so in Chicago. They wanted to get out of town.

Marshall drove Eddie, his mother and Green to South Bend, Indiana. There was a conference in the office of a lawyer friend of Marshall. The lawyer was a member of the United States Congress. The mother and son made signed, sworn affidavits.

Schwabauer stated that Henrichsen called him to Wagner's saloon about 11 p.m. on June 30 and told him that a rich man was in trouble and wanted to disappear for a while. Could the man hide out in Mrs. Sczech's house for a few days? There would be money in the deal.

Eddie said he okayed the proposition. Henrichsen did not mention Factor's name, Eddie added, and went on: "He [Buck] told me not to say anything to Roger Touhy about it."

Mrs. Sczech signed an affidavit stating that a man arrived at her home, by prearrangement with Henrichsen, in the early morning hours of that July day. She fixed a bed for the stranger in a second floor room and he retired, Mrs. Sczech stated.

She, her husband and their teen-age son were in the house alone with Jake the Barber until Eddie came home and went to bed about 5 a.m. Factor had slept in an unlocked room, without a guard.

Mrs. Sczech had gone shopping in the morning. She picked up a newspaper with a banner headline saying that Jake had been kidnaped. There was a picture of Factor on Page 1, and she recognized it. She went home, according to her affidavit, awakened her son and told him: "Tell Buck Henrichsen to get that man out of my house. I won't have any part of it."

All of this happened, it should be emphasized, in Mrs. Sczech's Des Plaines home, and not in the Glenview house, where Jake the Barber had testified so glibly to being confined, to visiting the toilet, to hearing the train whistles, to brushing against the shrubbery, to being threatened with ear-clipping, to hearing the strange-sounding footfalls on the stair tread.

The Glenview house was about five miles from Mrs. Sczech's home in Des Plaines.

Buck came to her place that afternoon, Mrs. Sczech said, and there had been a conference between him, Factor, Willie Sharkey and Ice Wagon Connors. Buck told her, she testified in the affidavit, that Factor would be taken away after dark.

Eddie stated in his affidavit that Henrichsen returned again between 8 and 9 p.m. with Connors and that another man may have been in a car outside.

Jake the Barber—unfettered, unblindfolded and seemingly unconcerned—had walked out of the house and been driven away, Eddie said. His mother had been in the house somewhere, he added.

Green testified later in court that Mrs. Sczech gave her affidavit freely but that she seemed to be apprehensive.

Q. What was she afraid of?

A. Bodily harm.

Q. From whom?

A. From the syndicate and the state's attorney's office.

Q. Did she tell you she was afraid of bodily harm.

A. That is why we took the statements out of town.

Q. What about Ed Schwabauer?

A. The same goes for him.

Green explained that Mrs. Sczech and her son wanted to be protected until after their affidavits were filed in Washington. That was a sensible precaution. Few, if any, terrorists have the courage to harm or murder witnesses in United States Supreme Court cases.

Morrie tried to take Eddie and his mother to Canada for safety, by way of Detroit. Their car was turned back because they had no proper papers, or a valid reason to visit the Dominion. Green drove them back to Kankakee, Illinois, and finally to Chicago.

Green now had proved me innocent, for all practical purposes—but he was far from finished. He interviewed Stevens and Kator in prison. I wasn't surprised, but I was a little hurt, by what Morrie learned from them. They had, in fact, been in on the Factor hoax. Buck Henrichsen had brought them into the deal. They had shared in the $70,-000 pay-off.

"We were afraid to let you know," Kator told me later. "Anyway, what in the bejesus good would it have done? We were hooked, especially after Ike Costner testified.

For Green, Kator pinpointed the house where Jake the Barber had spent his 12 beard-growing days to beat the British government. It was a place at Bangs Lake, Wauconda, Illinois, about an hour's drive from Des Plaines.

The owner of the house and an employee, according to Green's sworn testimony, said that Factor had been a free-to-come-and-go guest at Bangs Lake. After dark, they reported, Jake the Barber had taken walks around the town for exercise. He had played cards with his "captors," the witnesses told Green, and there never had been a blindfond on him.

For this restful vacation enjoyed by a swindler, I was serving 99 years, as were Stevens, Kator and Banghart. Costner, the Judas witness, never had been tried for the Factor snatch, which was understandable.

But Morrie Green's biggest accomplishment came when he located two men who billed themselves in Chicago taverns as "The Two Little Tailors." Fast patter, jokes and funny songs. They were Harry Geils and Frankie Brown. The depression had knocked them out of their regular jobs back in 1933, and they had made themselves into entertainers.

Buck Henrichsen had come to them with a proposition that they go out in the country to entertain a wealthy man, they said. In the basement of the Wauconda house, they had met Jake the Barber, bearded but happy. There had been no blindfold, no bonds, no guns in sight. Factor had given them money, drunk Johnnie Walker whiskey and played cards. They had visited him several times.

With the evidence that Green now had dug up, any jury in the land would have acquitted me. I felt certain that any judge would turn me loose if the facts now could be presented in court. But Morrie wasn't finished. He wanted more, and I told him to go ahead.

Among the many Chicago people he contacted were Sergeant Walter Miller and Lieutenant Thomas J. Maloney, who had been Chicago police officers during the summer of 1933. They had been detailed to guard Jake the Barber after his unshaven return to his customary life of luxury. They quoted Factor as telling them—as police officers—that he could recognize none of the "kidnapers." Miller, who had accompanied Jake to the Hamm trial at St. Paul, had the most important testimony.

Miller testified that in the fall of 1933, before my first Factor trial, an informant tipped him off on the Bangs Lake, Wauconda house as the place where Factor really had been. Miller said he took Jake the Barber there and that Jake told him: "This is it." In about five minutes, Miller went on, Factor reneged by saying: "I am not sure, I don't think it is."

Miller said he felt positive that the house was the real hide-out and that he telephoned the information to Gilbert. How did Tubbo react? Here is the answer, from Miller's sworn testimony: "Captain Gilbert told me to leave the house alone and to stay away from it . . . to forget about it."

Detective Green next went to Tennessee and picked up a few sworn statements. The affidavits proved that Ike Costner had not been in the Chicago area during late June or early July of 1933. He had been in Tennessee and so had Banghart.

One of the witnesses was Mrs. Ruth Mullinux, a resident of Knoxville for 23 years. She swore that on the night of June 30, 1933—the eve of Jake the Barber's alleged "kidnaping"—she and a woman friend had been with Costner and Banghart at wrestling matches in Knoxville's Lyric Theater. She was positive of it. Green, an eager searcher for verification, checked the back newspaper files and learned that, indeed, the Lyric had presented a wrestling show on the night in question.

On the Fourth of July, the forthright Mrs. Mullinux said, she and two women friends had gone with Banghart, Costner and Costner's brother, Rufus, to Gatlinburg. They stayed for three or four days, the witness continued, enjoying themselves with fishing and dancing. Another Knoxville witness, Marie Flinchum, said she was on the Independence Day outing with Mrs. Mullinux, the Costner brothers, and Basil the Owl. On July 1, Marie added, she and a friend went on a long drive with Ike Costner and Banghart, visiting several roadhouses.

Other witnesses who placed Ike and The Owl in Tennessee at the time of the Factor vanishing act included Walter Flanagan, a former Knoxville fireman; his sister, Grace Birmingham, a rooming-house operator; and Buford Roberts, a Knoxville resident for 49 years.

There were additional Tennessee witnesses, but the ones I have covered are sufficient. They proved that Ike Costner had been a spurious witness after he made his train trip to Chicago from Baltimore with Gilbert and the persuasive Jake the Barber.

Now, I do not contend, even today, that any one of the witnesses dug up by Morrie Green proved my innocence. But, taken collectively, those witnesses did deny my guilt and the guilt of Stevens, Kator and Banghart.

Let us sum up a little:

1. Mrs. Sczech and her son, Schwabauer, had shown in their sworn statements that Factor had not been kidnaped.

2. Brown and Geils, the entertainers, likewise had testified that Jake the Barber was no kidnap victim.

3. Kator and Stevens had admitted under oath that they were involved in the kidnap fakery.

4. The Tennessee witnesses—backed up by Banghart —had proved that Costner had been hundreds of miles away at the time during which he fingered me as a kidnaper.

5. The Chicago police officers, Miller and Maloney, had quoted Factor as saying he was unable to identify anybody. And Miller had sworn that he told Gilbert about the Bangs Lake house.

6. Buck Henrichsen had been shown to be an employee of Skidmore and Johnson, operators of Capone-mob gambling casinos.

242

7. My codefendants and I had been denied our constitutional rights by being forced to accept Stewart, a lawyer we didn't want and who didn't want us, at our second trial.

I was positive that Green's findings were more than enough to get me a hearing in court. So were Green and Attorney Marshall.

Among the Chicago newspaper reporters who believed me innocent was the late John Patrick Lally, of the *Chicago Daily News,* a fine and courageous man. He had visited me often over the years and now he began cooperating with Green.

A secretive man, as are many detectives and lawyers, Morrie didn't tell Lally everything he knew. He was afraid of premature publicity. We wanted to hold some things back to surprise the Illinois Attorney General's office, which certainly would oppose any appeal I might make. Prosecuting agencies are built that way.

At that time, which was 1938, bad luck began hitting me in batches. The Illinois Supreme Court turned down Attorney Marshall's appeal. It was the same old story: "Denied without a hearing." Marshall wasn't discouraged. He tried the U.S. Supreme Court. Again: "Denied without a hearing."

I was now as dead, legally speaking, as the old broken-down cons who get a $27 funeral at the state's expense, in a prison-made burial suit, out of Stateville. The only difference was that I hadn't been embalmed. The proof of my innocence had been gathered, but no judge would hear it. Still, I continued to hope.

Lally kept telling me that he had the proof to get me out of prison—that I never would spend another Christmas in Stateville. I believed him and I still think he had something big, although I never learned what it was. I know he wouldn't have built up false hopes in me. That would have been a wicked thing, and Lally was a decent, honest man.

Death by cancer took Lally out of my corner. He had been one of the great newspaper writers of his time. His death saddened and shocked me—partly for selfish reasons, I'll candidly admit.

But I wasn't hopeless. Not yet. I still had the magazine story, written by Lally's colleague, William Gorman, going for me. It was a good article and I had a warehouse full of optimism about it.

Came the day when Gorman showed me the rejection slips. The bottom fell out of the world for me. I went over the wall with Gene O'Connor, Basil the Owl, Eddie Darlak and the others.

Back in Stateville, after the killing of O'Connor and McInerney and the taking in custody of the rest of us, I did my punishment in the detention cells—the hole. It wasn't pleasant—but I didn't bellyache then and I won't now.

Attorney Harrington warned me of danger ahead, and he was right. A grand jury in the Will County Circuit Court at Joliet indicted me for aiding and abetting the escape of the 199-year-term policeman-killer, Darlak. They convicted me, too, in one of the rawest pieces of injustice since the burning of the witches at Salem, Massachusetts. I, the last man in on the break, hadn't aided or abetted anybody.

The real culprit in the escape had been Darlak's brother, Casimir. He had aided and abetted all seven of us escapees by delivering the guns at the flagpole. So what happened to Casimir? He turned state's evidence—and got his reward.

He was convicted of aiding and abetting Nelson and he picked up Nelson's one-to-twenty-year bit. No effort was made at Casimir's trial to prove that he had helped his 199-year brother to make the break. Casimir served 30 months and went free on parole.

My sentence was unconstitutional, as well as unfair, according to Judge Barnes, because the law requires that like punishment be inflicted for like offenses. My punishment had been immeasurably more stern than that of the main offender, Casimir Darlak.

The Owl also was indicted for aiding and abetting, but Illinois didn't keep him around long enough to try him. He had already made good on escapes from Atlanta, South Bend and Stateville. And he had ruined a truck on a try at Menard.

244

The federal government sent Banghart to Alcatraz, on the island in San Francisco Bay, to serve his time for the Charlotte mail robbery. Security was 100 per cent for him there, unless he could steal a boat or a pair of water wings.

Despite all his accomplishments, including flying airplanes, The Owl never had learned to swim.

Chapter 20

My Vindication in Court

I added up 99 plus 199 a lot of times for the next few months and the answer always came out the same—298 years in prison was what it meant for me. It would be 99 years and eight months, or long after my death, before I could even apply for parole.

The prospect of unending, drab, defeated years in prison left me dazed and numb at first. And then I came to realize that the extra 199 years didn't mean any more than kicking a dead dog.

My reasoning was that I still had Morrie Green's proof of my innocence in the Factor frame. If I could get the evidence before a reasonable judge, I could expect to be rid of the 99 years.

After that, the courts certainly would look favorably upon letting me out from under the aiding and abetting rap. Looking at it that way, I wasn't so much worse off than I had been before my escape, I thought.

Two lawyers, Charles P. Meghan and Howard Bryant, told me I was right in my theory. They filed petitions 12 times for writs of habeas corpus to get me into a court on the Factor conviction. The answer always was the same: "Denied without a hearing."

And then, in 1948, I got my biggest break since entering prison. A Chicago lawyer, Robert B. Johnstone, came to see me. Attorney Bryant had interested him in my case.

Bob Johnstone and I hit if off together from the very start. He was only a year or two past forty, and he looked younger. He was dynamic and aggressive. He had vision, resourcefulness and daring.

We talked together for four hours that first day in the visitors' room. Johnstone was no starry-eyed dreamer. He was a practical lawyer with a streak of toughness.

He questioned and cross-questioned me about my story, trying to catch me in a contradiction or a lie. He couldn't because I was telling the truth. At the end, he gazed at me in silence for two or three minutes and then burst forth with the hoarse voice he used at times of stress or strong emotion:

"I'm a damn fool, Touhy, but I'll take your case if you want me to." I told him that I'd be glad if he gave it a try. He warned me that it would be a long pull and that I should expect no miracles. Then he reached for his briefcase and left.

I watched him as he strode the length of the long, narrow room and climbed a short flight of steps at the end. He was a big man and he leaned forward a little as he walked. His mop of black hair could have used some grooming and his blue suit looked as if it might have been fitted to him by a tailor with astigmatism.

I had confidence in the guy. I knew somehow that he would do his damnedest for me. I was back in my cell before I realized that he hadn't mentioned a fee. I would pay him what I could, of course, but it was heartening to know that his first concern wasn't money.

His secretary and associates must have thought that Johnstone had flipped his lid when he reached his Chicago office the following day. I heard the story much later. He pulled open his desk drawers and filing cabinets. He threw copies of law suits, petitions, writs and other documents helter-skelter on a table.

"I'm referring all of that stuff to other lawyers," he told his secretary. "I'll give you a list of the lawyers and dictate letters to the clients. I can't be bothered with those things. I'm going to be busy on the Roger Touhy case."

Within a few minutes, he kicked away a law practice that it had taken him years to build. The cases which he sent to other lawyers would have earned him tens of thousands of dollars in fees. He didn't give a damn.

He not only wrecked his career but he also messed up his health working for me. What can I say about him? Only that he is the best friend a convict ever had.

Being Roger Touhy's lawyer was no social or professional asset. When his name showed up in the papers in connection with my case, his friends and associates would say in shocked tones: "Bob, why are you tied up with that terrible gangster? Why don't you represent decent people in court?" He tried for a while to explain that he was trying to right an injustice, but he soon gave up.

Johnstone is a determined—sometimes obstinate and irascible—man. Nobody could convince him that the second-division Chicago Cubs weren't going to win the National League pennant next year—or, anyway, the year after. He is strong-willed about many things, both important and trivial.

He and I had our first go-around on his third or fourth visit with me at Stateville. He opened up briskly: "Well, Rog, it's time for you to bring your wife and sons back from Florida. They should be with you at this time. I'll make arrangements through your sisters."

I told him that he wouldn't do any such damn thing. Clara had managed to set up a life for herself and the boys. Roger and Tommy were of college age. I wasn't going to mess up their futures.

"Don't be a blockhead," Bob said. "You're innocent. You have nothing to be ashamed of, and neither has your family. Clara and the boys *want* to see you. They want to show that they have faith in you. They have that right."

I wouldn't give in, but he foxed me.

I was in my cell on April 22nd, 1948. I was feeling low,

as cons do on special days. It was the 26th anniversary of my marriage to Clara. I kept thinking about how pretty she looked at the wedding and wondering why I hadn't stayed out of beer peddling.

A convict messenger came to the cell house with a ticket, or pass, for me to go to the administration building. It meant I had a visitor. I took the slip of paper and started the long walk.

My route took me through the mess hall, where 1,500 men could sit at a serving. The cons on duty were cleaning and disinfecting the place with jets of live steam. The tables had stone tops two inches thick and I recalled a warning given to me by a long-termer when I first arrived at Stateville:

"If there's ever another riot in the mess hall, Touhy, duck under a table. The guards' bullets won't go through those stone slabs."

There've been no riots while I've been in the joint, luckily, but I always kept the advice in mind.

From the mess hall, I went along a canopied sidewalk and smelled the fresh grass of spring and the newly turned earth in the yard.

Hundreds of cons, each assigned to a plot for growing flowers, were out with spades and trowels.

My progress was slow. Each time a person passes through a gate in Stateville, he must wait until the gate is closed and locked before the next gate ahead can be opened. And there are many, many gates and doors. I was in no hurry, of course—not with 298 years in sentences.

I reached the visiting room on the inmates' side and looked through the door.

My heart did a flip-flop. My knees turned rubbery. There they were—Clara and our two fine sons. They were looking up at me, and smiling.

I went down the stairs slowly, feeling as if I had been put in a trance. I sat opposite them, and I realized that I was wearing a silly grin. I was never happier. Bob Johnstone had been right.

It was ten years since I had seen Clara. There were lines in her face and gray in her hair, but she was pretty. She wore a tailored suit of the style I always admired on her. Her lips trembled a little as she said: "I hope it's all right, Roger. Mr. Johnstone told us to come back."

All right? It was wonderful!

I thought our sons were handsome. That's a father's privilege, but they probably won't thank me for saying so.

We talked for an hour. They were moving to Chicago permanently. My sisters, who had visited me so loyally over the years, were making arrangements for them. I asked the boys how it felt to visit their father in prison and Roger answered:

"Mother told us, as soon as we were old enough to understand, what had happened. She told us that you were innocent. We never were ashamed. We prayed for you every day."

I felt grand as I walked through the yard back to my cell. I was a family man again. I would ask for a spade or a trowel next day, by God, and go out and plant some flowers. I would try to bring a little beauty into the world, even if it was within a prison wall.

The next time I saw Johnstone, he didn't mention Clara and the boys. I tried to thank him, but he brushed aside my words. He was off on a new tack. He was determined to get Ike Costner into my corner, and I had an idea that might help.

An ex-con from Leavenworth had hit Stateville a few weeks before. He was celled not far from me and he brought word from Dutch Schmidt, one of Ike's partners in the North Carolina mail robbery. Dutch had sent his best regards and asked me to give him the word if there ever was anything he could do for me.

"The thing for you to do is to go to Leavenworth," I told Bob. "See Schmidt first, before you go to Costner. I have a hunch that Dutch will help us persuade Ike to come through with the truth."

When Johnstone arrived at the big Kansas federal pen, Schmidt wasn't in the least astonished to see him. Word had passed along through the prison-system grapevine that I wanted help from Costner.

"I was expecting you," Dutch told my lawyer. "I had a

talk with Ike and you won't have any trouble with him. He wants to get a load off his mind. He says he had no part in any kidnaping of Factor and that he lied against Touhy and the others."

Costner came through like a champion. He gave Johnstone a signed, sworn affidavit that he had perjured himself all over the place at the second Factor trial. Jake the Barber and Gilbert had persauded him to do it, Ike said.

The ground now was solid for my petition for a writ. My luck held for me when Judge Barnes agreed to hear it.

Barnes, who wore a full beard because he considered shaving to be a waste of time, was generally regarded as one of the most brilliant men in the history of the American bar. He was stern at times, but he had a deep well of courage, understanding and sympathy. He had a personal understanding of tragedy and loss, for two of his sons had been killed in combat during World War II.

Judge Barnes hated injustice and he despised influence peddlers. . . .

A former United States Senator once was interested in a case on Barnes' docket. The senator, a politically powerful character, waited for the judge at the doorway to his courtroom, flagged him down and told him: "Judge, I'd like to have a few words with you about an upcoming case."

The judge glared at him angrily and said: "Senator, if you so much as mention the name of the case to me, I will send you to jail for a year. You will go to jail, too, and you will serve every day of the term."

The hearing before Barnes was set for June   1949. I was brought from Stateville to the Cook County Jail for the duration.

I was optimistic and, at the same time, anxious about Bob Johnstone. He was as tense as a spring that had been coiled to the breaking point. He was edgy, so full of the Touhy case and so outraged by injustice that he seemed ready to explode at any time. I tried to warn him to relax a little. The only result was that he lost his temper.

Bob opened the hearing by saying that I was being illegally detained in prison. I had been improperly convicted by perjured testimony—with the knowledge of the prosecution—in the Jake the Barber frame-up, Johnstone said. The conviction on the aiding and abetting rap was unconstitutional, he added. He asked the judge to order me freed at once.

Ben Schwartz, an assistant Illinois attorney general, made his opposition opening strictly along legalistic lines. I had been convicted in the state courts, he said, and I must exhaust all state court remedies before going into federal jurisdiction. He contended that I had not used up all my Illinois State appeals and that Judge Barnes, therefore, had no right to handle my case.

The hearing went along for five days, with Johnstone calling our preliminary witnesses. Everything was going along fine, I thought. On the sixth day, there was a commotion in the corridor. Johnstone had collapsed. He was in a coma.

I saw them carry him away on a stretcher and I thought he was dying. His condition was critical, the doctors said. Judge Barnes continued the case until October 19. I don't think I've ever felt worse than I did as they took me back to Stateville.

What was I—a jinx to everybody? Bob had two young sons. If handling my case had killed their father or ruined his health permanently, there would be a lot of remorse in my future.

When the October 19 continuance date arrived, Johnstone was ready to go ahead, but Schwartz obtained some legal delays. It was not until September 8, 1953, that we got back before Judge Barnes again. From the stand came the stories of 57 witnesses, both by deposition and in person, over a period of 36 days.

I had a chance to tell the full true story of my stolen years for the first time in any court. Schwartz tried his best to overcome my testimony, but he couldn't. I was speaking the truth, just as I had told it to Bob Johnstone.

Morrie Green was there to tell how he had proven me innocent. So were Miller and Maloney, the police officers who quoted Factor as saying that he couldn't identify me.

Out came the true stories of Stevens, Kator, Banghart and, of utmost importance, Costner. Ditto for the testimony of Mrs. Mullinux and the other Tennessee witnesses.

Gilbert, Courtney and Crowley testified, denying that they knew anything about a frame-up against me. Johnstone gave Jake the Barber an unhappy time on the witness stand, prodding into his background. Jake had served a stretch since he last testified against me, and he didn't like to talk about prison life.

He had to admit, however, that he had lied about the Glenview house. And he conceded that the prosecution had known his testimony was false.

We also had some surprise testimony for Jake. It came from men who had served time with him in federal prison after he was tagged for swindling. They swore that Jake had told them remorsefully that he never was kidnaped. Factor called them liars.

The two witnesses who really gave me a jolt were Mrs. Sczech and Eddie Schwabauer. They told Johnstone they didn't want to testify, and when he got them on the witness stand they reneged on the affidavits they had made for Green in Indiana in 1938. Both now denied their previous sworn statements that they saw Factor unbound, unblindfolded and seemingly unconcerned in Mrs. Sczech's home on July 1, 1933.

It was a complete switch. Mrs. Sczech said she never met Factor in her life until she rode with him on a train to the Hamm trial at St. Paul. Neither, Mrs. Sczech testified before Judge Barnes, had she ever seen me.

Eddie's new story was that when he arrived home early on the morning of the Dells incident he saw Kator and Sharkey in the basement. They had Factor with them and he was blindfolded, Schwabauer now swore. He added that he told Kator and Sharkey to get Factor away from his mother's property. He, Mrs. Sczech and other members of the family drove to the summer resort area near Fox Lake, Illinois, for the week end and Factor was gone when they returned, Eddie added.

That testimony shook me up, but Johnstone told me not

to worry. He was right. Judge Barnes refused to believe the mother and son. He said in his finding that they undoubtedly told the truth in the Indiana affidavits, which showed that Jake really had never been snatched.

Johnstone had managed to obtain by subpoena from the state's attorney's office all of the available records on the Factor case. But the documents he got didn't include a statement by Jake the Barber to the authorities in the days immediately following his bearded return in 1933. Bob was certain that such a statement must have been taken—and that Factor in it had said he was unable to identify anybody.

As a witness, we called George R. McSwain, acting agent in charge of the Chicago F.B.I. offices. Judge Barnes ordered him to produce all FBI records of the case, including a statement by Factor, if any, and he refused. The judge sentenced him to jail for contempt and the Department of Justice appealed the case to the United States Supreme Court.

The high court reversed Judge Barnes, saying in effect that the F.B.I. files had to be kept sacredly confidential for the protection of informants. We never did obtain the Factor statement, if there was one.

After hearing all of the evidence we could produce, Judge Barnes took my appeal under advisement.

On the day of decision, August 9, 1954, Johnstone was standing nearby as my guards took off my handcuffs in a corridor of the United States Courthouse. "Rog, I don't think you'll ever be wearing those things again," he said. For all of his effort to seem confident, Bob was trembling. So was I.

The members of my family were in court, some of them sitting in the jury box. Clara waved to me and so did our sons. My newspaper friends smiled at me, but Schwartz didn't look so happy.

There wasn't a murmur of sound as Judge Barnes seated himself behind his big, elevated desk. I was listening so intently that the traffic noises from the street below cut off automatically for me. The bearded old gentleman's eye caught mine, and I thought I saw a twinkle.

The judge had a fine sense of timing and dramatics. He expressed his gratitude to the lawyers in the case. He voiced concern for Johnstone's health. He explained that his ruling was extraordinarily long, because the case was an involved one. Then he stroked his beard and began reading:

"The court finds that John Factor was not kidnaped for ransom, or otherwise, on the night of June 30th or July 1st, 1933, though he was taken as a result of his own connivance . . .

"The court finds that Roger Touhy did not kidnap John Factor and, in fact, had no part in the alleged kidnaping of John Factor."

Vindication had come to me at last. I had been exonerated. My stolen years were coming to an end. The judge went on to rule that the aiding and abetting conviction was unconstitutional. I was shed of the 199 years, too.

When the judge left the bench, there was a stampede. Reporters went out of court on a dead run, heading for telephones being held open for them to their offices. People slapped me on the back. I finally got away with Johnstone and a couple of friendly reporters who had no immediate deadlines to make.

We had coffee. I made a couple of half-blind stabs for the sugar bowl, got it and then dropped it. The bowl broke and sugar cubes were all over the table. A waitress cleaned up the mess, gave me a smile and said: "I recognize you from your pictures in the papers and I just heard a radio broadcast. Don't you worry, Mr. Touhy. You can smash every sugar bowl in the place and everybody will understand."

The name of Roger Touhy was in the headlines, but there was no stink attached this time. The newspapers were friendly, sympathetic toward me. The stories also carried stinging, bitter words by Judge Barnes against my prosecution and the witnesses who had lied against me. My repudiation was 100 per cent.

My happiness was complete, but it wasn't going to last. Even as I had dinner with my family that evening, the law took steps to slam me back into prison again. The fickle finger of fate was going to give me another jab between the ribs . . .

Before going into the shattering experience of returning to prison, after having been declared innocent, it is essential to deal with Judge Barnes' ruling. It is the most important —and, certainly, the best written—part of this book.

Chapter 21

A Great Judge's Opinion

J ohn P. Barnes, if he hadn't decided to become a lawyer and a judge, would have been a fine, compelling, honest author, I believe. He had all the talents—a sense of timing, comedy, suspense, understanding and zest. His vocabulary was superb and his integrity was beyond question.

Convicts read hundreds of books in prison, and some of them become better than green hands as literary critics. Many of the men in my cellhouse studied Judge Barnes' written decision in my case. It kept them entranced for hours.

The opinion ran about 60,000 words, the length of the average book. It covered every facet of the Factor frame-up, including many long and involved legal precedents to back up his decision. Presented here will be Judge Barnes' words on the facts of my case and the personalities concerned.

The judge, a moderate man, refrained from bad names in summing up Jake the Barber. Instead, he used this scholarly, but piercing, language:

"John Factor has an extraordinarily agile mind—certainly the most agile mind of anyone the court has observed in connection with this case . . .'[1]

"He has learned all that a boy and man can learn as a bootblack, wash-room attendant, newsboy, barber, high-pressure stock salesman, Florida land salesman, bucket-shop operator and confidence man—except to be honest.

"So far as the so-called business morals are concerned, he is completely amoral."[2]

Another section on Factor in the opinion read:

"John Factor's appearance and demeanor on the stand and about the court room, and the testimony of all witnesses who dealt with him, all indicated that Factor was eminently well qualified by character, ingenuity, mental resourcefulness and experience to devise and perpetrate a kidnaping hoax.

"Furthermore, he had money which he was willing to spend. Finally he had a motive. He was in real trouble. He faced a long prison sentence when he went back to England."[3]

After blistering Factor, Judge Barnes took care of another poisonous trial witness against me:

"The court is of the opinion that Isaac Costner was not in Illinois on June 30th, 1933, and did not come to this state until August, 1933; that aside from making telephone calls to Factor . . . Costner had nothing to do with the Touhy case until John Factor and Captain Gilbert contacted him in the Baltimore jail . . . and bribed him with the promise of a five-year sentence for robbery in North Carolina, to testify against Touhy.

"It is true the government did not keep the promise made to Costner, but that is not the point. *The promise made by Factor and Gilbert was the payment for his perjury.*"[4] [Author's Italics]

In commenting on me, the judge made no effort to mold me into a plaster saint. He pointed out that I was "in the business of violating the prohibition law"[5] by peddling beer and running slot machines, but he gave me an even break:

"He had never been convicted of a felony. He was a family man, having a wife and two sons of whom he was

258

very proud. He had a brother Tommy who had a criminal record with whom, in the public mind, Roger was sometimes confused."[6]

The judge then went into the motive for railroading me:

"He [Touhy] had incurred the dislike of Captain Gilbert and the enmity of the Capone mob . . . principally because of his aiding labor union officials in their fight against the taking over of their unions by the Capone mob."[7]

Judge Barnes reviewed the situation in the state's attorney's office under Tom Courtney during my two trials. He stated that Courtney and Crowley were men of "relatively little experience," while Tubbo Gilbert had a long background as a labor unionist and a police officer.[8]

"In 1933 and 1934, of the three men, Captain Gilbert, because of his age and experience in life, would be expected to be the dominant personality,"[9] the bearded judge observed.

Judge Barnes used gentle language when he dealt with Mrs. Sczech, but it was impossible for him to be gallant. Not with the fabric of lies she had woven on her busy loom. The judge remarked:

"As has been noted, Mrs. Sczech does not always tell the truth. The court is convinced that Factor went to her home [and not to the Glenview house] on the night of June 30th-July 1st, 1933, and remained there until the night of July 1st.

"Buck Henrichsen arranged for Factor to stay there, but did not tell Mrs. Sczech who Factor was. . . . Factor was not under restraint. He was free to use the telephone and come and go at will."[10]

When Mrs. Sczech learned Jake the Barber's identity from newspapers, she insisted to her son, Eddie Schwabauer, that Factor be taken from her Des Plaines home, the judge stated, and it was done.[11]

Regarding the testimony of Mrs. Sczech and Schwabauer, Judge Barnes said:

"In the court's opinion, they only told the truth when they felt free of the state's attorney's power and Factor's money. The court thinks that Mrs. Sczech and Schwabauer told the truth only in the affidavits which they made [at South Bend] in 1938."[12]

In evaluating the testimony of the mother and son in his court, Barnes said: " . . . there is an obvious explanation for their conduct on the stand here—fear of reprisals from Captain Gilbert and the state's attorney's office, and the influence of Factor's money."[13]

Reviewing the sworn statements made by Stevens and Kator in 1938, Judge Barnes said he believed them. Both Kator and Stevens had sworn that Jake never was under restraint or, in fact, kidnaped, the judge remarked, adding:

"Roger Touhy knew nothing about the meeting on the proposed kidnaping of Factor."[14]

Of the so-called ransom money, Judge Barnes expressed this opinion:

"That some financial institution or other responsible agency did not keep a record of the amount of money paid, the denominations of the bills and the [serial] numbers of the bills strikes the court as an extraordinary characteristic of this case."[15]

The judge pointed out that Gilbert, immediately after the reported kidnaping, charged that the "Touhy gang" was responsible.

It was rather extraordinary, the judge found, that none of my associates and I were arrested, questioned or charged until 19 days later, when Sharkey hollered "t-i-m-b-e-r" as the pole went down at Elkhorn, Wisconsin.

"The court is of the opinion that the incident of June 30 and July 1, 1933, was a hoax planned by, and executed under the direction of, John Factor in order to avoid extradition to England,"[16] Judge Barnes said.

As for who was responsible for Jake the Barber's success in beating removal to England, the distinguished federal jurist pointed out:

"The purpose of the hoax—the keeping of Factor in this country—was accomplished. The responsibility of State's Attorney Courtney for its accomplishment was admitted by Mr. Courtney, who testified that he went to Washington and talked to the President [Roosevelt].

"Factor is in this country today because of that intercession [by Courtney]."[17]

Judge Barnes found that Factor had lied in his stories of having seen me partly concealed behind a blanket.

"The court is of the opinion and finds that the only reasonable inference is that the statement contained material unfavorable to the State's theory of the case. Every item of evidence that was produced on the question of identification by Factor (other than Factor's testimony of visual identification) tends to establish Factor's utter inability to identify Touhy and the prosecution's knowledge of this inability. Taken together these items are overwhelming, and establish to a certainty that Factor could not identify Touhy, and that the State knew he could not. The court is of the opinion and finds that Factor's testimony, elicited by the prosecution, of a visual identification was false and was known to be false, and a case of material subornation of perjury has been made out."

He also dwelt upon the statements made by Jake the Barber to newspaper men, police officers and others in July that he could identify none of the purported "kidnapers:"

"Captain Gilbert and Factor have sought to explain Factor's many statements prior to the Touhy trial that he could not identify any of his alleged captors by saying the F.B.I. agents and Captain Gilbert told him to deny that he could identify any of his alleged captors.

"So far as the F.B.I. agents are concerned, this statement is impossible to be believed. The F.B.I. agents are thoroughly trained investigators and it is difficult to believe that any of them would ever tell a prospective witness upon whom they were going to have to rely to identify another person, to deny ability to identify that other person and thereby to lay himself open to successful impeachment."[19]

"Captain Gilbert had 16 years of experience as a thief catcher and investigator when, according to Mr. Factor's story, he is supposed to have told Factor to lie in response to questions as to whether he could identify his captors and thereby to lay himself open to successful impeachment when he testified otherwise.

"Lawyers and investigators almost invariably advise witnesses not to talk, but good lawyers and good investigators never advise witnesses to lie."[20]

Judge Barnes stated flatly that the state's attorney's office knew in advance that testimony against me and my codefendants was false:

"The court finds that both with respect to Factor's identification testimony and Costner's entire testimony, guilty knowledge on the part of the prosecution was established . . ."[21]

"The state is directly chargeable with knowledge that Factor actually stayed at the Wauconda, Bangs Lake house. Captain Gilbert suppressed important evidence on this point by directing Officer Miller 'to forget the place, leave it alone'. . . ."[22]

"The state is charged with knowledge that the actual place where Factor stayed the first night was in Schwabauer's [and Mrs. Sczech's] house in Des Plaines, not in Glenview, and with failing to disclose this information to the court and the defense."[23]

In pointing out the changes in Factor's testimony in the second trial as against the first—on such important matters as the Glenview house basement and the lifting of the blindfold—Judge Barnes said:

"First Assistant State's Attorney Wilbert F. Crowley's methods of handling the evidence in the second trial demonstrates the state's own awareness of the deficiencies in Factor's testimony both in the matter of identification and location."[24]

"Under ordinary circumstances, no favorable inference could be raised from a prosecutor's change in the method of presenting the state's case in a second trial."[25]

"Here the changes were so marked and so obviously designed and calculated to bolster a thin case on identification, that it having been otherwise shown that the identification was designedly false, the prosecution's awareness and knowledge of the falsity of such testimony appears."[26]

Judge Barnes punched another hole in the cloth of my conviction when he wrote:

"One of the strongest single factors pointing to the

inability of Factor to identify Touhy in July was the fact that he [Touhy] was not kept in Chicago. He was returned to Wisconsin . . . and later was sent to trial in St. Paul on what the government knew was 'a very weak case'."[27]

Before Judge Barnes, Johnstone introduced scores of July, 1933, Chicago newspapers quoting Jake the Barber as saying that he could recognize none of his "kidnapers." Also, there were quotes in the papers by lawyers for the British Crown that the kidnaping was a sham.

Prior to June 30-July 1, there had been headlines on the efforts to extradite Factor to England and about the disappearance of Jerome Factor. In this connection, the judge commented on testimony by Tom Courtney, indicating a belief that Courtney had been less than candid, at least:

"State's Attorney Courtney denied ever having heard about Factor before the date of the alleged kidnaping, but his later testimony, when asked about the incident involving Factor's son, indicated the contrary.

"In the 1949 hearings, Judge Courtney admitted he read the papers every day. In the 1952 hearings, he said first he didn't follow the case in the papers but later admitted that he did."[28]

Judge Barnes dealt with Johnstone's charges that I was convicted as a result of a conspiracy by state and federal authorities. The judge said:

"With respect to the state's attorney's office, this has been abundantly shown . . . . State's Attorney Courtney admitted that he was the motivating factor in getting the State Department to withhold execution of the extradition warrant and permit it to lapse . . .

"Secondly, the prosecution was apprised at all times of Factor's predicament, of the gaping holes in his story with respect to identification and location, and of the existence of the plot involving the 'railroading' of Touhy, both from the British authorities and from Father Weber . . .

"Finally, the state . . . indulged in numerous stratagems and artifices . . . consistent only with a design to bring about the conviction of Touhy at any and all costs . . . "[29]

The proof of conspiracy by the federal government was not so conclusive, Judge Barnes said, adding:

"However, the fact is that the Department [of Justice] did evince an astounding disregard for Touhy's rights and indulged in practices which . . . can not be condoned . . . Keenan's assistance was indispensible in enabling the state to administer the death blow in the second trial through the use of the spurious witness Costner."[30]

Judge Barnes ruled, therefore, that Factor, the state's attorney's office and the Department of Justice "worked and acted in concert to convict Touhy of something, regardless of his guilt or innocence . . ."[30a]

One of the sternest criticisms of Captain Gilbert came in a section of the ruling which said:

"Once Touhy was introduced as an actor in the drama, sinister motives of Captain Gilbert and the politico-criminal syndicate for wanting to remove him permanently from the scene of action, seemed to intensify the state's efforts to pin a conviction on him."[31]

Regarding Jake's chumminess with Tubbo, the judge said:

"With respect to Factor, all the evidence establishes that the relationship between him and the prosecution was far more than the ordinary relationship between prosecuting witness and prosecutor. This will be more fully developed hereafter, but standing alone, it would justify charging the state with Factor's own guilty knowledge and improper motive in the case."[32]

Pointing out that Courtney and Gilbert knew Jake the Barber's finesse as a swindler and liar, Judge Barnes said further:

"The state can not deny knowledge of Factor's capability as an inventor and narrator of untrue stories and of his capacity for deceit and trickery."[33]

The "timeliness" of kidnapings in the Factor family came in for discussion by the judge:

"The supposed kidnaping in his case was the second to occur in the family of the victim within a relatively short period of time, two and a half months.

"The supposed kidnaping of Jerome Factor took place

at a time when the sympathy of the public for the victim of the supposed kidnaping and his family might be expected to be helpful to a member of that family in his enterprises.

"John Factor had given a bond for his appearance before the Supreme Court of the United States.

"It is certainly not a violent presumption that he did not want to appear in a jurisdiction [the District of Columbia] where the crime with which he was charged in England might be more clearly spelled out than it was in the statutes of Illinois."[34]

Judge Barnes remarked:

"The supposed kidnaping of his son furnished an excuse for his not going to Washington."[35]

Of Factor's personal kidnaping story, the ruling stated:

"The Supreme Court of the United States, by its order of May 29th, 1933, foreshadowed the final order that it did render." [The final order was that Jake be sent back to England, although the order never was carried out.]

"Within five weeks after the order of May 29th, 1933, John Factor was himself supposedly kidnaped. *This supposed kidnaping furnished an excuse for his not going back to England.*"[36] [Author's italics]

The judge said he thought it unusual that Factor, soon after the presumed kidnaping of his son, would visit the Dells, "known to be run by members of the so-called Capone syndicate, located outside of the city of Chicago . . . along a lonely road . . ."[37]

Judge Barnes remarked that the Capone mob operated gambling and other rackets in Cook County, and commented:

"The relationship between the state's attorney's office, under Courtney and Gilbert, was such that during the entire period that Courtney was in office no syndicate man ever was convicted of a major crime . . ."[38]

"To put it mildly, Roger Touhy was not an acceptable person to Captain Gilbert. Touhy and the opposition with which he was identified was an obstacle in the drive of the politico-criminal Capone syndicate to control and dominate the labor unions . . .

"That criminal syndicate could not operate without the approval of the prosecutor's office . . . They did continue to operate and thrive without interference from Courtney or Gilbert . . .

"That the arrangement between Gilbert and the syndicate was closer than a mere tolerance is evident from his function as a go-between in the Horan and Wallace surrenders and from the fact that his men were put in key posts in the Capone-dominated unions, as well as from his ability to place Henricksen with the Skidmore-Johnson outfit."[39]

The opinion pointed out that the F.B.I. or the state's attorney's office obtained signed statements from Factor's wife, from F.B.I. agents, from employes of the Dells and from other witnesses. Certainly, the judge commented, a statement was taken promptly from the most important witness—Factor, himself. Barnes went on:

"That the F.B.I. had a complete statement of Factor's testimony is clear from Factor's testimony. . . . The relator [Roger Touhy] and the court did everything possible to secure production of this statement in this case without success . . . "[40]

"The question persists, why wasn't any statement of Factor ever produced by the state? . . . "[41]

"The court is of the opinion and finds that the only reasonable inference is that the statement contained material unfavorable to the state's theory of the case."[42]

In other words, Judge Barnes deduced that a statement was taken from Factor sometime soon after July 12, 1933 —and that it was held out because Jake the Barber said officially, perhaps under oath, that he could describe or recognize no kidnapers.

Such a statement would have had much more weight in my behalf, of course, than did quotes by Factor in the newspapers.

An element of humor entered the ruling when Judge Barnes recalled a deposition by Herman Becker, a convict who had driven a garbage truck in the federal prison at

Sandstone, Minnesota. Jake the Barber was a helper on the odorous, untidy truck.

The judge reviewed Becker's sworn statement with these words:

"Becker said that a lot of fellows over there [in Sandstone] wouldn't talk to him and when he inquired they said they didn't like him because he was hanging around with that rat, meaning Jake, who framed Touhy . . .

"At the incinerator, Becker asked Factor whether he was the guy they called Factor and Factor said: 'Roger Touhy, I ain't worried about him, let him and his family take care of him; to tell you the truth, the man ain't guilty.' . . .

"Becker then said: 'What did you put him in for?' and Factor said: 'Well, if I didn't go along with the [attorney] general, the lawyer, the state's attorney—otherwise I would be deported back to England because me and my friends took $5,000,000 over there'. . . .

"And Becker said: 'Why put another man in jail?' and Factor said: 'Well, I am looking out for my own skull, I have got two sons and a wife on the outside'."[43]

It seemed pretty wonderful to me that multimillionaire Jake—welcome in the finest hotels and flossiest night clubs —would be shunned as an outcast in prison.

Judge Barnes made a few remarks that were genuinely pleasing to me and to my family about the testimony of my wife's girlhood friend, Emily Ivins. Said the distinguished judge of Miss Ivins:

"She testifies unequivocally that Roger Touhy was at home with his family [on the front porch] at the time of the alleged kidnaping. If what she said is true, Roger Touhy could not have been guilty of kidnaping John Factor.

"Emily Ivins seems like a responsible person and one who would not intentionally tell an untruth. The court believes she is worthy of belief and does believe her."[44]

The judge said he also believed testimony by our aunt, Mrs. Morgan, and by my wife and two sons. All of them said I was at home practically all of the time when Jake the Barber claimed I was negotiating with him for ransom.

The testimony of Mrs. Ruth Mullinux and other Knoxville witnesses proved beyond doubt, of course, that Costner and Banghart had been in Tennessee during the period of Jake the Barber's Alice-in-Wonderland caperings, Judge Barnes found.

I sort of think the judge was grinning in his beard when he commented on the adventures of Basil the Owl and Ice Wagon in trying to collect the additional $50,000 on the deal with Jake to make his kidnap story look good. The judge said:

"That when the two police officers . . . drove out in the country . . . to deliver the supposed 'supplemental ransom' their firearms were stored underneath the seat of the cab so that they had to stop the cab, remove the seat and reassemble the parts of the machine gun before they could go into action, strikes the court as being a rather extraordinary thing."[45]

[The judge kept using the words "rather extraordinary thing" for what I would call just plain damn foolishness. But he had a better vocabulary than I.]

The judge evidently placed full credence in Harry Geils' testimony of having entertained Jake in the Bangs Lake house in Wauconda. His Honor's comment was:

"Geils saw Factor . . . Factor was sitting at a table in the basement . . . he had dark glasses on. They were drinking down there. Factor was not tied in any way. Witness [Geils] did not see him under restraint. Witness did not see any guns there. He was in Factor's presence for about half an hour. There were no guards at the doors, there was no unpleasantness of any sort while the witness was there, everybody was happy, laughing, kidding, and telling stories, there was a quart of Johnny Walker whiskey on the table and there was some beer in cases."[46]

Discussing an appearance of William Scott Stewart before him, the judge wrote in the opinion:

"Mr. Stewart's testimony makes it clear that serious differences had arisen between him and Roger Touhy and that he did not want to represent Roger Touhy in his second trial and that Roger Touhy did not want Stewart to represent him. "Mr. Stewart's testimony also makes it clear that Roger Touhy desired to testify in his own behalf but that Stewart forbade his testifying."[47]

In his summing up, Judge Barnes pointed out that no one bit of proven perjury by Gilbert's witnesses, and no single piece of evidence uncovered by Morrie Green and Bob Johnstone could absolve me of guilt and establish the Factor kidnap story as a hoax. As the judge commented:

"No one of the foregoing facts, or supposed facts, nor all of them together, without other facts and circumstances . . . would warrant the court in overturning the work of the state courts, but all of the foregoing facts, or supposed facts, are in the background of the case at bar and help to make the climate of the case."[48]

The eclat with which the federal government accused me of having kidnaped William Hamm, Jr., at St. Paul also came in for some discussion:

"That Touhy was indicted at all on the Hamm matter is something for which the Department of Justice should answer. They knew it was a very weak case. The only identification witness was . . . completely spurious. . . . The state has admitted that Alvin Karpis was guilty of this particular crime."[49]

Of the public officials who tried their best to put me in prison or sit me down in the electric chair, Judge Barnes had some kind remarks for Wilbert F. Crowley:

"Mr. Crowley, who tried the two Touhy cases, twice testified in this court in this case. He was and he is still a highly respected judge of the Superior Court of Cook County, Illinois. He made an excellent impression as a witness. He was frank and told the truth as he remembered it."[50]

When he slammed into a résumé of the Factor frame-up, Judge Barnes left no possible doubt of my innocence:

"In the opinion of the court, Costner was a completely spurious witness. He was in Tennessee during the entire kidnaping period of June 30th, 1933, to July 13th, 1933 . . . "[51]

"The court finds that Touhy was at home after midnight of June 30th, 1933, which is when the kidnaping is supposed to have occurred . . . . "[52]

"The court finds that John Factor was not kidnaped for ransom or otherwise on the night of June 30th and July 1st, 1933, although he was taken as a result of his own connivance . . . . "[53]

"Roger Touhy did not kidnap John Factor and, in fact, had no part in the alleged kidnaping of John Factor."[54]

Then came the clincher of the ruling, on a point which Bob Johnstone had stressed throughout the Barnes hearings:

"Perjured testimony was knowingly used by the prosecutor to bring about Touhy's conviction—this being the case, his conviction can not stand, regardless of the motive [of the prosecution]."[55]

Thus did Judge Barnes knock out every vestige of legality in my conviction in the Factor sham. His words proved me innocent, over and over again.

He next attacked my conviction and sentence of 199 years for aiding and abetting the escape of Darlak.

He stated that my constitutional rights had been violated all to hell when I got 199 years and Darlak's brother—the real aider and abetter—was let off with only three years. It was a violation of the sound, sacred principle of law that offenders must receive like punishment for like offenses. Out the window, therefore, went the second conviction and the 199-year term.

Judge Barnes ordered me freed—and it was done. But I knew freedom for only 47 hours.

Assistant Attorney General Schwartz appealed Barnes' finding to the U.S. Court of Appeals. Schwartz didn't deny that I was innocent of kidnaping Jake the Barber—in fact, he later admitted that perjured testimony had been used against me. He didn't really contradict Barnes' ruling that the 199-year sentence was unconstitutional.

But he insisted that I hadn't exhausted state court remedies before taking the aiding and abetting conviction to federal court. The Appeals Court agreed with him. The technicalities of the law, no matter what hardships might be inflicted, must be met. I was ordered back to prison, pending a review of the case.

Johnstone telephoned me the bad news. I got a cab and went at once to the U.S. Courthouse. What a reception awaited me there! Sheriff John Babb was waiting for me. He had lined up a dozen squads of deputies and city police. On went the handcuffs, along with chains and an escape-proof belt.

I went back to Stateville with the effects of a desperate criminal captured in a gun battle, rather than as a man who had surrendered voluntarily on a court order. I didn't care much, since I was optimistic for an early release.

My optimism was as ill-advised as the hope of a man condemned to the electric chair that electricity might go out of style. The U.S. Court of Appeals reviewed my case —but the decision was against me. The finger of fate was leaving me bruised all over.

There was no question involved about my innocence of the Factor charges. The 199-year term for the escape was the hitch-bitch. The Court of Appeals agreed with Schwartz that I hadn't used up my sources of remedy in the Illinois courts.

In order for me now to go free on a court order, I would have to carry the 199-year conviction all the way through the state courts, probably getting turned down, and return to federal jurisdiction. It would take years, not because Judge Barnes was incorrect, but because I had to unwind the red tape of the law.

Bob Johnstone and others filed appeals for me in both state and federal courts. Johnstone was joined by Frank Gagen, Jr., Daniel C. Ahern and Kevin J. Gillogly, all capable, hard-working lawyers.

Legal technicalities blocked me at every door to freedom. Judges, in their zeal to follow the letter of the law, seemed to forget that the evidence showed I was innocent. My best bet was to appeal to Illinois' Governor William G. Stratton and to the Illinois Pardon and Parole Board.

The board granted me a hearing in 1957. I was allowed to tell my story, and I thought the board members were sympathetic. The hearing room in Stateville was crowded with newspaper people and many of them held up two fingers in a hopeful V-for-Victory signal for me. Camera flashbulbs flashed.

I answered the board's questions and then sat down, thinking it was all over.

And then a dark, youngish, compactly-built man stood up in the audience and asked to be heard. I recognized him from his newspaper photographs. My hopes sank. He was Benjamin S. Adamowski, state's attorney of Cook County, in the job Tom Courtney had held. His words could condemn me.

Adamowski spoke softly, but firmly. I jittered. He said he did not know the minute details of the Touhy-Factor case, but that he had consulted with people who did. He did not believe, he said, that I was guilty of kidnaping Factor.

The prosecutor paused for a moment, said he would have no objection to my release from prison and added quietly:

"In fact, I would urge it."

A great feeling of relief surged through me. At last, for the first time, an important Illinois state official had come over to my side. My happiness was almost as great as when I heard Judge Barnes' decision or when I saw Clara and the boys in the visiting room after ten years.

The board recommended to Governor Stratton that he commute my sentences. He agreed—cutting the kidnap term from 99 years to 72 years, making me eligible for parole on that one, since I had served 24 years, or one third of the sentence. He reduced the 199-year term to three years.

The upshot was that I became eligible for release late in 1959. By that time I would have spent more than a quarter of a century in prison for a crime that never happened.

This is the end of my story. I am thankful for the opportunity of telling it—for the sake of my family, and also, to set the record straight. It was my privilege, thank God, under the American way of life, to tell my story.

I have no bitterness, no enmity toward anyone. Instead, I have the deepest sense of gratitude toward the many people who have befriended me.

My hope is to live out the few years remaining to me in peace and quiet—and freedom—with those I love and respect.

(¹) - *U.S.A. ex rel Roger Touhy v. Ragen*, U. S. District Court, No. Dist. of Illinois, Eastern Divison No. 48 C 448, Opinion of Court, p. 333

(²) - *Ibid.*, p. 333
(³) - *Ibid.*, p. 395
(⁴) - *Ibid.*, p. 334
(⁵) - *Ibid.*, p. 334
(⁶) - *Ibid.*, p. 334
(⁷) - *Ibid.*, p. 334
(⁸) - *Ibid.*, p. 332
(⁹) - *Ibid.*, p. 332
(¹⁰) - *Ibid.*, p. 339
(¹¹) - *Ibid.*, p. 339
(¹²) - *Ibid.*, p. 339
(¹³) - *Ibid.*, p. 394
(¹⁴) - *Ibid.*, p. 343
(¹⁵) - *Ibid.*, p. 364
(¹⁶) - *Ibid.*, p. 375
(¹⁷) - *Ibid.*, p. 397
(¹⁸) - *Ibid.*, p. 441
(¹⁹) - *Ibid.*, p. 405
(²⁰) - *Ibid.*, p. 406
(²¹) - *Ibid.*, p. 425
(²²) - *Ibid.*, p. 434
(²³) - *Ibid.*, p. 433
(²⁴) - *Ibid.*, p. 434
(²⁵) - *Ibid.*, p. 436
(²⁶) - *Ibid.*, p. 436-437

(²⁷) - *Ibid.*, p. 405
(²⁸) - *Ibid.*, p. 426
(²⁹) - *Ibid.*, p. 461-462
(³⁰) - *Ibid.*, p. 462
(³⁰ᵃ) - *Ibid.*, p. 463
(³¹) - *Ibid.*, p. 464
(³²) - *Ibid.*, p. 425
(³³) - *Ibid.*, p. 428-429
(³⁴) - *Ibid.*, p. 361
(³⁵) - *Ibid.*, p. 361
(³⁶) - *Ibid.*, p. 361
(³⁷) - *Ibid.*, p. 361
(³⁸) - *Ibid.*, p. 474
(³⁹) - *Ibid.*, p. 481
(⁴⁰) - *Ibid.*, p. 439
(⁴¹) - *Ibid.*, p. 440
(⁴²) - *Ibid.*, p. 441
(⁴³) - *Ibid.*, p. 415
(⁴⁴) - *Ibid.*, p. 350-351
(⁴⁵) - *Ibid.*, p. 366
(⁴⁶) - *Ibid.*, p. 335
(⁴⁷) - *Ibid.*, p. 351-352
(⁴⁸) - *Ibid.*, p. 366
(⁴⁹) - *Ibid.*, p. 466
(⁵⁰) - *Ibid.*, p. 486
(⁵¹) - *Ibid.*, p. 418
(⁵²) - *Ibid.*, p. 460
(⁵³) - *Ibid.*, p. 484
(⁵⁴) - *Ibid.*, p. 484
(⁵⁵) - *Ibid.*, p. 471

John P. Barnes
—a Profile

BARNES, John Peter, judge; born in Ohio
Township, Beaver County, Pennsylvania, March
15, 1881; son of Albert and Olive A. (Jack) B.;
B.S., Geneva Coll. (Beaver Falls, Pa.), 1904, hon.
LL.D., 1936; LL.B., U. of Mich., 1907, hon.
LL.M., 1933; LL.D., John Marshall Law School,
1954; married Sara A. Darr, 1908; children—
John Peter, Rufus Darr (dec.), Mrs. Sara Louise
Suster, Mrs. Catherine Olive Hooper, Paul Harry
(dec.), Hugh Douglas (dec.). Private practice of
law, Chicago, 1907-31, except for 1913-14, when
first asst. county atty., Cook County; judge
U. S. Dist. Court, Northern Dist. of Ill.
since 1931. Northwestern University, Centennial
Award, 1951. Mem. Am., Ill. State and Chicago
bar assns. Student editor Mich. Law Rev., 1906-
07. Home: Avalon, R. D. 3, Elgin, Ill. Office: U. S.
Courthouse, Chgo.

from **Who's Who in America**
Volume 30, 1958-59
—by permission

A man accused of impersonating a federal employe
stood in United States District Court in Chicago.
Behind him was a deputy United States marshal, holding a
pair of handcuffs in readiness. The judge on the bench
scanned documents dealing with the case and addressed
the deputy sternly.

"Mr. Marshal, you will put those manacles away at once," he said. "You will not handcuff this defendant, or fingerprint him, or photograph him. That is the order of the court.

"The defendant never before has been accused of a crime. He may be not guilty at this time, although he has been indicted. He is presumed to be innocent until proven guilty.

"If he is convicted, you then may incarcerate him, fingerprint and photograph him for your files. Until then, you will not put a finger on him."

The speaker, John P. Barnes, was a paradox of the federal bench.

On that same day, he had sentenced a dope peddler to ten years, the maximum term, for selling a small amount of heroin. The average judge would have let the man off with a year or two, probably.

In his chambers, Judge Barnes discussed his actions of the day with a friend:

"The dope peddler is a repeater. When he gets out of prison, he probably will resume selling heroin and addicting new people to the terrible stuff. It was my job to keep him out of circulation for as long a time as possible.

"The man charged with impersonation is a first offender. Suppose I had allowed him to be fingerprinted and photographed for the federal government files and further suppose that he is found to be innocent. What then?

"I'll tell you what. He would have difficulty ever getting a job in federal service. His record would work to his disadvantage for promotions if he went into the United States armed services. It might have created hardships for him for the rest of his life."

It developed that the judge was right in both cases.

The dope peddler was paroled after four years, went back to selling heroin and was convicted again. The judge had kept him confined, as a menace to society, for as long as he could.

The government dropped the charges against the impersonation defendant, quashing the indictment with an apology that it had been a mistake. Judge Barnes had saved an innocent man from humiliation and a record file that might harm him in the future.

Persons who understood the judge frequently contrasted the story of the dope peddler with the case of the innocent defendant in efforts to explain His Honor's sometimes seemingly unpredictable conduct on the bench. It wasn't easy.

Judge Barnes could be stern, almost implacable, in one case, and deeply sympathetic in the next. He could broil, fry and boil a hypocritical defense lawyer or a too-eager prosecutor with incendiary language. An hour later he might be conferring sympathetically with an out-of-work, wife-expecting-a-baby, young husband charged with stealing letters from mail boxes.

A jury in his court returned a verdict of guilty against a bank cashier, the father of four young children, for embezzling about $2,500. The amount of the defendant's salary came out during the trial and, when sentencing time came, Judge Barnes delivered an angry and noisy oration for the benefit of bank presidents and board chairmen:

"When you pay a man $90 a month, it is dangerous to allow him to handle money. You are asking for trouble. This defendant had to feed his family on $90 a month, or steal more. He stole."

The United States attorney's office had recommended a sentence of five years for the cashier, but Judge Barnes let him off with probation.

The decision caused grumbling among some financiers along the line that Judge Barnes, in effect, had issued a blanket license to steal to all underpaid money-handlers. The judge blithely ignored the criticism. He prized justice above all things. He despised injustice.

John P. Barnes grew up pitching hay, milking cows and hoeing corn on his parents' farm near Beaver Falls, Pennsylvania. In high school he met and fell in love with a classmate, Sara Darr, and he never fell out of love. "She was the prettiest, nicest, sweetest girl in Pennsylvania, or anywhere else," he said. "And she never changed."

Barnes dish-washed his way through the University of Michigan law school and upon his graduation in 1907 he headed for that outrageous boom town, Chicago. He got a job, at $40 a month, at the first law office where he applied. In six months his pay was raised to $60 and he sent for Sara Darr. They were married.

There were years of scrimping for Barnes and his bride, but his income crept upward. He became a corporation lawyer, the most lucrative form of practice. He represented railroads, banks, real-estate corporations and other important clients.

There came a New Year's Eve in the early 1920's when he could tell his wife that he had made $1,000 a week, and more than $50,000, during the past year. It was a princely figure, especially for those times, and it kept increasing.

Barnes handled many bankruptcy and receivership cases. When the great depression hit, he had more clients than he could handle. His income passed $2,000 a week. He built a fine suburban home. He was invited to join the best clubs.

A federal judgeship opened up in Chicago in 1930. A number of his colleagues in law approached Barnes. He was a staunch Republican. President Hoover probably would look favorably upon nominating him for the bench. His record was spotless and he had a vast knowledge of the law.

Barnes went home that evening and joked with Sara over the dinner table. "Just imagine it," he said, chuckling. "They suggest that I throw away my law practice for a $10,000 a year judgeship." After another mouthful of food he added with another chuckle: "Just imagine it."

Sara Darr Barnes knew her husband as well as he knew the law, or perhaps better. As she poured his coffee, she told him: "John Barnes, you want that appointment. You know you want it and so do I. Accept it. We'll manage without the money, never fear."

Judge Barnes did accept. He gave up his corporation practice and took a salary shrinkage of $90,000 a year. There never was any indication that he ever regretted it. He served as a federal judge for 26 years. He seemed to enjoy every minute of it.

Barnes had bought a farm outside of Chicago, and

there he went with Mrs. Barnes to live quietly and to rear their three sons and two daughters. He was a busy man, bringing home briefs from court and working harder than he had as a young law clerk trying to get ahead in the world.

As the years passed, he decided while scraping with a razor in front of his bathroom mirror one morning that shaving was a waste of time. He finished shaving and dressing, strode briskly to the breakfast table and told his family: "I will never shave again. I will use those ten or more minutes a day for exercise, instead."

The added exercise, swimming in a Chicago pool and walking on his country acres, preserved a trim figure for him throughout his life. The beard became a symbol of justice in the Chicago courts. He trimmed it at medium length, cut off squarely beyond the chin and resembling—as one prominent Chicago lawyer said after an unnerving time in Barnes' courtroom—the business end of a bulldozer.

He was a truly great pillar, always, in support of the United States Constitution and the Bill of Rights. No defendant ever got short-changed on his precious civil rights as an American citizen before Barnes.

Judge Barnes was impatient at times, even hot-headed or belligerent. But he never was too hasty to hear out the plea of a deserving defendant. He was patient with young lawyers doing their best, but any hint of fakery in his court would upset and outrage him.

Judge Barnes never carried his impatience home and, even when he showed it deservedly in court, he seemed remorseful thereafter, his bailiffs and court clerks said. He once was impressed—and perhaps a bit embarrassed, in an amused way—upon reading an ancedote about one of his great heroes, Oliver Wendell Holmes, the Magnificent Yankee who was chief justice of the United States Supreme Court.

It seemed that Justice Holmes stomped out of his home angrily one morning after being unable to find a legal document which he needed in court. After his departure, Mrs. Holmes found the paper exactly where it should be—on a desk in the chief justice's study where he had left it.

Mrs. Holmes thumb-tacked the document to a wall, where her husband could not miss it. Above it she placed two small American flags and underneath a hand-lettered notice which said: "I am an old man and I have had many troubles—most of which never happened."

After reading the story, Judge Barnes was extra solicitous around the house for days. The truth was, however, that he seldom, if ever, was annoyed by trifles. Injustices and shams would set fire to his anger, but not human failings.

There were times, his colleagues said, when Judge Barnes seemed almost to agree with Mr. Bumble in *Oliver Twist*. Readers of Charles Dickens may recall that Mr. Bumble was quoted as saying: "If the law says that, the law is an ass."

Barnes held the law in too great esteem, generally speaking, to make such a comment. But he sometimes was indignant when the law was, in his opinion, improperly administered.

There was the case of a young defendant, under a sentence of life imprisonment, who came before him on a writ of habeas corpus—just as Bob Johnstone brought Roger Touhy. The judge read the records of the case and then exploded.

"Young man," he said, "you were only 23 years old when you were convicted as an habitual criminal. You were too young to be an habitual anything. It was a shame that a grand jury ever indicted you on such a charge."

The defendant finally got his sentence reduced, won a parole and became—of all things—a clergyman in Kansas. He lived a fine, respected, constructive life until polio killed him after about 15 years.

Midway in Barnes' judicial career, the United States Supreme Court discovered that convicts in Illinois penetentiaries were being stopped from mailing out petitions for writs of habeas corpus. Regardless of the circumstances of their convictions, the development of new evidence or other extenuating circumstances, the convicts had no right of appeal. It was suspected by some lawyers that

Judge Barnes called the matter to the attention of the Supreme Court.

Anyway, the high court held that hundreds of Illinois convicts were "on a legal merry-go-round" and at "the end of blind alleys" in violation of their constitutional rights. Every person has the right to petition for habeas corpus.

The Supreme Court asked Judge Barnes to do something about the situation, and he did. He threatened to send to jail any prison warden who refused to allow an inmate to mail a petition for a writ.

Hundreds of convicts promptly petitioned Barnes for relief. Many of the applications obviously were preposterous and others had no standing in law. A small percentage of the petitioners received hearings in court and most of them were turned down. A magazine writer wrote that, of the applicants, only seven were freed as falsely convicted. Judge Barnes read the comment and seemed to be aghast.

"What does he mean by *only* seven?" the judge said. "If *only* one had been freed, it would have been worth the effort. And if *not one* justifiable case had been found, these men still should not have been denied their constitutional rights."

Personal tragedies weighed heavily upon the judge. Of his three sons, one died in infancy. The other two, Hugh and Paul, were killed within six weeks in combat during World War II. Barnes mourned, but he never let his broken heart show through his black judicial robes.

On September 15, 1957, Judge Barnes retired from the federal bench. His age was 77, and he thought it was time for him to make way for a younger man. His perceptions and ready grasp of the law had not given way, but he feared the day when they might.

He was asked to state which one of his decisions would live longest in the history of American jurisprudence. "The Roger Touhy case," he replied without a second of hesitation.

In retirement, Judge Barnes occupied himself with leisurely walks and his hobbies of oil painting and refinishing old furniture. He lived for less than seven months and, on April 12, 1958, he died in the Sherman Hospital at Elgin, Illinois.

The funeral was private, but there was a memorial service in the dingy, old-fashioned courtroom of the sooty, antique United States Courthouse in downtown Chicago where Judge Barnes had presided for so long. Lawyers, judges, businessmen, bankers, publishers, realtors and others were there. One of the speakers said:

"He had a realization of the frailties of humans and a sympathy for the friendless and the downtrodden."

That is a fitting epitaph for John P. Barnes.

—Ray Brennan

THE STUDY OF BENTHIC COMMUNITIES

A MODEL AND A REVIEW

Elsevier Oceanography Series, 9

THE STUDY OF
BENTHIC COMMUNITIES
A MODEL AND A REVIEW

by

ROBERT H. PARKER

Coastal Ecosystems
Management Incorporated,
Fort Worth, Texas, U.S.A.

ELSEVIER SCIENTIFIC PUBLISHING COMPANY *Amsterdam - Oxford - New York 1975*

ELSEVIER SCIENTIFIC PUBLISHING COMPANY
335 Jan van Galenstraat
P.O. Box 211, Amsterdam, The Netherlands

AMERICAN ELSEVIER PUBLISHING COMPANY, INC.
52 Vanderbilt Avenue
New York, New York 10017

Library of Congress Card Number: 73-20941

ISBN: 0-444-41203-4

With 92 illustrations and 13 tables

Printed in The Netherlands

This book is almost unique as a publishing venture; in that much of its contents involve one large, original research study, the likes of which seldom is published in a scientific journal. A project of such magnitude as discussed here was actually too large to be included in a single issue of any journal. Because the project (a complete analysis of a complex marine ecosystem) covered a number of disciplines and could serve as a model for a wide variety of studies in the now extremely relevant ecological sciences, it was decided that a hard-covered book, available to all, would be appropriate.

The primary objective of this study was to design and carry out an eco-systems survey of a small area in such detail that it would be possible to delineate precise sea bottom community boundaries and to determine the environmental conditions which influence them. It is with some pride that I can state that the objectives were reached with greater success than antici-pated. In a sense, the success of this project gave me hope that it could be used as a model for future community studies in the sea and on the land. In order to emphasize this study as a *model*, similar studies, both local and worldwide, were reviewed and compared with the present one. What is more important, it was possible to show that previous subjective studies of a similar nature were still substantially correct when compared with the present more objective approach to the problem and its results. In addition, I tried to show how the model could be used to solve applied problems by giving results of some of the more successful applications.

A final objective was to see if such a large body of data could be collected and integrated by a small, full-time staff typical of a project unit within a large institution or company. Although the bulk of the collection of data and all sorting of faunal samples were done by only three people, many other persons were involved in the analysis of data and final identification of the animals to the species level. The responsibility of writing the earlier computer programs, which are the critical portion of the results, lay primarily with Mr. Anthony B. Williams, one of my research assistants. Programs used at Texas Christian University, Fort Worth, Texas, were written by Dr. Woodley Sconyers and the I.B.M. Systems Engineer, Mr. David Carthauser. Without their concentrated effort in devising the statistical methods used to bear out our original hypotheses, this study would have floundered in a morass of uncorrelated data. Mr. Williams did the major share of work in getting the various kinds of data into computer form and storage by which they could be processed by conventional and unconventional statistical techniques.

Several research assistants contributed enormously to both the collection and identification of the organisms in this study. It would have been impossible to process and identify some 10,000 animals a week without the tireless efforts of both Mr. J. Stewart Nagle and Mr. Andrew Driscoll, research assistants in the Program. Mr. Robert Kaufman also spent two summers as a summer assistant in our program in sorting the samples and assisting in identification of the polychaetes. All three of these assistants have earned my deepest gratitude for their interest and industry during their tenure with this program. Miss Karen Lukas, also briefly employed in the Systematics—Ecology Program, was responsible for running the first half of the sediment samples while Mr. Williams completed the suite of some 220 complete sediment analyses. Two research assistants at Texas Christian University, Messrs. Jack Kuehn and Douglas Currer devoted considerable time towards tabulating results of the Texas Christian University computer analysis and in checking and reorganizing the IBM cards. Assistance from other members of the technical staff of the Systematics—Ecology Program, particularly Mr Peter Oldham and Mr. Stewart Santos, is also gratefully acknowledged.

A number of post-doctoral fellows, visiting investigators and consulting systematists have carried out the major share of taxonomic work on this study. I am particularly grateful to Dr. Neil C. Hulings, formerly of Texas Christian University, for his identification of the Ostracoda in a rather short time; Dr. Louise Bush, Drew University, for identifying the Turbellaria; Dr. Robert P. Higgins, Wake Forest College, for working with the Kinorhyncha; Dr. Charlotte Mangum, visiting ecologist in this Program, Dr. Joseph Simon, Post-doctoral Fellow in Systematics also of this Program, and Charlene Ward, Museum of Comparative Zoology, Harvard University, for identifying and checking the Polychaeta; Mr. J. Stewart Nagle and Dr. Edward L. Bousfield, the latter from the National Museum of Canada, Ottawa, Canada, for identifying and checking the Amphipoda; Mr. Dehn E. Solomon, Coastal Ecosystems Management, Inc., Fort Worth, and Dr. Roland Wigley, U.S. Bureau of Commercial Fisheries, Woods Hole, for Cumacea; Dr. Kerwin Hyland, University of Rhode Island, for checking the marine mites; Dr. Thomas Bowman, U.S. National Museum, for Isopoda; and Dr. Duane Hope, U.S. National Museum, for his assistance with the Nematoda. Groups with smaller numbers of individuals, such as echinoderms, barnacles, decapods and mollusks, were identified either by the author or with the assistance of the general staff of the Systematics—Ecology Program.

Special acknowledgement with gratitude is due Dr. Melbourne R. Carriker, Director of the Systematics—Ecology Program, who made this study possible by acquiring funds and permitting free rein to organize and execute this research, even though this was a somewhat unorthodox approach. He also spent considerable time in thorough and excellent editing of this manuscript.

By far my deepest appreciation is for the untiring efforts of my wife, Elizabeth L. Parker, in typing, compiling and checking the manuscript, endless tables of numbers and scientific names and giving me constant encouragement to complete this book.

These studies were aided by Contract Nonr. 3070(03) (1964-65) between the Office of Naval Research, Department of the Navy, and the Systematics—Ecology Program, Marine Biological Laboratory; by Grants GB 561 and GB 4509 from the National Science Foundation to the Systematics—Ecology Program, Marine Biological Laboratory; and by Texas Christian University, Research Foundation Grant No. 6677. Systematics—Ecology Program contribution No. 148.

CONTENTS

CHAPTER 1

INTRODUCTION

A few years ago, the study of marine bottom-living animals and plants was primarily the province of basic research. With the exception of some studies devoted to establishing the productivity of bottom fishing grounds, emphasis was placed on satisfying our own scientific curiosity as to life history studies of non-commercial bottom animals, physiology of these same creatures, and the composition and abundances of benthic communities. This present study of benthic community ecology was initiated for the same reasons — to satisfy scientific curiosity and to learn more about the detailed interactions of animals and plants and their relation to the total marine environment. In the intervening years between 1963 (when this study was initiated) and 1972, there has been a steady shift in the study of benthic communities from the basic to the applied aspects, such as the effect of oil pollution on benthic standing crops and productivity.

This study has particular relevance to today's problems of human disturbance of natural ecosystems in that it serves as a model for establishing the "baseline" or conditions in the undisturbed state. It is only through careful observations as to behavior and distribution of environmentally sensitive organisms in an undisturbed habitat that we can identify major deviations from the "normal", when environmental disturbances do occur. The data contained herein were collected in a relatively undisturbed environment and under conditions which were typical of a long period of time. Although it is unlikely that industrial or domestic pollution might become a major factor in disrupting the smoothly operating ecosystem of Hadley Harbor, Massachusetts, it would be possible to determine the exact amount of damage sustained there in the event that a sudden disaster, such as an oil spill, might occur. The value of this study is not limited to the Cape Cod region alone, as one can use the techniques outlined here to establish baseline conditions in any part of the world. It also should be possible to make definitive decisions (which can stand up in a court of law) as to the amount of damage sustained by benthic communities, through using objective mathematical methods described herein for correlating animal distributions with environmental damage.

Since this study was completed in 1968, this author has had ample opportunity to test the various hypotheses and techniques outlined on polluted or disturbed habitats in other parts of the world. For example, using these same methods of data collection and analysis it has been possible to identify the degree of damage sustained by two major oil spills (Watson et al., 1971) and to assess the effects of continuous discharge of oil field salt brines into Texas estuaries (Parker and Blanton, 1970). The fact that this large body of data exists as to the causes of minute changes in populations and community composition, it is infinitely easier to determine whether changes in benthic community density and diversity are natural or man-made. It is the express-ed hope that continued use of this model can be made in other parts of the world and for other types of habitats and ecosystems, eventually contribut-ing to a cleaner and more esthetically satisfying world.

Investigations of marine benthic communities, with relatively few excep-tions, have been concerned with describing the aggregation of species of infaunal animals in relation to broad geographic areas of uniform sediments, depths, and salinity. The majority of these studies has emphasized distribu-tion of marine benthic invertebrate communities as they are related to sub-stratum preferences, the principle approach of Petersen (1913, 1914, 1915), Thorson (1957), Lie (1968), and Rhoads and Young (1970) and most of the other Danish and European investigators. Other studies have related marine faunal aggregations to salinity gradients (Gunter, 1945; Parker, 1955, 1959; Sanders et al., 1965), and less frequently, to the stability of the external environmental factors (Parker, 1960; Parker et al., 1965; Hessler and San-ders, 1967; Parker and Blanton, 1970; Wade, 1972). Depth facies have been established by Thorson (1957), Parker (1964a, c), Sanders (1968), and Stan-ton and Evans (1971), where temperature range and stability of the water are probably the controlling factors as a function of depth. Less investigative effort has been devoted to detailed studies of biological interactions as possi-ble primary influence in determining the composition and extent of marine benthic communities, a possibility suggested by Thorson (1957) and hy-pothesized by Slobodkin (1960).

By and large, the greatest number of benthic community studies has em-phasized the larger and less-motile invertebrate organisms as the predominant or indicator animals for various associations or "communities". Published quantitative studies (summarized by Holme, 1964; Longhurst, 1964; Parker, 1964a; Carriker, 1967) generally have been based on animals of a size larger than 1—2 mm. Few studies have been concerned with the smaller subtidal meiofauna (0.25—1 mm), with the exception of Sanders (1958, 1960), Wieser (1960), Jones (1961), Wigley and McIntyre (1964), Fenchel (1969), Harris (1972a, b) and, to some extent, Reish (1959, 1961) and Wade (1972). Earlier meiofaunal investigations have demonstrated that the bulk of the benthic fauna in terms of total number of individuals per unit volume of the bottom lies in size classes below 1 mm. However, in terms of biomass, the smaller animals, although several orders of magnitude more abundant, form a minute portion of the total living weight. More important is the fact that these large numbers of small animals provide the basic food for many of the larger forms. If most of the larger invertebrates are selective in their food, either as predators or selective deposit feeders, then their distribution and population densities are apt to be dependent upon the specific distributions of meiofaunal species of invertebrates.

Although the relationship between certain environmental variables (such as salinity, temperature, and sediment parameters) and the distribution of megafaunal elements has been hypothesized, virtually nothing is known about the influence these commonly measured factors may have on the meiofauna. In previous studies, such variables as current strength and direction, light penetration, dissolved oxygen, redox-potential (Eh), hydrogen-ion concentration (pH), and bottom topography have seldom been compared with benthic faunal distributions and abundance. These data usually consisted of single sample points without duplication, either as many widely spaced samples at one single sampling period or single sample points over a large area and over a fairly long time span. This kind of information does not provide the scope necessary to determine if any real environmental influences are exerted on a community or on a species throughout its life span. Caution should be used when mapping benthic communities based on a single season's collection, since the aggregations may move seasonally into different habitats or be composed of different elements on a seasonal basis. It should also be stressed that most benthic studies have been carried out in areas covering hundreds to thousands of square kilometers, where sampling density was at best only one sample to every square kilometer and, more frequently, one sample for every 4—100 km^2. With sample intervals so great, it is not possible to determine either degree of patchiness of marine benthos or sharpness of boundaries between different benthic communities.

The present study was initiated to investigate some of these problems mentioned in an earlier paper by Parker (1964b) and to examine in detail questions raised in a study of faunal complexes in the Gulf of California (Parker, 1964a). Of particular significance in testing the instability of marine communities is the fact that water temperatures of the Cape Cod region fluctuate between $-2.0°C$ in the winter and $+25.0°C$ in the summer, an extreme seldom duplicated anywhere else in the marine world. Thus, striking seasonal changes might be expected both in composition and abundance of animals within marine benthic communities in this region. It is also important to note that salinities in the vicinity of the Marine Biological Laboratory are extremely stable, 31—32‰, below normal open ocean salinity of 35‰, and do not vary more than 1.5‰ throughout the annual cycle. Salinity was therefore not considered a limiting factor in the area, except that values of

31‰ might exclude a very small number of wholly marine species of animals.

To test the hypothesis that marine benthic communities exist in the terrestrial sense and to examine the question of whether sharp or indistinct boundaries exist between them (a difficult concept to test in the Gulf of California), we investigated a small area of sea bottom confined by natural land boundaries, the Hadley Harbor Complex. Because little is known of the true influence that external physical—chemical and sedimentary factors may exert on invertebrate animals, we measured some 15 environmental parameters on a weekly basis. At the same time at least one quantitative sample of the marine benthos was taken in five different habitats per week within the chosen one-third square kilometer of sea bottom. Over 280 biological samples were collected and 800 stations for physical—chemical measurements were occupied throughout a two-year sampling period. We believe that this provided an unprecedented opportunity to test, with both conventional plotting and conventional and somewhat unconventional statistical methods, the hypothesis that communities of organisms can be discerned on the sea floor. The concept that the areal extent and composition of communities are controlled by certain inanimate aspects of their environment was explored; and to a certain degree the influence of biological interactions on benthic community composition was also investigated.

PREVIOUS COMMUNITY STUDIES IN THE WOODS HOLE REGION

One of the more important and earliest comprehensive studies on the distribution of benthic invertebrates in the Woods Hole region, which includes the Hadley Harbor Complex, was a survey by the Bureau of Commercial Fisheries under the direction of A.E. Verrill, S.I. Smith and O. Harger (Verrill, 1873; Verrill et al., 1873). Subsequent discussions of Verrill's results deal with a reprinted version of these papers (Verrill and Smith, 1874). This study includes much ecological information relating to faunal distributions and serves as an important base for estimating faunal changes which may have occurred in the past hundred years. Verrill's work was extended by the equally important work of Sumner et al. (1913) which assayed the fauna in a more systematic manner and contains more detailed information on the ecology of the area.

A good deal of qualitative information on the Hadley Harbor Complex before disappearance of the eel grass (*Zostera marina*) was reported by Allee (1922—1923). An unpublished catalogue of the distribution of common invertebrates in the Woods Hole region was found in the library of the Marine Biological Laboratory (Allee, 1922c), which describes the relative abundance of many invertebrate species. Localities as given by Allee, which are of interest to this study are: Northwest Gutter (mud, sand gravel and eel grass), Northwest Gutter (rocks and seaweeds), Southwest (West) and Southeast (East) Gutters (mud, sand and eel grass), Southwest (West) and Southeast (East) Gutters (rocks and seaweed), and Lackey's Bay. Unfortunately, many of the identifications of organisms reported were made by students, and, in certain groups where the systematics is now better understood, cannot be trusted fully.

Of particular importance is a quantitative investigation of Northwest Gutter made by Stauffer (1937) after the eel grass had completely disappeared (Milne and Milne, 1951). Stauffer compared the distribution and abundances of common species of invertebrates in the absence of eel grass with that reported by Allee and his students when eel grass abounded. The present study is particularly significant in this respect, as it was made after the eel grass had almost attained its previous luxuriance.

Several benthic ecological studies have been made in nearby waters, where most of the species dealt with in the present study are found, albeit in somewhat different habitats. Lee (1944) carried out a quantitative survey of the bottom fauna in Menemsha Bight, approximately 12 km across Vineyard Sound close to Martha's Vineyard. His results are not comparable to ours as his samples represented only animals over 1.8 mm in size; these constitute but a fraction of the fauna collected in the present study.

Investigations in Buzzards Bay by Sanders (1958, 1960), in Barnstable Harbor by Sanders et al. (1962), and in Pocassett Estuary by Sanders et al. (1965) are similar to the present study in that they dealt with about the same size organisms on a quantitative basis. However, Sanders' Buzzards Bay stations generally were taken in an area of much greater environmental stability, both areally and temporally, and were in considerably deeper water and on softer substrata than those occupied in this study. His faunal composition was thus quite different from ours. It is remarkable that a number of his stations were taken only a few kilometers from Hadley Harbor, yet none of his benthic communities were duplicated in Hadley Harbor except in a gross way. Sanders et al. (1962) also explored the biological structure of communities in Barnstable Harbor on the north side of Cape Cod, some of which resemble those found in the shallower portions of the Hadley Harbor Complex.

The largest number of organisms collected in this study consisted of the meiofauna, and it is of interest that a number of specific meiofaunal investigations have been carried out relatively close to the Hadley Harbor Complex. Wieser (1960), in conjunction with Sanders' studies, investigated the meiofauna of Buzzards Bay and provided a basis for comparison with the present study. Wieser and Kanwisher (1961) also investigated components of the meiofauna in a small marsh on Penzance Point, just across the Woods Hole from Hadley Harbor. Pennak (1942a, b) studied some of the elements of the meiofauna, primarily in the intertidal sands in the vicinity of Woods Hole. These studies were not comparable to ours, because the intertidal portion of Hadley Harbor was not studied intensively during this investigation. One other study, a quantitative comparison of the meiobenthos and macro-benthos south of Martha's Vineyard, should be mentioned (Wigley and McIntyre, 1964). It is not possible to compare Wigley and McIntyre's results with the present study as depths of their stations ranged from 40 to 567 m, while the deepest Hadley Harbor stations were in less than 7 m; and their faunal counts were made on sieve fractions down to 72 μ rather than on organisms larger than 250 μ.

Numerous papers have been published on the systematics, physiology, and autecology of animals collected in the Hadley Harbor Complex and its environs, but few of them contribute in any major way to an understanding of the synecology of the communities encountered during this investigation. These papers are indexed in a bibliography of the Cape Cod region prepared by Yentsch et al. (1967).

CHAPTER 2

STUDY AREA AND METHODS

The Hadley Harbor Complex (Fig. 1), a part of the Elizabeth Islands Chain, contains approximately one-third of a square kilometer of sea bottom and consists of a series of tidal channels connecting Woods Hole, and both Buzzards Bay and Vineyard Sound. Buzzards Bay, in the vicinity of Woods Hole, has a tidal range of about one and a half meters, while Vineyard Sound, on the opposite side of the Elizabeth Islands Chain, has a tidal range of less than a meter (Redfield, 1953). These large tidal differences across a distance of only a kilometer are explained by tidal node and interference phenomena relating to the shapes of both Vineyard Sound and Buzzards Bay and the movement of the tidal surge along the northeast coast of the United States (Redfield, 1953). As can be expected, the tidal height differentials in the Hadley Harbor Complex produce swift tidal races through its so-called "gutters". In fact, within the narrow, partly artificial constrictions of these gutters, current strengths of over six knots have been observed. In addition, there is a net flow of water from Buzzards Bay into Vineyard Sound which has yet to be calculated.

In terms of stability of the marine environment, the Hadley Harbor Complex was not an ideal choice for a detailed study, as the complicated circulation arising from the many entrances to the Complex produce a large variety of small micro-habitats. A preliminary appraisal of this area, based primarily on the relatively uniform salinities throughout the area and throughout the year and uniform temperatures throughout the Complex at any one time, would suggest that the Complex might contain a relatively uniform benthic fauna closely allied to that living in adjacent Buzzards Bay and Vineyard Sound. The investigation demonstrated, however, that the Complex contains many different micro-environments and several habitats which coincide with micro-variations in the environmental factors.

Detailed close-spaced sampling of the fauna and broad areal observations of the environmental factors were the ultimate aims of this study. Normally, one-time transects across the axis of each portion of the Complex and additional transects of samples down the axis of the gutters would have been the approach needed to assay the biological and physical—chemical factors in a region of this configuration. Unfortunately, this approach would have produced only a single set of observations per unit area during the period of

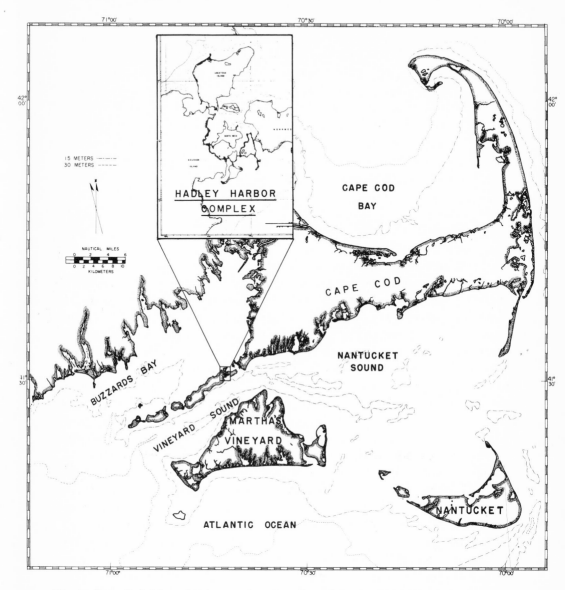

Fig. 1. Cape Cod, Massachusetts, and surrounding islands with the location of Hadley Harbor Complex.

study, and the variation in environmental factors and populations would not have been realized. Consequently, a more or less random-sampling approach with a weekly sampling at 29 fixed environmental stations was selected after some 65 preliminary semi-quantitative grab samples had been taken during the first six months of study. A sampling program and sample treatment routine was established which gave the maximum amount of information with the least amount of effort. This was done by marking the Complex in consecutively numbered squares, each measuring roughly 50×75 m in area (Fig. 2). We attempted to collect at least two samples in each square over the two-year period, no two samples taken at the same season. Physical, chemical, and sediment parameters were measured at every biological station while an areal survey of the physical—chemical factors only was carried out once a week at a series of 29 permanent buoy-marked stations (Fig. 3). In all, 288 biological samples were collected and over 800 physical—chemical stations were occupied (see Figs. 9 and 10 for some data), resulting in over 200,000 variate values, relating to 700 variables.

MEASUREMENT OF PHYSICAL—CHEMICAL VARIABLES

From the onset of this study it was realized that in order to measure and understand the small-scale changes of environment in the Complex, it would be necessary to make a large number of environmental measurements at frequent time intervals. In most marine ecological investigations, it has been customary to take individual surface and bottom water samples for the measurement of salinity, temperature, oxygen, pH, and Eh. It was soon realized that a planned one-day-a-week sampling program of up to 34 stations, at surface and bottom, would involve collecting a minimum of 68 bottles of water a day for analysis in the laboratory. Other alternatives were: (1) collecting water samples in the normal fashion, but running on-the-spot analyses in a boat, using short-electrode electronic instruments; or (2) making in situ measurements of all variables, using long-lead electrodes which could be dropped on and into the bottom. We chose the latter method, although because of various electronic failures all three methods were used at one time or another.

For the most part, several long-electrode devices were used to measure salinity, water temperature, air temperature, dissolved oxygen, hydrogen-ion concentration, reduction—oxidation potential, and light penetration (Parker, 1964b). Although sensing instruments used were the best available at that time, they were difficult to handle simultaneously. The major inconvenience of the multiple "black box" method (Hedgpeth, 1967, p. 708) was the necessity of hanging at least ten separate wires over the side, and attempting to read six different meters while jotting the individual values from either digital or dial readouts on to station sheets. We used a Buehler Turbocraft 17-ft. boat (Fig. 4) which operated on a 185-h.p. inboard engine equipped with alternator and inverter, permitting the operation of the instruments which required stable a.c. 120 V power. As can be seen in Fig. 4, space for various boxes was limited. In spite of the difficulties encountered in using multiple

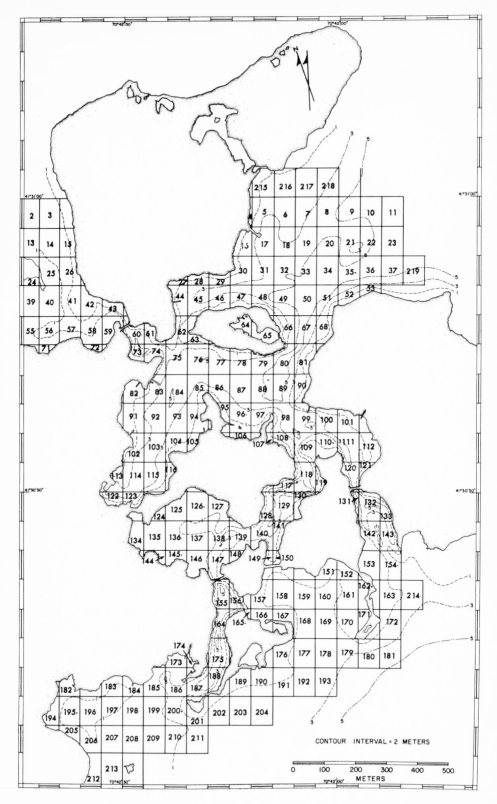

Fig. 2. Numbered grid used to locate stations for computer data storage, Hadley Harbor, Massachusetts.

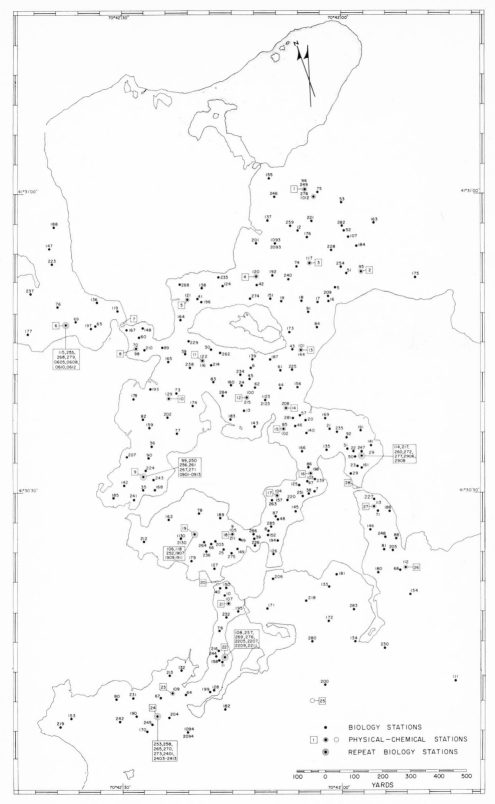

Fig. 4. Inside of Turbocraft boat with boxes, wires, and equipment used for sensing the marine environment.

cables and making individual lowerings of each sensor, it was possible to complete a station, including surface and bottom measurements, of all variables in less than 15 min. We could thus sample most of the 29 permanent physical stations during one stage of the tide, or in about four to five hours, without additional analytical work at the laboratory.

Salinity and water temperature were measured with an Industrial Instruments (Division of Beckman Instruments) RS—5—2 Induction Salinometer. Readout values could be obtained with accuracies to hundredths. Water samples were taken frequently to calibrate this accuracy and checked further on the Woods Hole Oceanographic Institution precision salinometer. For the most part, our values agreed within 0.02‰ of those obtained at the Oceanographic Institution. A Yellow Springs, Teletemp tele-thermometer with 30 ft. electrode and calibrated between $-30°$ and $+40°\,C$ was used to measure air temperatures and to verify the temperature readout on the salinometer. Redox-potential and pH were measured with a line-operated Radiometer pH meter and with specially developed 10 m long electrodes, protected by a plastic holder which permitted insertion into the bottom. Accuracy was 0.01 pH units or 10 mV Eh and readings were checked periodically against a standard Beckman Model G pH meter. The greatest problem resulted from delay in replacement of frequently broken electrodes which had to be shipped from Copenhagen, Denmark. Dissolved oxygen was measured occasionally with a Jarrell—Ash oxygen meter. Unfortunately, this instrument did not perform satisfactorily in both air and water temperatures below 0°C. Most of our early reliable oxygen measurements were made on water samples using a modified Winkler method. Light penetration was measured with an Ocean Research Equipment (O.R.E.) Company photometer, developed by C. Yentsch formerly of Woods Hole Oceanographic Institution. Measurements were first made by calibrating the photo cell at the surface and taking a reading of the same cell on the sea bottom and then calculating the percentage of the total ambient light. Later measurements were taken with two cells, a deck cell and a bottom cell, kept in constant balance within a recording system so that the readout would always relate to a percentage of total surface light.

Current measurements were taken infrequently, with the exception of a four-day survey of two tidal cycles, using a Marine Advisors ducted current meter suspended in a vaned holder as shown on Fig. 5. Currents as low as about 6 cm/sec and as high as 820 cm/sec could be measured with this device, although difficulties were encountered with corrosion, connectors,

Fig. 5. Current strength and direction sensor, vaned so as to head into the current. Recording case and O.R.E. light cell in foreground.

and electronics. A small Geodyne Savonius current meter was tested in the high-current portions of the gutters which stalled at velocities of over three or four knots. It also was too large to measure current speeds as close to the bottom as we desired to sample.

TESTING AND USE OF MARINE WATER MONITORING SYSTEM

Shortly after initiating the use of individual instruments for sensing the marine environment, it was realized that a single system for measuring all variables simultaneously would be an immense improvement (Parker, 1964b). In the fall of 1964, we therefore decided to invite the Philadelphia Division of Honeywell, Inc., to construct a marine water quality sensing system. Honeywell was selected because they already were marketing a fresh-water quality monitoring system which had been operating successfully for several years (Cory and Davis, 1965; Keyser, 1967). Unfortunately, the established monitoring system was designed to have the water pumped from the bottom into a stationary land-based well, with the recording system fixed on land. As it was necessary in the present study to have a mobile system which could be transported in a small boat, many modifications were needed. We also felt strongly that the sensors should be lowered directly into the marine environment rather than into a small well where the water would be brought to them, as such parameters as pH, water temperature, dissolved oxygen, and Eh may vary considerably over a vertical distance of nine meters and across horizontal distances of even greater magnitude.

The original system was designed to measure water temperature, dissolved oxygen, air temperature, conductivity (as a function of salinity), turbidity, and pH, while the present study necessitated slightly different variables, including Eh, light penetration rather than turbidity, current strength and current direction. The necessity of placing the sensors on the bottom or in the water column presented new design problems, especially in the case of the pH, Eh, and reference electrodes. Although construction of this device was begun in October, 1964, the device was not fully perfected to our satisfaction until one year later, too late to be used to its full capacity for this project. Major difficulties with the instrument were encountered, mainly electrolysis, heating of the recording package, and inconsistent operation of the pH and Eh amplifiers at both high and low temperatures.

The system was in operation intermittently throughout spring, summer and early fall of 1965, and was described briefly at the Marine Technology Association meeting in Washington, D.C. (Parker, 1965). Essentially, the system consisted of a stainless steel circular frame for holding six of the sensors (Fig. 6), a precision thermocouple, a Kelvin bridge conductivity cell,

Fig. 6. Stainless steel frame holding sensors for the portable marine water quality system.

a dissolved oxygen probe, a pressure-compensating pH, Eh and reference electrode sensor (all manufactured by Honeywell) and a submerged photo cell, manufactured by Ocean Research Equipment Company of Falmouth, Massachusetts. Each sensor had separate leads running directly to the recording module and were bound together with a zip-jacket to make a 1.2-inch diameter cable for raising and lowering the holder. Each sensor had individual leads so that, if one of them malfunctioned, it could be removed without disturbing the others. The cable arrangement can be seen in Fig. 6. All six sensors proved to operate satisfactorily, except that electrolysis set in on the outside of some of them because of a mixture of metals. The system was designed for depths of at least 15 m, and all sensors appeared to be effective to these depths. To take the strain off the electrode cables, the holder was actually suspended by a heavy nylon cord attached to the ring at the top of the holder. The holder was balanced and proved to be stable, even in currents over 3 knots (360 cm/sec). It should be added that a bottom screen was provided to protect the electrodes in the bottom ring from rocks. However, in soft substrata the screen was removed and the electrodes were permitted to penetrate the top two centimeters of sediments.

The current meter and current directional sensor had to be mounted in a

Fig. 7. Complete marine sensing system as operated from the Turbocraft boat. Note recorder on engine housing in center of cockpit.

separate holder which was designed by A. Williams (research assistant). Because the current meter must always face into the area of maximum current, the holder had to be dynamically stable, be maintained vertically, and rotate easily and smoothly. The current sensing system is shown on Fig. 5. It was not always satisfactory as the ducted meter was an early model, needing much improvement.

The recording module consisted of an 8-channel Electronik 15, Honeywell Recorder with pH, Eh, and recording amplifiers mounted in the portable, tropic-pac, shock-proof case (Fig. 7). Each variable was recorded in a different color and as consecutive points of a cycle of the eight variables. In the beginning a full cycle of recording took a little over 3 min. In the final version the recording of a full cycle took only 40 sec; thus, the data for three complete cycles of all physical—chemical variables taken at both surface and bottom could be obtained and recorded in less than 5 min. This provided a rapid areal sensing system, whereby 50—80 physical stations could be occupied in the Complex during an 8-hour day. Although not considered pertinent to this investigation, the system also proved to be a valuable monitor of the salt-water intake of the MBL salt-water system, where the sensing holders were suspended just above the intake when not in use in Hadley Harbor. Continuous records of eight physical—chemical variables were obtained here over 2—6 week periods. Both tidal and diurnal cycles could easily be discerned[1]. This system was later modified by technicians at Dow Chemical Company, Texas Division, Freeport, Texas, and used with variable success for a study of estuarine ecosystems of the Brazos and Colorado Rivers (Parker et al., 1969).

TREATMENT OF SEDIMENT SAMPLES

Most samples for sediment analyses were taken simultaneously with the quantitative biological samples. Using a modified $1/25$ m^2 Van Veen grab sampler (Fig. 8), two samples were taken at each station — one for biological

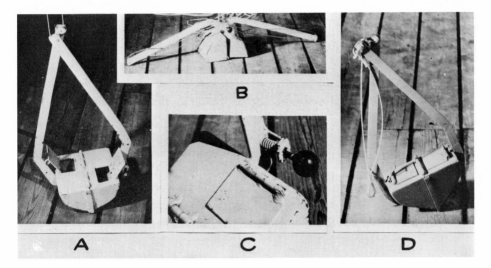

Fig. 8. Van Veen grab sampler. A. Closed. B. Open. C. Trigger mechanism. D. Model with latch trigger.

analysis and the other for sediments. Surface material from the undisturbed grab sample sufficient to fill a 6-ounce jar was removed. These samples were stored under refrigeration until analyzed from one to four months later. Sand fractions after wet sieving, which prevented the breaking up of aggregates and faecal pellets, were analyzed with the Zeigler Rapid Sediment Analyzer (Zeigler et al., 1960; Zeigler et al., 1964) at the Woods Hole Ocean-

---

[1] Additional data on this system, now on the market, may be obtained from C.W. Wilkins III of Honeywell, Inc., Philadelphia Division, Fort Washington, Pennsylvania.

ographic Institution. Finer materials were analyzed by the hydrometer method (Krumbein and Pettijohn, 1938). Median diameters and sorting coefficients were calculated and the percents of sand, silt, and clay were plotted on a triangular diagram of sediment types as proposed by Shepard (1954). Several transects were made in critical areas, where close-spaced samples were taken specifically for sediment analysis. Sediment samples were taken also at weekly intervals at two stations, one on the outer sand flats and the other in the clayey silts of the Inner Harbor. Additional samples were taken biweekly at four other stations. These stations were occupied over a 6-month period to test the hypothesis that seasonal changes occur in sediment composition.

MISCELLANEOUS ENVIRONMENTAL PARAMETERS

Depths were measured with a Bendix DR—19 recording fathometer with a readable accuracy of about one-third of a meter. The micro-bathymetry of the Complex was drawn up by contouring some 350 fathometer depth values obtained as part of the collection of standard station data during this study.

Several measurements of benthic chlorophylls were made in the two most contrasting habitats, the sand flats and Inner Harbor, by Dr. D. Hope currently of the U.S. National Museum. Dissolved carbohydrate analyses also were made of surface and bottom waters in various portions of the Complex by Dr. G. Walsh, then a Research Associate in the Systematics—Ecology Program.

COLLECTION AND TREATMENT OF THE BIOLOGICAL DATA

Most of the biological samples were taken with a modified Van Veen grab (Fig. 8). The first 66 samples were taken with a 1/50 m² grab, the remainder with a 1/25 m² grab with a bite 10 cm deep. Several stations were sampled with a modified Ockelmann Detritus Dredge (Ockelmann, 1965), which provided purely qualitative data. Stations 95 through 121 (Fig. 3) were taken only with a small gravity corer designed by Dr. M. Buzas, U.S. National Museum, who investigated the foraminiferal populations of the Complex. Earlier in the study some organisms, primarily algae, were collected by means of scuba diving by Dr. I. MacKenzie Lamb and associates of the Herbarium for Cryptographic Botany at Harvard University.

All sediment taken in the grab, which was completely filled on nearly every trial, was washed through a set of five 14-inch U.S. Standard stainless steel screens, with precision openings of 4 mm, 2 mm, 1 mm, 0.50 mm and

0.25 mm. All living organisms in the 4-mm and 2-mm screens were removed by hand, while the smaller fractions were treated with a light sugar solution which caused approximately 99% of the animals to float to the surface where they could be removed with fine bolting silk. Faunal counts were made on samples treated with sugar solution and also on untreated samples. It is significant that higher numbers always resulted from the treated samples. Furthermore, equal numbers of organisms were obtained by this method from paired samples (Driscoll, 1964). Each sieve fraction was dealt with separately. Animals were fixed in formalin for 24 h and then transferred to alcohol on sorting. Sorting of the whole sieved fraction for larger-sized material, and fractions of the elutriated material for the smaller animals, was carried out under a dissecting scope. Frequently the 0.25-mm fraction contained so many organisms that it had to be divided into eight equal fractions. If three of the fractions produced equal or near-equal counts for each taxon, the average counts per taxon were then multiplied by 5/8ths to provide the totals; if counts were not equal for three fractions, then the whole sample was sorted and counted.

Within two days of collection the samples were sorted at the higher taxa level and, when possible, to the species level in certain groups. Each taxon was stored and labeled separately by size fraction on special data sheets. Totals for the sample and totals per square meter were then calculated.

Time did not permit the weighing of each organism, nor did we obtain biomass of total samples; therefore, we do not have a quantitative measure of the amount of living organic matter per unit area. A relative measure of the rate of change of species growth and change in populations was calculated from counts of individual species for each of five fractions at five stations sampled weekly for nearly six months. Since samples were taken in each of the discernible major habitats each week throughout the investigation (though not at the same spot), it may be possible to calculate a rough measure of productivity on the basis of relative sizes of animals for these habitats. Biomass can be calculated if representations of each size class of each species could be weighed.

Some idea of life cycles of many of the invertebrate species was obtained, even though larval forms were not specifically studied. Since data were available for these species for five size classes, the smallest, being about 250 μ, just settled or juvenile populations could be ascertained by sudden appearances of large numbers of any one species in the smallest size fraction.

In most cases identified organisms were stored as part of a study collection in the George M. Gray Museum and can be obtained upon request from the Resident Systematist of the Systematics—Ecology Program. Certain groups of animals, particularly the ostracodes, isopods, nematodes, kinorhynchs, mites, and turbellarians, have been retained by the specialists in the respective groups for later study. A named set of individuals of representative developmental stages of many species collected was sent to the George M. Gray Museum for reference. Those groups which proved impossible to identify before the conclusion of this study are: copepods, most of the oligochaetes (majority destroyed in shipping), nematodes, nemerteans, ectoprocts, and about one-third of the specimens of polychaetes. Major difficulties in identifying these groups could be attributed to the large numbers of individuals that require mounting or sectioning and intensive microscopic work for positive identification.

REGISTRATION OF THE DATA BY COMPUTER TECHNIQUES

From the inception of the project in 1963 it was realized that a large body of environmental and biological data would be collected and would need systematic storage for rapid retrieval and data reduction. For this reason, an IBM card-filing system was devised, similar to the one originated by the author for a broader investigation in the Gulf of California (Parker, 1964a). Field station data sheets were devised so that data were columned to correspond to columns on IBM cards and that these data could be punched soon after returning from the field. Most of the environmental data were entered on to "Station Data Cards", prefaced by the station number. Data included on this card consisted of values relating to time, location, environmental data (surface and bottom), sediment type (coded according to the classification of Shepard, 1954), sampling devices (numerically coded), and the only biological data consisting of total animal counts per station. Besides regular biological stations with new numbers each week (as each biological station had an unique location), there were 29 permanently placed stations for weekly measurements of environmental data alone. Whenever a biological station was taken close to a permanent physical or environmental station, the physical station number was also entered onto the card adjacent to the biology number. The computer listing of these data went through considerable trial and error as to the order and headings. A sample of the final version used is reproduced on Fig. 9, the format now on file at the National Oceanographic Data Center, Washington, D.C.

A second card was devised to record biological data related to individual species occurrence. The "Species Data Card" contains available information pertinent to an individual species at a particular station. A sample listing of this information as it pertains to the pelecypod *Solemya velum* is shown on Fig. 10. A numerical code system was devised to key the species names on the IBM cards. An 11-digit code number for the species is given first, followed by the station number at which the species was found. Biological data

```
                     SALINITY TEMP IN  OXYGEN   PH     EH      CURRENT        %                          WEIGHT
 S                   /   %  //   CENT.  / ML/L   /     //  MV / D                  L  TOT      MED SORT/     %      /
 T    L P     D    T  S  B   A  S   B   S  B   S  B  S  B  E          G  S  I   A   D   C    S  S   C   C
 A    O S     A    I  U  O   I  U   O   U  O   U  O  U  O  P V      D  E  E  G   N   I   O    A  I   L   O
 T    C       T    M  R  T   R  R   T   R  T   R  T  R  T  T E      I  A  D  H   I   A   E    V  L   A   D
 NO.  .NO    E .  E. F . M .   . F . M .   . F . M .   F . M . F . M . H L . R . R .C . T . M .   . M . F . D. T. Y. E.
       04112464103532343220009008200830          810          11           0003 0056
       05112464105032423242090078406 77          805    329    04                0078
 188014 112464105732323323009007990800           8007803493 0406        10030100880148        230 126   98  1   1  1
       06112464110532343220100079608 04          810    359    04                0094
       07112464111232303230095078807 80          805    339    04                0040
       08112464111632355322209507600730          805    339    14                0063
       171124641120323232340980763 0742          8007053492 1918        0003 0025
 189127191124641132323432440950635 0620          8007553540 4903        10010300411408         20 261   25 68   7  3
       181124641143325232140980715 0696          800    329    09                0057
 190198241124641150321632161000682 0690          81081033933902         10030100950509        400 136   95  2   3  1
       091124641342324032240800703 0565          790695239.3111          0003 0026
       10112464135032288323200807400530          800    269    13                0024
       111124641355324432380800753 0752          800    309    05                0028
       12112464140032303240080078005 48          760    329    14                0027
       131124641402323532280790750 0567          820    329    15                0025
 191101291124641410323032120810740 0748          79070033317903        00010200951180         56 331   48 47   5  2
       151124641419323232250800784 0782          780    329    04                0085
       161124641424323532380800776 0776          79069027419910          0003 0038
       211124641437323432350820740 0742          790    269    16                0027
       221124641442324432320850737 0742          820    309    05                0060
       261124641447324432380800882 0882          820    331    06                0082
       271124641452322732200800750 0745          815    319    15                0032
       02120264095532443310-0505320530           850    349    08                0085
       011202641002327032640404600460            800    344    04          0003 0081
 192031041202641020320723295000044 00352         78078734925010        10010300183475         57 182   45 50   5  3
       091202641035330232920010215 0216          780    349    08                0025
 193083101202641047329032920090258 0254          800610349-1104         00010400440097         18 203    8 76  16  4
       111202641055329832900100272 0276          820    289    10                0012
       161202641057328032420010029 00284         810    314    03                0072
       121202641100327532820090334 0300          820    289    14                0009
       151202641105328532740100455 0468          840    329    03                0095
       171202641153242327601102700225           860    319    16                0004
 194141  120264113032893288011024 20258          83077031915904        00010100321443        142 246   76 17   7  1
       131202641145327532800210388 0388          870    344    11                0012
       2412026415553258    0100247                                02                0095
 195156211202641600328032670050328 0355          84083321918911        00010100010411        520 135   98  1   1  1
       07120864   323232280000040 40408          870          06                0077
       021208640950323232232-1004920490           815          14                0066
       011208640955323232320000492 0492           810          06                0058
       041208641055329322324-0104680388           825          10                0066
 196045051208641003324032140000374 0378          830          06          00010300953050        020 303  027 63 10 03
 197058061208641030323832440010407 0400          835835        03          00010200960683        060 231  047 47 06 02
       081208641035324532420030370 0364          825          08                0074
 198118161208641045324432420030440 0442          825          13          00010300562912        023 298  029 59 12 03
       171208641050323632340050436 0422          830          20                0037
       181208641054325432370050310 0306          830          11                0087
       191208641059325032440070390 0298          825          03                0098
       211208641104324032380100382 0370          830          14                0035
 199188221208641104324032300130384 0380          830          10          00010100740841        235 263  082 16 02 01
       2412086411153242232250100375 0382          835          03                0098
 200193251208641122323632340150548 0542          830830        06          00010100840193        440 129   98  1   1  1
       261208641135323032420200044 00438         830          06                0095
       271208641137324032220150438 0435          830          14                0046
```

Fig. 9. Computer listing of station data for biological stations and physical stations as now stored in the files of the National Oceanographic Data Center, Washington, D.C.

entered on this card include: (1) total number of individuals for that station; (2) number of individuals for each size fraction; (3) number of males, females, and juveniles; (4) number of gravid females; and (5) if they carried eggs, the number of eggs per female.

The third card was used to store information on higher taxa, as we had better counts and identifications at higher taxa levels than at the species level. For the most part these cards are identical to the "Species Data Cards", except that they are keyed at a higher taxonomic level. In addition, "Species Name Cards" were made for each of the 350 species identified. These cards give the code number and the correct scientific name, describer and date for both species and higher taxonomic categories. A sample listing

```
1304101 101 SOLEMYA (PETRASMA) VELUM SAY,1822

SPECIES NO   STATION   SUM  4MM  2MM  1MM  HMM  QMM  OVI  EGG  MAL  FEM  JUV
1304101 101     87      1    1    0    0    0    0    0    0    0    0    0
BIO NO LOC  PS  DATE   TIME    SALINITY    TEMPERATURE   OXYGEN      PH      REDOX    DEPTH  GEAR  LIGHT  BUGS
                                           AIR SUR BOT   SUR BOT   SUR BOT   SUR ROT
 87   129   0  6 23 64 1425  31.8332.02  23.020.5019.70  11.510.40  7.958.00  244 209    8   1003   0.22   1093
SEDIMENT   MU BAR  ESO SAND SILT CLAY TYPE
 0.070MM   4.79  0.51  .41  .08  2

SPECIES NO   STATION   SUM  4MM  2MM  1MM  HMM  QMM  OVI  EGG  MAL  FFM  JUV
1304101 101     8H      2    0    0    0    0    0    0    0    0    0    0
BIO NO LOC  PS  DATE   TIME    SALINITY    TEMPERATURE   OXYGEN      PH      REDOX    DEPTH  GEAR  LIGHT  BUGS
                                           AIR SUR BOT   SUR BOT   SUR BOT   SUR ROT
 88   143   0  6 23 64 1600  31.8531.95  25.019.8018.80   0.  0.   8.108.15  209 249   14   1003    0.    1061
SEDIMENT   MU BAR  ESO SAND SILT CLAY TYPE
 0.217MM   1.61  0.82  .13  .05  1

SPECIES NO   STATION   SUM  4MM  2MM  1MM  HMM  QMM  OVI  EGG  MAL  FFM  JUV
1304101 101     89     10    0    0    6    4    0    0    0    0    0    0
BIO NO LOC  PS  DATE   TIME    SALINITY    TEMPERATURE   OXYGEN      PH      REDOX    DEPTH  GEAR  LIGHT  BUGS
                                           AIR SUR BOT   SUR BOT   SUR BOT   SUR ROT
 89    74   0  6 31 64 1050  31.9031.94  22.519.7019.85   0.  0.   8.058.10    0    0    5   1003   0.30     0
SEDIMENT   MU BAR  ESO SAND SILT CLAY TYPE
 0.019MM   5.56  0.32  .53  .14  3

SPECIES NO   STATION   SUM  4MM  2MM  1MM  HMM  QMM  OVI  EGG  MAL  FEM  JUV
1304101 101     92      4    0    0    0    2    0    0    0    0    0    0
BIO NO LOC  PS  DATE   TIME    SALINITY    TEMPERATURE   OXYGEN      PH      REDOX    DEPTH  GEAR  LIGHT  BUGS
                                           AIR SUR BOT   SUR BOT   SUR BOT   SUR ROT
 92   111   0  6 30 64 1357  32.0132.10  25.019.7019.85   0.  0.   7.857.99  265 229    4   1003    0.      0
SEDIMENT   MU BAR  ESO SAND SILT CLAY TYPE
 0.203MM   4.29  0.61  .34  .05  2

SPECIES NO   STATION   SUM  4MM  2MM  1MM  HMM  QMM  OVI  EGG  MAL  FEM  JUV
1304101 101     94      3    0    0    1    0    0    0    0    0    0    0
BIO NO LOC  PS  DATE   TIME    SALINITY    TEMPERATURE   OXYGEN      PH      REDOX    DEPTH  GEAR  LIGHT  BUGS
                                           AIR SUR BOT   SUR BOT   SUR BOT   SUR BOT
 94   200   0  7  8 64 1250  31.7331.77  23.021.4221.43   0.  0.   7.958.00    0    0    3   1001    0.      0
NO SEDIMENT DATA

SPECIES NO   STATION   SUM  4MM  2MM  1MM  HMM  QMM  OVI  EGG  MAL  FFM  JUV
1304101 101    125      6    0    0    0    0    0    0    0    0    0    0
NO PHYSICAL DATA
NO SEDIMENT DATA

SPECIES NO   STATION   SUM  4MM  2MM  1MM  HMM  QMM  OVI  EGG  MAL  FEM  JUV
1304101 101    128      8    0    0    1    0    0    0    0    0    0    0
BIO NO LOC  PS  DATE   TIME    SALINITY    TEMPERATURE   OXYGEN      PH      REDOX    DEPTH  GEAR  LIGHT  BUGS
                                           AIR SUR BOT   SUR BOT   SUR BOT   SUR BOT
128   188   0  8  4 64 1503  32.0432.06  23.020.4020.33   0.  0.    0.  0.    0    0   11   1001   0.26   3006
NO SEDIMENT DATA
```

Fig. 10. Computer listing of data for the mollusk *Solemya velum*, as it occurred from Stations 87 through 128. (Print-out is of data taken in early stages of study when sums were not subdivided by size fractions).

```
13035000000    CEPHALASPIDEA
13035160101 ACTEON PUNCTOSTRIATUS (C.B.ADAMS,1840)
13035170101 HAMINOEA SOLITARIA (SAY,1822)
13035180101 CYLICHNA ALBA (BROWN,1827)
13035180102 CYLICHNA ORYZA (TOTTEN,J.G. 1835)
13035190101 RETUSA CANALICULATA (SAY,1827)
13035200101 DIAPHANA DEBILIS (GOULD,1840)
13037000000     NUDIBRANCHIA
13037010000   ELYSIIDAE
13037010101 ELYSIA CATULA (GOULD,1870)
13037020000   AEOLIDIDAE
13037020101 EMBLETONIA FUSCATA GOULD,1870
13036000000     PULMONATA
13040000000       PELECYPODA
13041000000     PALAEOCONCHA
13041010000   SOLEMYIDAE
13041010101 SOLEMYA (PETRASMA) VELUM SAY, 1822
13042000000       PROTOBRANCHIA
13042010000   NUCULIDAE
13042010101 NUCULA PROXIMA SAY, 1822
13042020000   NUCULANIDAE
13042010201 YOLDIA (YOLDIA S. STR.) LIMATULA (SAY,1831)
13043000000     FILIBRANCHIA
13043010000   MYTILIDAE
13043010101 MYTILUS EDULIS LINNE,1758
13043020000   PECTINIDAE
13043020101 AEQUIPECTEN (PLAGIOCTENIUM) IRRADIANS IRRADIANS (LAMARCK,181
13043030000   ARCIDAE
13043030101 ANADARA (LARKINIA) TRANSVERSA (SAY,1822)
13044000000       EULAMELLIBRANCHIA
13043040000   CRASSATELLIDAE
13043040101 CRASSINELLA MACTRACEA (LINSLEY,1845)
13043050000   OSTREIDAE
13043050101 CRASSOSTREA VIRGINICA (GMELIN,1791)
13044150000   LUCINIDAE
13044150101 PHACOIDES (LUCINOMA) FILOSUS (STIMPSON,1851)
13044010000   CARDIIDAE
13044010101 LAEVICARDIUM MORTONI (CONRAD,1831)
13044010201 CERASTODERMA PINNULATUM (CONRAD,1831)
13044020000   VENERIDAE
13044020101 MERCENERIA MERCENARIA (LINNE,1758)
13044020201 GEMMA GEMMA (TOTTEN,1834)
13044020301 PITAR MORRHUANA (LINSLEY,1845)
13044030000   TELLINIDAE
13044030101 TELLINA (ANGULUS) AGILIS STIMPSON,1858
13044030201 MACOMA (MACOMA S.STR.) CALCEREA (GMELIN,1790)
13044030202 MACOMA (PSAMMACOMA) TENTA (SAY,1834)
13044030203 MACOMA BALTHICA (LINNE,1758)
13044040000   SEMELIDAE
13044040101 CUMINGIA TELLINOIDES CONRAD,1838
13044040201 ABRA AEQUALIS (SAY,1822)
13044050000   SANGUINOLARIIDAE
13044050101 TAGELUS (MESOPLEURA) DIVISUS (SPENGLER,1794)
13044060000   MACTRIDAE
```

Fig. 11. Computer listing of code numbers and equivalent taxa arranged phylogenetically from Cephalaspida (Gastropoda) to Mactridae (Pelecypoda).

is shown on Fig. 11. The value of these cards is that scientific names, rather than 11-digit numbers, can be listed as part of the results derived from computer analysis of species and environmental data.

The final data storage card is the "Sediment Data Card". Each card, again prefaced by the station number, gives detailed sediment information including median diameter, sorting coefficient, percent sand, silt and clay, and, finally, the code number for the Shepard sediment types. A print-out of data from this type of card also is shown on Fig. 10.

Most of the information obtained during this study has now been entered on IBM cards and transferred to magnetic tape[1].

---

[1] All of the storage procedures, some of the statistical testing, and programs for handling input of the data for analysis were conducted at the Woods Hole Oceanographic Institution Information Processing Center. The computer used for preliminary factor analysis and preparation was the General Electric 225. The concentrated cluster and factor analysis was initiated at The Computation Center of the Massachusetts Institute of Technology on an IBM 7094 computer. Computer time was arranged through the gracious assistance of Prof. I. Sizer, Chairman of the Department of Biology, Massachusetts Institute of Technology. Final analyses were performed on the IBM 360—50 computer at the Southwest Center for Advanced Studies, Dallas, Texas. We are exceedingly grateful to Dr. D. Spencer, Woods Hole Oceanographic Institution; the staff of the Information Processing Center, Woods Hole Oceanographic Institution; the staff of the Computation Facility of the Massachusetts Institute of Technology; and to the staff of the Texas Christian University Computer Center, particularly Dr. W. Sconyers, for their assistance and time spent on these computer programs.

CHAPTER 3

RESULTS OF THE PHYSICAL—CHEMICAL INVESTIGATIONS

The major physical and chemical factors which characterize the area are each discussed in detail as a basis for correlation of these factors with the distribution of individual species populations and communities, and to separate biological interactions from the influences of the physical—chemical factors and sediments; although it is obvious from the data that all are interdependent.

CIRCULATION, CURRENT VELOCITY, AND WAVES

The fact that the Hadley Harbor Complex is dominated by tidal exchange between two large bodies of water of differing tidal characteristics suggests that water movements are of primary importance in influencing such environmental factors as sediments, light penetration, redox-potential, and water transport, as reflected in the density difference between Buzzards Bay and Vineyard Sound. The circulation also appears to influence the distribution of eel grass, and thus that of epifaunal animals, and ultimately that of infaunal animals.

Wave and current data[1] presented represent a generalized picture of circulation and wave influence deduced from several concentrated studies of these factors alone through the tidal cycle and over the entire Complex.

Two different circulation patterns were produced, according to whether the water was flowing through the Complex from the north (from Buzzards Bay and the Woods Hole), or from the south (from Vineyard Sound). The circulation pattern with the greatest influence on sedimentation was that produced by the current flowing south into Vineyard Sound since, at this stage of the tide, the water level in Buzzards Bay was almost a meter higher than in Vineyard Sound. The approximate circulation pattern for the southward flowing currents is shown on Fig. 12. The significant features were: (1) a major eddy in the eastern portion of the Inner Harbor; (2) two large weak eddies in Grassy Pond, which is an offshoot of West Gutter; (3) a small eddy in East Gutter just south of the bridge; (4) a small eddy in the wide portion

---

[1] These data were collected by J.S. Nagle and K. Lukas.

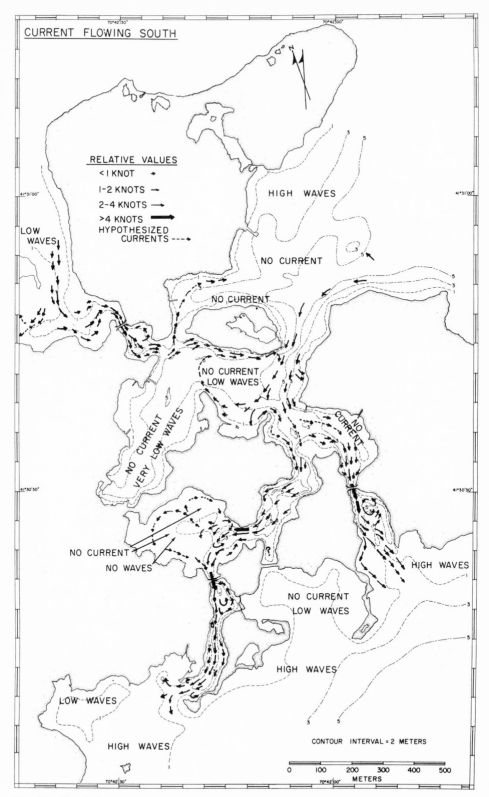

Fig. 12. Circulation pattern in Hadley Harbor, Massachusetts, with tidal currents flowing south.

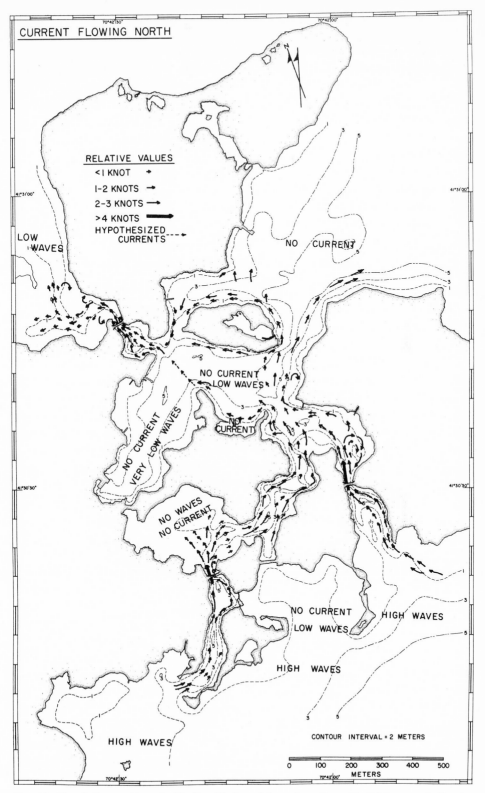

Fig. 13. Circulation pattern in Hadley Harbor, Massachusetts, with tidal currents flowing north.

of the eastern portion of Northwest Gutter; and (5) two small eddies between the two constrictions in the central part of West Gutter. It is significant that sediments were generally finer and more poorly sorted in the centers of these eddies. The areas indicated on Fig. 12 and 13 as having no currents were regions where no detectable currents could either be measured or observed. As could be expected, these regions were characterized by clayey silts or silty clays, and the sediments were well sorted but in the very fine size range. The areas marked by high wave action were naturally only at the exposed outer portions of the Complex and were always marked by well-sorted, sand-sized material.

The circulation pattern for the northward flowing current, i.e., when the tide was low and water was flowing from Vineyard Sound into Buzzards Bay, is shown on Fig. 13. Water levels of the two bodies of water are more equal when the water is flowing in the opposite direction. In general this circulation pattern was much less dynamic, and current strengths were considerably less than those observed when the current was flowing in the opposite direction. The significant features of this circulation pattern were: (1) water flowed around Bull Island in a counterclockwise motion regardless of current direction through the Complex; (2) with the exception of the fairly strong eddy just north of the bridge in the East Gutter, all flow was straightforward from south to north with no associated small eddies; and (3) the strong flow of water tended to move on the east side of the gutters, demonstrating on a minor scale the effect of Coriolis Force. Note that when water flowed from north to south (Fig. 12), the flow generally was strongest on the west sides of the gutters. The center portions of the gutters, regardless of flow direction, usually had the quieter waters. Areas of no current and high waves tended to be the same as those during the time of opposite water flow. When these charts are compared with those of the distribution of sediment, eel grass, depth, and light, it can be seen that the controlling influence for these factors seems to be the tidal currents themselves, modified by and also modifying the bottom topography.

MICRO-TOPOGRAPHY OF THE BOTTOM

It is difficult to say whether currents carved out the bottom features in the Hadley Harbor Complex, or whether the bottom features already existed as a result of the deposition of terminal moraine during the last glaciation and tend to control the current pattern (Woodworth and Wigglesworth, 1934). Although the U.S. Coast and Geodetic Survey have drawn several bottom charts for the Inner and Outer Harbor, no contoured bottom charts of the gutter portions of Hadley Harbor have ever been constructed. Earliest charts of the Complex were made in 1845 as part of the U.S. Coast and Geodetic Survey Buzzards Bay Chart No. 160. A later, more detailed chart was drawn in 1887 as "Register 1833", and is reproduced as Fig. 14. The most detailed chart of the Complex, no longer used for navigation but still obtainable, is Coast and Geodetic Survey Chart No. 348 for Woods Hole. Unfortunately, this chart leaves off the southwestern portion of the Complex. The first edition was printed in 1857; the last in 1961. The latest navigational chart of the area is the first one to show the whole Complex, but is of too small a scale to be very useful. This is Coast and Geodetic

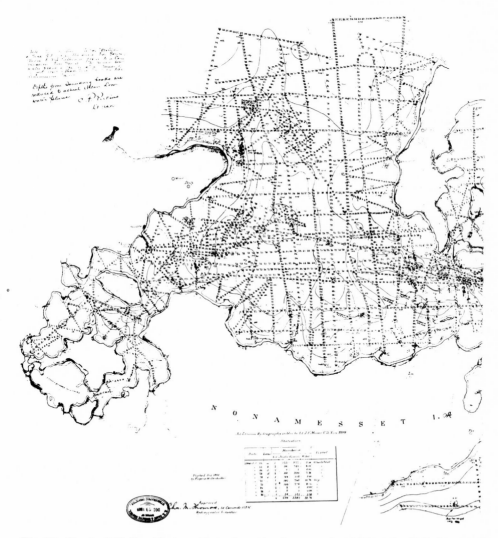

Fig. 14. Chart of Hadley Harbor, Massachusetts, drawn up in 1887 by the U.S. Coast and Geodetic Survey (Chart No. 160).

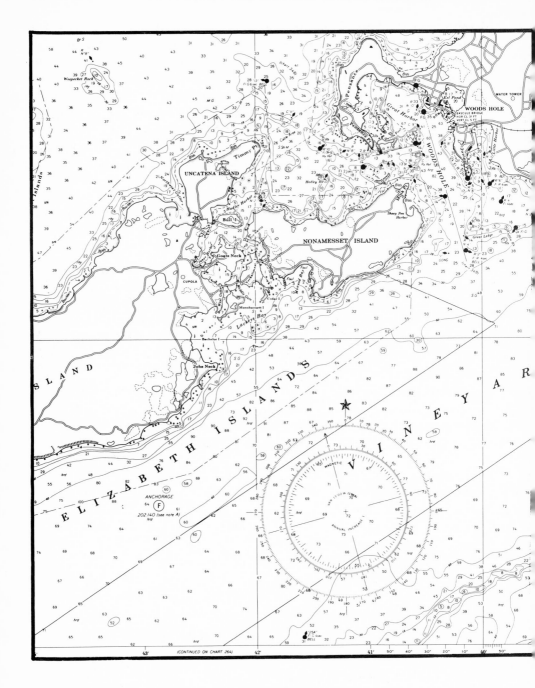

Fig. 15. Chart No. 260, U.S. Coast and Geodetic Survey, latest navigational chart of Hadley Harbor, Massachusetts, published in 1964.

Survey Chart No. 260, Falmouth to Buzzards Bay (Fig. 15). The officers and crew of the U.S. Coast and Geodetic Survey vessel "Whiting" in 1966 completed a detailed bathymetric study of the Vineyard Sound side of the Complex, but results had not been published at this writing.

More useful to this survey than existing charts were the U.S. Coast and Geodetic Survey large-scale aerial photographs. These air photos, roughly 3.5 × 5 ft. in size, were our principle means of navigation and location of stations. One of them (Fig. 16) was made just eleven years before the inception of this study. Note the lack of eel grass throughout much of the Complex. Although eel grass was beginning to return after its complete destruction by the wasting disease in the early thirties, it was still rather scarce, and much of the Complex was characterized by clean sand flats. The photo taken in 1962 (Fig. 17), only a year before we started sampling, shows a noticeable increase in the distribution of eel grass cover. Many formerly white sandy areas are now black with grass. Both photos were taken on the same day and month and under the same cloud conditions. The latter aerial photo was used for navigation and location of stratum, as it showed clearly every rock, point, and shore artifact. By taking three of four horizontal sextant angles on the various shore points which could also be seen on the photo, a point could be located with an accuracy of a meter by plotting the angles with a three-armed protractor on the traced map used for a field sheet. The aerial photograph of 1962 is the basis for the configuration of the land used in the illustrations in this book.

Because none of the published charts was satisfactory for demonstrating the bathymetry, a new one was constructed from our own fathometer soundings, evidence of the shape of bottom features from published charts, and from the aerial photographs. This chart is shown on Fig. 18.

The bathymetry of the Hadley Harbor Complex (Fig. 18) generally reflected the circulation patterns, the deep areas appearing wherever the current appeared to be deflected by the shoreline features. Depths greater than 6 m occurred only in the eastern portion of the Outer Harbor and Inner Harbor and in a deep hole in the northern portion of West Gutter. A suggestion of an earlier channel into Lackey's Bay was indicated where a rock dike was constructed across what was formerly the Middle Gutter. There also appears to be two small basins in the Inner Harbor which trended towards a former open connection from Inner Harbor into Grassy Pond, an offshoot of West Gutter.

SEDIMENTS OF HADLEY HARBOR

Bottom sediments are thought to be the major factor which determines

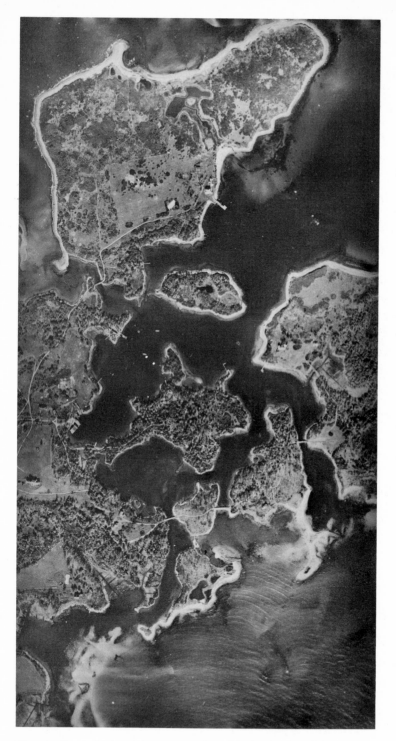

Fig. 16. Controlled aerial photograph of Hadley Harbor, Massachusetts, taken in September, 1952. Light areas are clean sand flats, lacking vegetation.

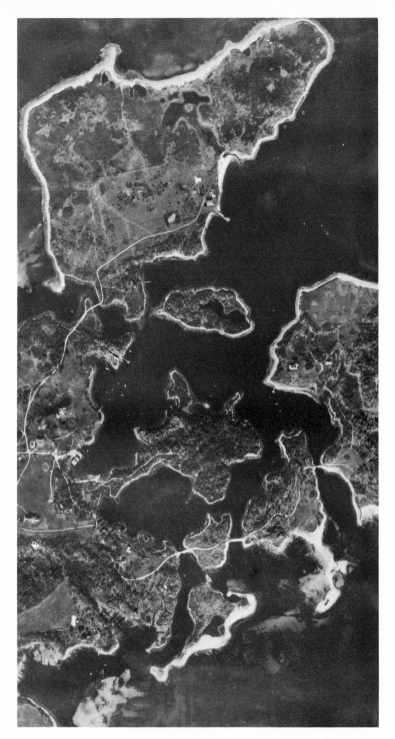

Fig. 17. Controlled aerial photograph of Hadley Harbor, Massachusetts, taken in September, 1962. Note that former light areas on Fig. 16 are now dark or black and covered by eel grass.

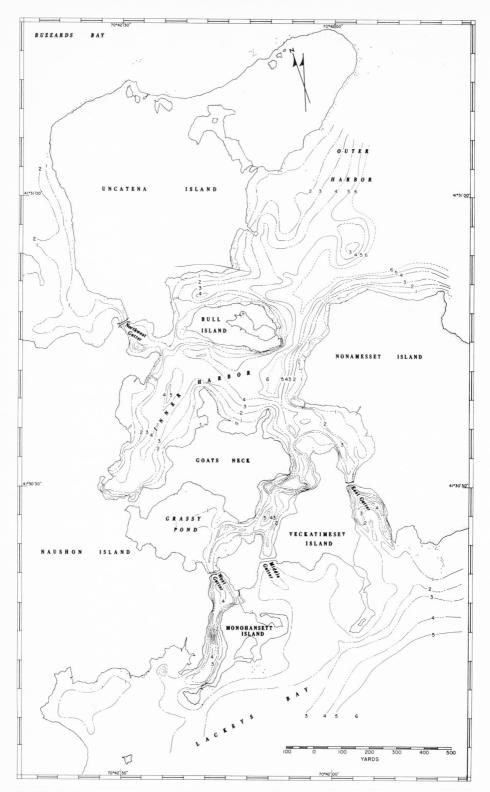

Fig. 18. Bottom contour chart of Hadley Harbor, Massachusetts, constructed from depths obtained during this study and adjusted to contours visible on aerial photograph (Fig. 17). Contour interval = 1 m.

the areal distribution of infaunal marine animals. In the majority of European studies, sediments are poorly defined on an approximate size basis as being sand, sandy mud, muddy sand, or mud bottom. Few mechanical analyses of the sediments are reported in their classifications, and what might be a sandy mud in one locality might be termed by another investigator in the same locality as a muddy sand or a mud. Examples of this sort of sediment description as a basis for community separation can be found in Petersen (1913, 1914, 1915), Allee (1923a,b), Segerstråille (1933, 1960), Pratt (1953), Thorson (1957), and Holme (1961). Biologists' use of objective terminology for describing sediments is discussed briefly in Parker (1964a). Some investigators have reported sediment analyses in terms of median diameter, particularly Sanders (1956, 1960), Wieser (1960), Reish (1961, 1963), Sanders et al. (1962), Wigley and McIntyre (1964), Lie (1968), and Wade (1972). Others have used median diameter or percent of sand, silt, and clay (Parker, 1956, 1959, 1960, 1964a; Brett, 1963; and Wade, 1972) and/or sorting coefficients (McNulty et al., 1962; Brett, 1963; Wigley and McIntyre, 1964). There seems to be little agreement among benthic ecologists as to what sedimentary parameter is most important in influencing animal distribution, nor is there agreement among the investigators as to what constitutes sedimentary parameters, so that few valid comparisons can be made among the various studies. The only investigator who has used most of the available measurable sedimentary parameters in examining infaunal distributional relations is Brett (1963). Brett and Parker are the only two investigators known to have used the sedimentary nomenclature suggested by Shepard (1954) to describe the amounts of sand, silt, and clay, as determined by mechanical analysis. Their's, therefore, are the only two studies in which meaningful comparisons can be made between faunal distribution and statistical sediment parameters.

The author's previous studies on benthic aggregations were concerned with only one sedimentary parameter (percents of sand, silt, clay) as an ecologic factor; however, several other methods of describing the sediments were used in the present study. The percentage of sand, silt, and clay were plotted on the Shepard (1954) triangular diagram and then superimposed on the chart of Hadley Harbor. This was done first for all stations shown on Fig. 19, and then repeated seasonally for determination of changes in sediment composition over the two-year period. The sediment map (Fig. 19) was based on the analyses of approximately 220 sediment samples, enough to give an accurate picture of the general distribution of sediment types, but an insufficient number of samples to demonstrate the true patchiness of sediments in such a variable region. The significant feature of the map is the predominance of sand and silty sand sediments in the eastern portion of the Complex, generally following the configuration of the gutters. Sand is the

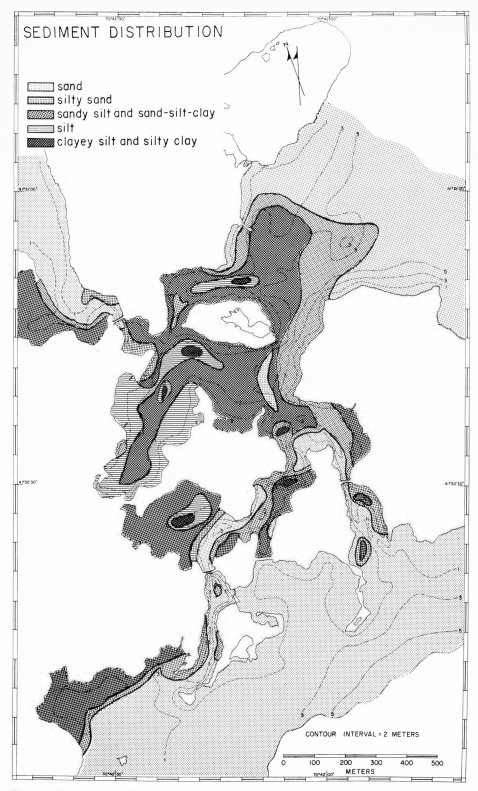

Fig. 19. Distribution of sediment types, determined by size analysis, and plotted as percentages of sand, silt, and clay on a three-dimensional triangular graph. Sediment names are derived from divisions of this triangular diagram plot as described by Shepard (1954).

dominant sediment in all of the entrances, while the finer sandy silts, silts, and clayey silts are typical of the Inner Harbor and the backwash areas or small coves, where currents and waves are low or non-existent. Sources of the sand appear to be Buzzards Bay and Vineyard Sound rather than the shores of the Complex, most of which are rocky. It is noteworthy that the majority of the deeper holes within the gutters are characterized by sediments with high percentage of silt. Silty-clay sediments (clay forming the predominant fraction as defined by Shepard, 1954) were found only in the center of the Inner Harbor and a small area just north of Bull Island. Clayey silts (predominant fraction being silt) are the finest sediments reported from the Woods Hole region by other investigators (Hough, 1940; Sanders, 1958; Moore, 1963), although Manheim et al. (1964) indicate a large area (based on three cores) designated as "clay" in a bottom-sediment chart of Great Harbor just across the Hole from Hadley Harbor. As there is virtually no source of fine sediments in the Cape Cod region (no large silt or clay-laden rivers), it is probable that the same sediments are being reworked by the local waves and currents. Only in the quietest areas, where organic matter settles and decomposes, did clay-size material accumulate.

The second parameter which was explored related to the median diameter of sediments as defined by Krumbein and Pettijohn (1938). These were plotted areally, both as data for all samples and on a seasonal basis, in order to note changes occurring between winter and summer. The areal plot is shown on Fig. 20. Comparison of this chart with Fig. 19 shows a certain correspondence of median diameter with percentages of sand, silt, and clay. Five size classes modified from the Wentworth classification were used to characterize the median diameters: 4—$16\,\mu$ (fine silt and clay), 17—$62\,\mu$ (coarse silt), 63—$250\,\mu$ (very fine sand), 251—$500\,\mu$ (fine sand), and over $501\,\mu$ (medium to coarse sand). The major difference between the sand—silt—clay map and that of median diameters is in the areas classified as sand (more than 80%), which split into three different size classes of sand on the basis of median diameter.

Although sorting coefficients (Inman, 1949) have been cited in connection with ecological studies involving marine benthos, correlation of species with sorting coefficients per se has not been attempted. Brett (1963) and Wigley and McIntyre (1964), for example, included sorting coefficients for sediment samples collected in conjunction with biological stations, but little use was made of them in correlating species distribution or abundance. Sorting coefficients were calculated for the Hadley Harbor sediments and plotted areally (Fig. 21). There is some agreement between well-sorted sediments and size distribution of sediments, and a much better agreement with degree of sorting and current velocities (Fig. 12, 13). Well-sorted sediments were not restricted to channels or outer wave-effected sand flats, but were actual-

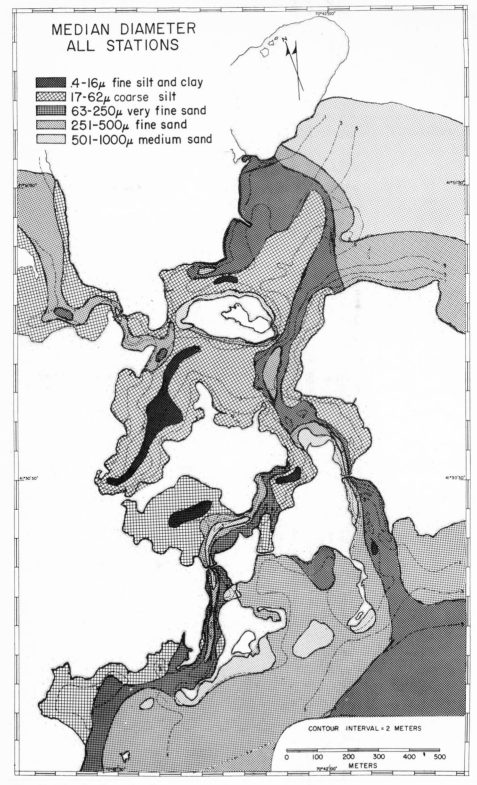

Fig. 20. Distribution of sediments according to median diameter, using a modified Wentworth classification.

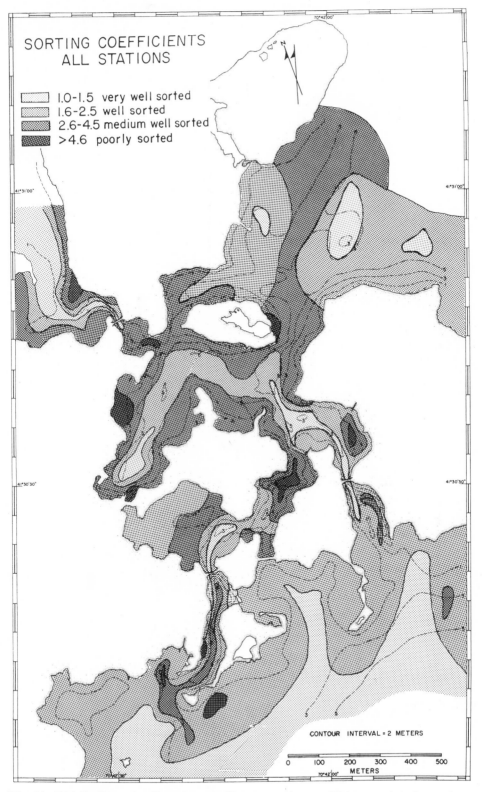

Fig. 21. Distribution of sediments according to sorting coefficients, using the methods and terminology devised by Inman (1949).

ly related to two processes, each very different from the other. As noted in Fig. 21, well-sorted sediments occurred in the southern portion of the Inner Harbor where very quiet waters permit the settling of the finest material, and again in channel centers where strong currents tend to sort sediment material, and finally at the shallow outer entrances to the gutters where sediments are sorted by the waves. The most poorly sorted sediments were found in the backwashes of the current areas where gravel and pebble-sized particles predominated. It is significant that the sorting coefficients changed seasonally, as the currents and wave patterns are also seasonal in direction.

A final sediment parameter used in this study was obtained by a factor analysis of combined sediment and other environmental data. As expected in an area of highly dynamic physical processes, sediment distribution resulted from a combination of many variables. Factor analysis was originally performed on a test program of 72 stations, for all of which there were valid data on the measured physical—chemical factors of the water and sediments. One of the sediment factors provided a high degree of correlation between median diameter, percents of sand and silt, and lesser correlation between these variables and sorting coefficients and salinity. As the GE 225 computer at the Woods Hole Oceanographic Institution was limited to a $35 \times 35 \times$ unlimited third component matrix (in this case, stations), the analysis was run in the R-mode, where we had less than 35 variables. Linear relationships between variables were examined.

Factor scores for the "sediment factor" were plotted areally and isoplethed at levels -2 to -1, -0.9 to 0, $+0.01$ to $+0.9$ and $+1$ to $+2$, which seem to be the significant breaks in the data (Fig. 22). These plots do not represent any single sediment variable, but a combination of all the variables examined, and suggest the physical processes which control them. In this respect, the areal plot is probably more meaningful than the plot of only one of the variables. As a small number of stations were used in the calculation of this analysis, the zones of sediment types encompass larger areas than those depicted on the previous charts of the individual variables. There is, however, a general correspondence between the factor score plots and the distribution of sand, silt, and clay (Fig. 19). The partially enclosed areas (Inner Harbor, Grassy Pond) and backwash areas show close similarity in sediments. Likewise, the gutter regions are distinct from the rest of the Complex, and the highest-energy portions, such as the wave-effected outer reaches and the scoured portions of the gutter, are characterized by the highest factor scores.

A second factor analysis was computed on 100 variables and 137 stations, of which 85 variables were species and their size fractions and 15 were physical—chemical variables. The rotated matrix produced 31 "factors", only one of which could be considered a sediment factor; whereas in the

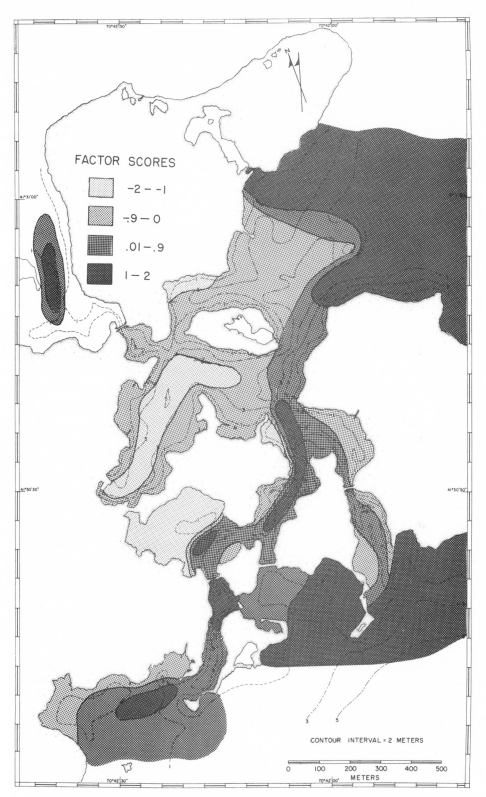

Fig. 22. Plot of factor scores for the "sediment factor" as derived from the matrix of 35 × 35 variables × 72 stations.

original factor analysis of 35 variables and 72 stations the sediment factor consisted of only the four sediment variables as high loadings (highly correlatable), the larger matrix resulted in a factor with three species of invertebrates, bottom Eh, salinity, and light as relatively high loadings, decreasing the influence of the very high loadings for percentage silt, percentage sand, and median diameter. Using the same intervals that were plotted for the previous analysis (Fig. 22), the "factor scores" were plotted for this modified sediment factor, resulting in the map of sediments shown in Fig. 23A. With the exception of 29 low positive and low negative scores, all were either very highly positive or highly negative. Positive loadings were for percent of silt; thus, positive scores indicated silt-sized sediments. Negative loadings indicated sand or large median diameters; thus, scores for sandy sediments were highly negative.

It is evident from the plot of these scores (Fig. 23A) that fine sediments accumulated in the Inner Harbor region and in cul de sacs where they can be trapped, whereas the coarse or sandy sediments were characteristic of the channels, the outer portions of the Complex, and some of the shorelines. Intermediate scores, representing intermediate sediment types, were so rare that the physical factors influencing them cannot be hypothesized. As was demonstrated in the previous plot (Fig. 22), the distribution of two main sediment types which is related to physical forces can be ascertained: (1) channel and outer Complex sands influenced by current and waves; and (2) Inner Harbor silts, influenced by quiet waters and gravity.

In an attempt to quantify and impose a greater degree of objectivity to the factor analysis score plotting, all data for the scores and locations of the stations used were put on IBM cards and fed into a special CALCOMP plotting program. Through the generosity of the Dallas office of the California Computer Corporation, a 10,000 card plotting program was adapted to the special problems presented by contouring in the dissected topography of Hadley Harbor. Using the same intervals that were isoplethed in Fig. 23A, data were fed into a program which would separate contours mathematically by calculated distances, always guided by shorelines. It is hoped that such a process would eliminate bias brought about by prior knowledge of shorelines and sediment distributary processes. Unconscious knowledge of these dependent factors may cause the person contouring such data to adjust lines to fit data, rather than to contour data alone. As the results on Fig. 23B indicate, there probably needs to be more data defining shorelines and more factor scores or station points to connect areas of equal intensity. The process does show promise for contouring pollution variables in the open sea, when data are being continuously monitored and plotted by computer for a nationwide pollution monitoring program.

Two papers include a discussion of a similar factor analysis on these major sediment variables relating to size and sorting. Klovan (1966) using sediment analyses on 69 samples taken in Barataria Bay and working only in the Q-mode found that three significant factors emerged from the analysis of 10 grain-size variables. These roughly corresponded to: (1) a surf energy dominated factor; (2) a current energy dominant factor; and (3) a gravitational energy factor. Plots of samples representing the three factors corresponded closely to areas where these forces predominate in Barataria Bay, even though none of these physical environmental variables were measured and no a priori relationships were hypothesized. Although our factor analysis was performed in the R-mode, factor scores for the sediment factor give almost exactly the same results as the study by Klovan. The -2 to -1, and to some extent the -0.9 to 0, scores plot areally as an individual factor representing gravitational energy. The $+0.01$ to $+0.9$ scores plot in areas dominated by current energy, and the $+1$ to $+2$ scores, for the most part, plot in areas of high wave energy, or wave plus current energy. There is, therefore, considerable agreement between the first Hadley Harbor sediment factor analysis and that performed on Barataria Bay sediments, and also some agreement with the larger Hadley Harbor factor matrix, although the Louisiana and Massachusetts ecosystems are quite dissimilar.

The second paper dealing with this technique, although not as successful in terms of factor analysis treatment, is by Lynts (1966). Using 19 stations repeated 4 times (76 in all) in Buttonwood Sound, a small offshoot of Florida Bay, Lynts measured depth, temperature, salinity, pH, and Eh at the sediment—water interface, roughly the same factors that were measured in the present Hadley Harbor study. Although the variables were said by Lynts to have been measured by in situ techniques, most of them were not: water depth was checked by sounding with a core tube, water temperature was taken with a glass thermometer (accuracy to $0.1°C$), salinity was measured by titrating on the spot, and pH and Eh were taken on samples *removed* from the bottom and run immediately on deck, even though changes may have taken place in the time interval between sample collection and analysis. The only sediment parameters tested by factor analysis were sand, silt, and clay percentages using Shepard's (1954) nomenclature. Although only 19 stations were occupied (1 per approximately 1 km^2), 76 samples were used in the analysis, virtually the same number used in the Hadley Harbor small factor matrix. Lynts found no significant linear relationship between sediments and his "ecologic" variables, the only relationship being between sand and silt or clay, which already existed in the ratio relationship. Buttonwood Sound is low in kinetic energy (there is little wave and current action — it is virtually one big settling basin), which probably accounts for the fact that Lynts' results did not give clusters similar to those of Klovan (1966). It is of great significance to this study, however, that the chart of abundance of

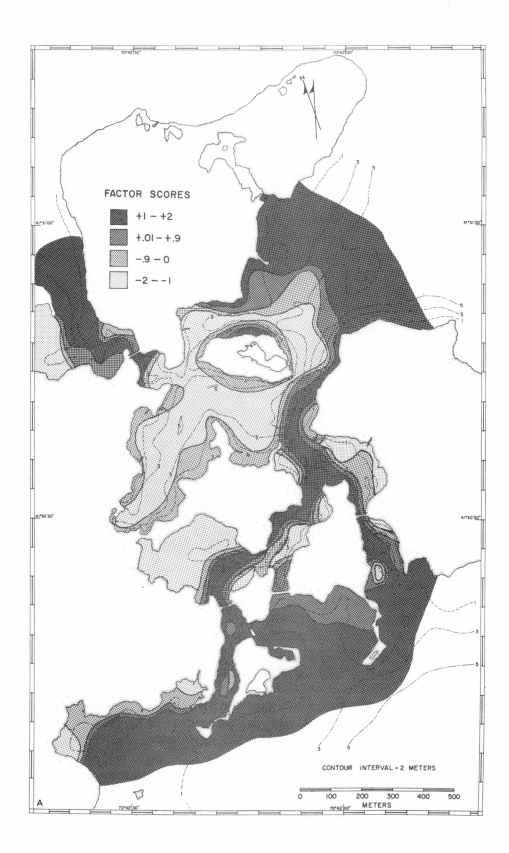

FACTOR SCORES

+1 — +2
+.01 — +.9
−.9 — 0
−2 — −1

CONTOUR INTERVAL = 2 METERS

0   100   200   300   400   500
METERS

A

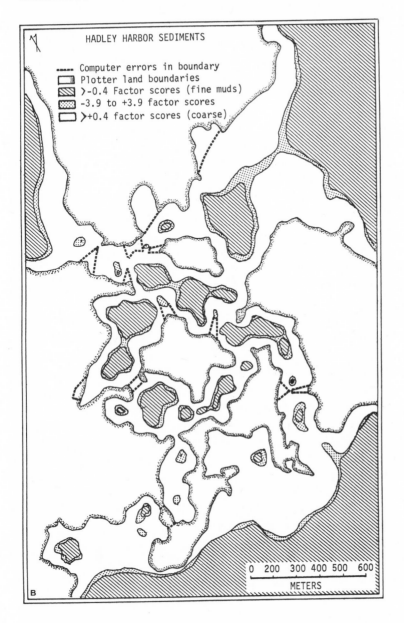

Fig. 23. A. Plot of factor scores for a sediment factor derived from the matrix of 100 ×
100 variables × 137 stations. B. Plot of factor scores for a sediment factor derived from
the matrix of 100 × 100 variables × 137 stations. Isopleths are generated through a
computer program from the library of California Computer Corporation, Dallas, Texas,
office. Shoreline derived from a plot of coordinates fed into the computer program, thus
only slightly resembles the shoreline shown in Fig. 23A, which contains the same data.

turtle grass (*Thalassia testudinum* König) abundance, the southern equivalent to eel grass, corresponded almost identically to the sand—silt—clay distribution chart, indicating that the dominant control of sediments was exerted by the sea grass abundance. This also proved to be a significant variable in the seasonal and areal composition of the sediments in Hadley Harbor.

EEL GRASS COVER

Though not a physical or chemical parameter, the relative abundance and distribution of eel grass (*Zostera marina*) on the bottom of the Hadley Harbor Complex is intimately related to the distribution of sediment variables (as mentioned previously) and also can be correlated with the circulation of water. This essentially biological variable is therefore discussed in context with the sediment and circulation studies. Relative abundance of eel grass was measured in 1966, during the last six months of the study; wet weights per $1/25 \, m^2$ grab sample were taken at each biological station. In addition, several special trips were made during the summer to further assay the relative distribution of eel grass. This was done by making traverses across various portions of the Complex and taking quantitative measurements of the plants at fixed intervals along the traverses. These synoptic data were then plotted with those of the individual stations to produce a map of the relative abundance of eel grass as related to its distribution (Fig. 24). The boundaries of distribution were adjusted to the degree of cover shown on the 1962 aerial photograph. It is emphasized that the map represents density and distribution of eel grass at the peak of its seasonal abundance, and that this fluctuated greatly from season to season.

It is significant that in areas of highly well-sorted sediments of both fine and coarse material, the eel grass was usually absent. Depth and degree of light penetration may also be significant factors in limiting eel grass production in highly well-sorted fine sediments. In general, only 2—20% of the surface illumination penetrated to the bottom of the Inner Harbor and deeper portions of the Outer Harbor. Little current or wave action were found in this region, permitting the continued suspension of fine sediment and phytoplankton particles in the water, thus cutting off a significant portion of light which could reach the bottom. The absence of eel grass in the highly well-sorted, coarse sediments, both in major channels of the gutters and in the shallow sand flats, can be attributed to the constant movement of the substratum or to lack of sufficient porosity of the sediments to permit establishment of a root system. Lynts (1966) found similar correlations between sediment size and abundance of turtle grass in Florida Bay.

The greatest amounts of eel grass (or optimal localities for eel grass

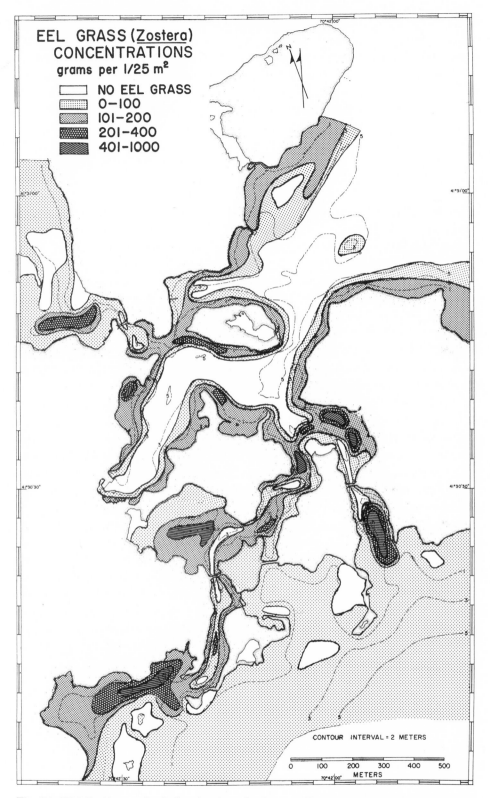

Fig. 24. Distribution and relative density of eel grass (*Zostera marina*) by weight, calculated as grams per 1/25 m^2, taken by the Van Veen grab, during late spring and early summer of 1965.

growth) in Hadley Harbor occurred at depths ranging from 1.5 to 4 ft. at mean low tide, in water flowing just rapidly enough that the residence time of suspended particles was short enough that they would not reduce light penetration over the eel grass, but long enough to supply dissolved nutrients. Areas of intermediate abundance were found along the borders of the gutters, Inner Harbor, and Outer Harbor. Current velocities were reduced, but water clarity was still relatively high permitting "normal" eel grass growth.

The strong seasonality of eel grass growth is attributable to the great differences in temperature and light between winter and summer. The seasonality of *Zostera* and other benthic marine plants for Great Pond, just across the Sound from Hadley Harbor was discussed at length by Conover (1958). Areas of high eel grass abundance persist until late fall (Fig. 24), the eel grass getting taller and more dense in regions characterized by the 101—200 g weights of the plant. Starting in late fall and early winter, the eel grass begins to die down, and in certain areas disappears almost completely by early spring, when small shoots start up from the bottom again. Whereas, eel grass virtually dies down on the outer grass flats and outer portions of the gutters in winter (areas of 0—100 g weights), the densest patches become reduced but do not disappear and the areas of intermediate abundance seem to remain green throughout the winter.

The seasonality of the eel grass was also reflected in seasonal changes of the sediments. With the spread of eel grass patches to unoccupied areas, grain size decreased proportionally in these formerly bare sediments. During minimum-growth periods, sediments were mainly silty sand, and during maximum-growth attainment, the sediments changed to a sandy silt. Changes were even more striking in the areas where eel grass disappeared. In the summer when eel grass was present, sediments were normally in the sandy silt range, or coarse silt to fine sand. However, when the eel grass died down completely in the winter, sediments become pure sand, and changed to the medium sand range. Sorting coefficients changed slightly from well-sorted to very well-sorted sediments when the eel grass died. With the exception of Ginsburg and Lowenstam's (1958) paper dealing with turtle grass as a stabilizing influence on sediment parameters and the previously mentioned work of Lynts (1966) in the same Florida Bay region, the effect of eel grass or other marine grasses on sedimentary processes has been little studied, and should be systematically investigated on a seasonal basis.

LIGHT PENETRATION

As penetration of light to the bottom is a function of depth, circulation (particles in suspension), and phytoplankton production (as plankton particles also are light scatterers), this ecological variable is discussed in context with sedimentary factors. Availability of light is closely related to eel grass and algal abundance as light is needed for growth, and its degree of penetration in the water changes with the diurnal position of the sun, the seasonal inclination of the sun, and the amount of cloud cover. At first it was thought that turbidity would be an important factor to measure, and a Hydro-Products light-path turbidity meter was tested. Unfortunately the sensitivity was so low that virtually no differences in turbidity could be measured from one part of the Complex to the other. With the possible exception of Grassy Pond and Inner Harbor, water flowed through the Complex too rapidly for accumulation of any quantity of suspended material in one place. It was found that two of the most important factors relating to the benthos are eel grass concentration and algal production on the bottom, therefore, the amount of ambient surface light reaching the bottom was considered a critical variable to measure, and turbidity per se was omitted. Because the amount of light reaching the bottom was measured as a percentage of surface ambient light (calculated from nearly simultaneous surface and bottom readings of the photo cell), light measurements were independent of the altitude of the sun or cloud cover. Measurements were also an index of turbidity in that, aside from water depth, light extinction is a function of the quantity of suspended materials in the water column between the two photo cells.

Light penetration was plotted first as seasonal values on an areal basis (Fig. 25A—D) and finally as an overall plot of all values taken at the biological stations (Fig. 26). As can be expected, seasonal differences in light penetration were great, the least amount of light reaching the bottom in the spring and summer months when standing crops of plankton were the highest. During spring and summer, light values in the deeper portions of the Complex ranged only from 3 to 18% (Fig. 25C,D) while in the same spots during fall and winter the values increased to 22—40%, being almost twice as intense (Fig. 25A,B). There was a corresponding increase in light in the gutters and at the shallow entrances, and a significant difference between total light reaching bottom during the spring and summer of 1964 and 1965. Examination of illumination figures from the weekly physical—chemical stations during these two years showed conspicuously clearer waters in 1965 than in 1964. The worst drought on record in the Cape Cod area occurred in 1965. With no rainfall of any significance, there was virtually no runoff. The resulting lack of land-derived nutrients possibly reduced phytoplankton production sufficiently to create clearer water. The pH of both surface and bottom waters during these two years also changed radically, indicating less CO_2 uptake in photosynthesis. Another possible explanation for this change is a shift of offshore Gulf Stream waters closer to shore, and there are indications that Hadley Harbor waters were warmer in 1965 than in 1963 and 1964.

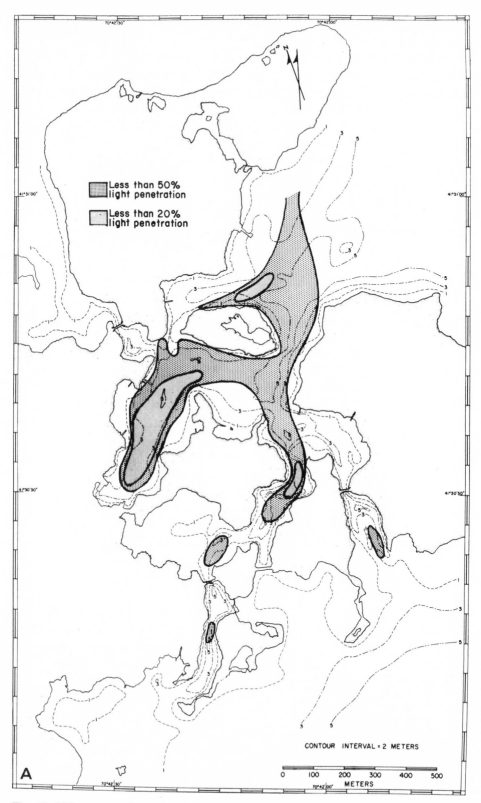

Fig. 25. Light penetration values as percent of light transmission to the bottom. A. Fall, 1964. B. Winter, 1964—65. C. Spring, 1965. D. Summer, 1965.

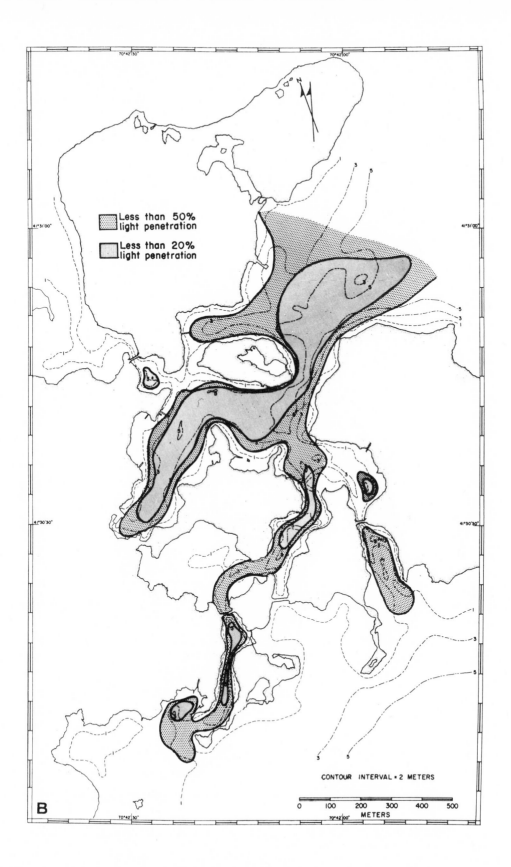

Less than 50% light penetration

Less than 20% light penetration

CONTOUR INTERVAL = 2 METERS

0   100   200   300   400   500
METERS

B

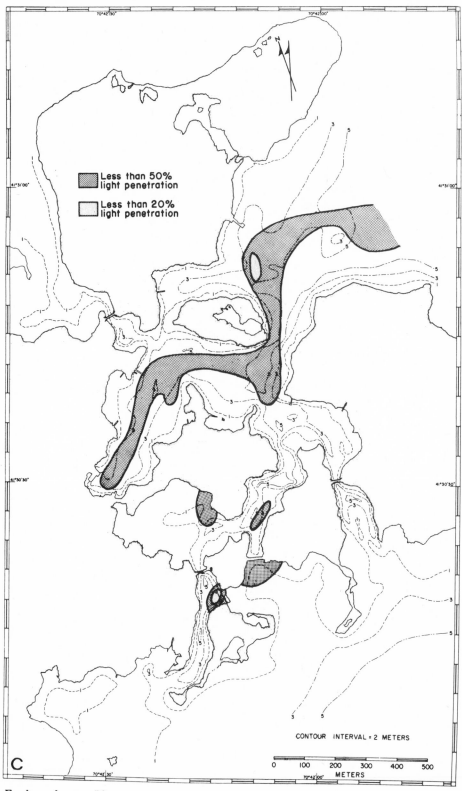

Less than 50%
light penetration

Less than 20%
light penetration

C

CONTOUR INTERVAL = 2 METERS

0   100   200   300   400   500
METERS

For legend see p. 50.

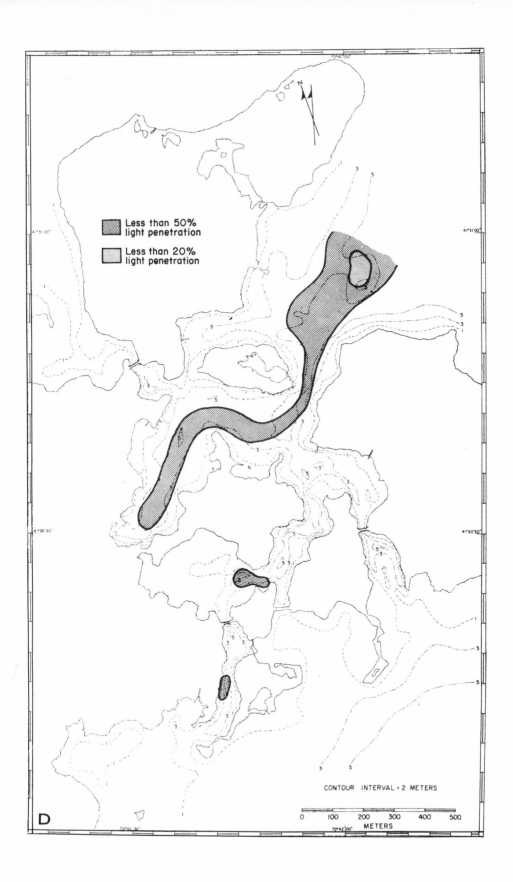

Less than 50%
light penetration

Less than 20%
light penetration

CONTOUR INTERVAL = 2 METERS

0   100   200   300   400   500
                METERS

D

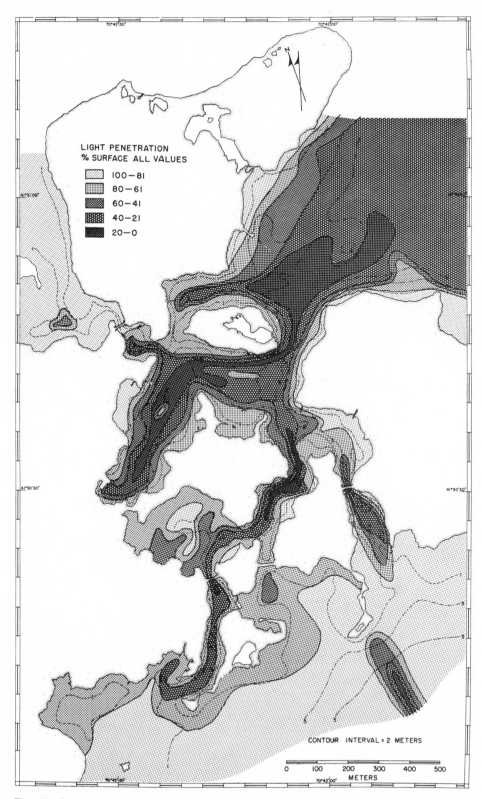

Fig. 26. Composite plot of light penetration as percent of light transmission to the bottom, using all light values obtained throughout the study.

The plot of all light values taken at the biological stations (Fig. 26) indicates overall areas of high and low light intensity which correlate, in general, with depth, circulation, and eel grass cover. With the exception of two high light intensity patches, the Inner and Outer Harbors were characterized by very low light penetration. The centers of the gutters, particularly the deep settling basins, also had low light values. The highest values were found on the clean sand flats and in areas with low eel grass cover. Factor analysis in the R-mode of the 72 selected stations and the physical—chemical variables also showed very high correlation between light values, depth, and eel grass cover, substantiating conclusions reached from inspection of areal plots of these variables.

HYDROGEN-ION CONCENTRATION (pH) OF THE BOTTOM

During the initial stages of this study, measurement of pH was considered of doubtful value, as it was expected that pH of coastal marine waters should show very little variation from the "normal" expected range of 7.90—8.20. As the study progressed however, it was observed that there was not only wide areal variation within Hadley Harbor, but also major seasonal differences. Bottom pH values actually range through almost three complete pH units — remarkable for a wholly marine environment. Four seasonal areal plots of pH are depicted in Fig. 27A—D. Major changes in pH took place between 1964 and 1965. In the spring and summer of 1964, minimum pH values were 7.90 and the overall average was 8.01; whereas values in the spring of 1965, with one exception, were below 7.85 and averaged 7.55. This was thought to be related to the decay of the measuring electrodes, until it was noticed that pH values[1], measured during the same period in 1965 for the salt water system of the Marine Biological Laboratory, also showed a gradual decrease (Fig. 28). It is probable that pH values obtained in the Hadley Harbor study were roughly related to benthic and planktonic plant production, as well as microbial decomposition of accumulated organic matter. Similar fluctuations were noted by Conover (1958).

All of the values for the two years were plotted on the same chart (Fig. 29), which gives a composite picture of areas of low and high pH. Throughout most of the Complex, pH values were close to those expected for normal sea waters, or 8.00—8.30. However, low values below 7.00 appeared consistently in the small coves or cul de sacs on the western side of the Complex. All of these areas are free of currents and have little wave action. The very low pH values of 6.00—6.49 on the western side of the

---

[1] Values taken by Dr. M. Carriker and D. van Zandt of the Systematics—Ecology Program.

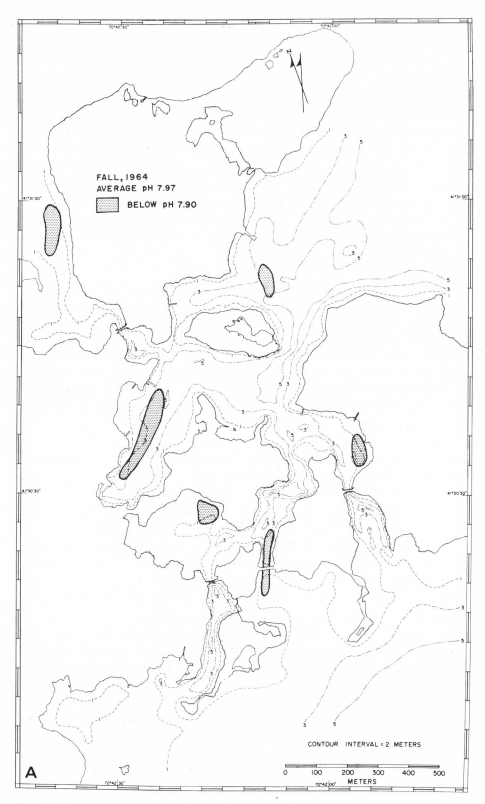

FALL, 1964
AVERAGE pH 7.97

BELOW pH 7.90

CONTOUR INTERVAL = 2 METERS

0   100   200   300   400   500
METERS

A

Fig. 27. Hydrogen-ion concentration (pH) values, plotted seasonally. A. Fall, 1964. B. Winter, 1964—65. C. Spring, 1965. D. Summer, 1965.

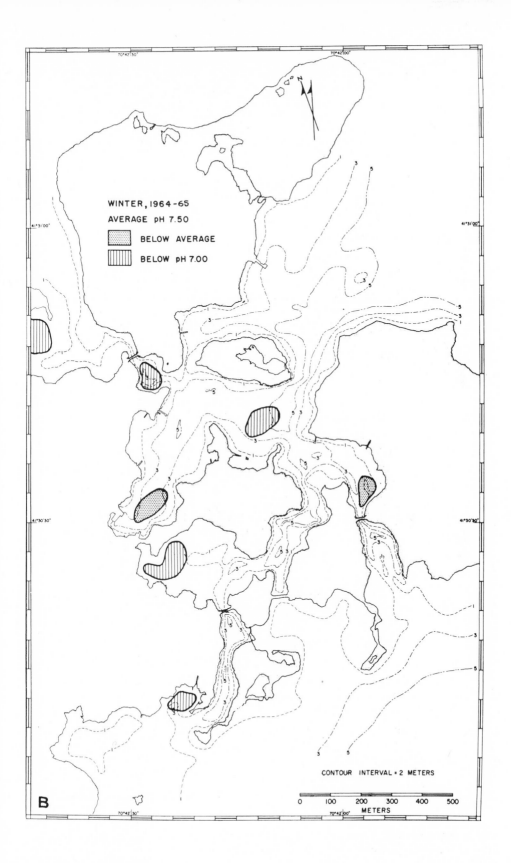

WINTER, 1964-65
AVERAGE pH 7.50

▦ BELOW AVERAGE

▥ BELOW pH 7.00

CONTOUR INTERVAL = 2 METERS

0   100   200   300   400   500
METERS

B

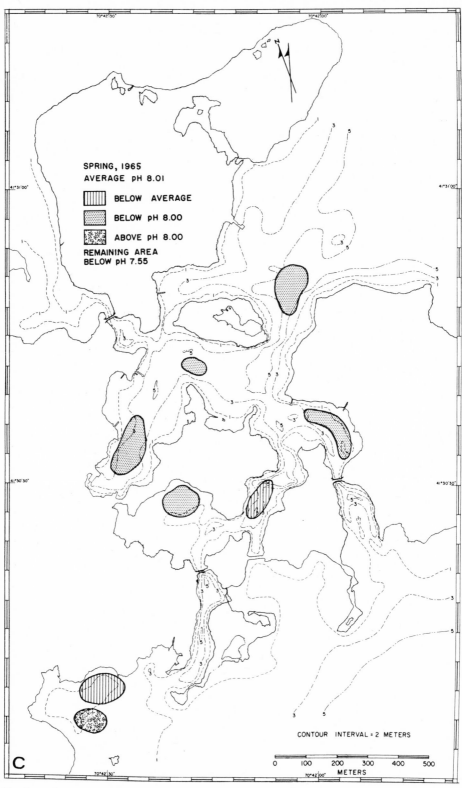

SPRING, 1965
AVERAGE pH 8.01

||||| BELOW AVERAGE

▦ BELOW pH 8.00

▨ ABOVE pH 8.00

REMAINING AREA
BELOW pH 7.55

CONTOUR INTERVAL = 2 METERS

0   100   200   300   400   500
METERS

C

For legend see p. 56.

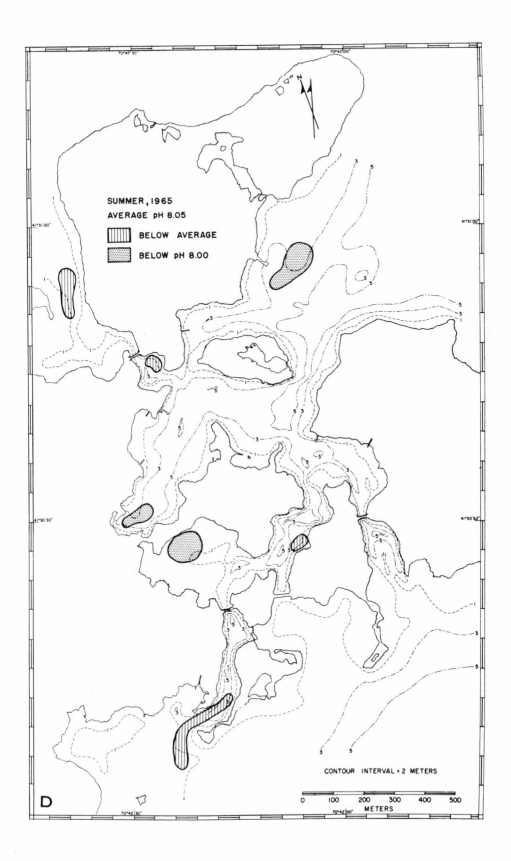

SUMMER, 1965
AVERAGE pH 8.05

BELOW AVERAGE

BELOW pH 8.00

CONTOUR INTERVAL = 2 METERS

0   100   200   300   400   500
METERS

D

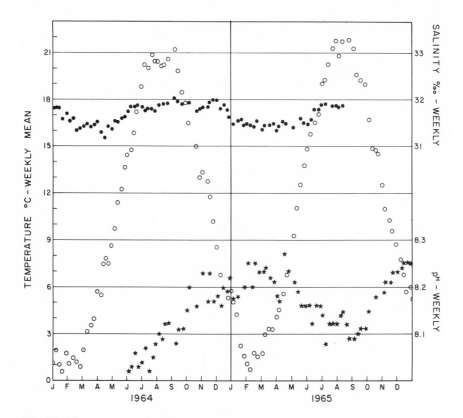

Fig. 28. Measurement of pH, salinity, and temperature of sea water taken over a two-year period (1964—65) by M.R. Carriker and D. van Zandt in their salt water tables at the Marine Biological Laboratory, Woods Hole, Massachusetts. ○ = temperature ° C; ● = salinity ‰; ★ = pH.

Inner Harbor may be attributed to a sewer outfall and the presence of pens and grazing areas for sheep and horses which were located in the vicinity. According to Oppenheimer and Kornicker (1958), Oppenheimer (1960), and Lynts (1966), pH of the sediments is a result of CO_2 and H_2S production during microbial decomposition of organic matter. Values isoplethed in this study are for the most part sediment pH's.

REDUCTION—OXIDATION POTENTIALS (Eh) OF THE BOTTOM

The redox-potential of sediments has been measured in a number of studies relating to sedimentation and benthic communities, although the significance of the measurement is still not fully understood. Zobell (1946) discusses the relationship of Eh to marine sediments and some of the chemical processes involved. There is evidence to show that oxygenated sediments

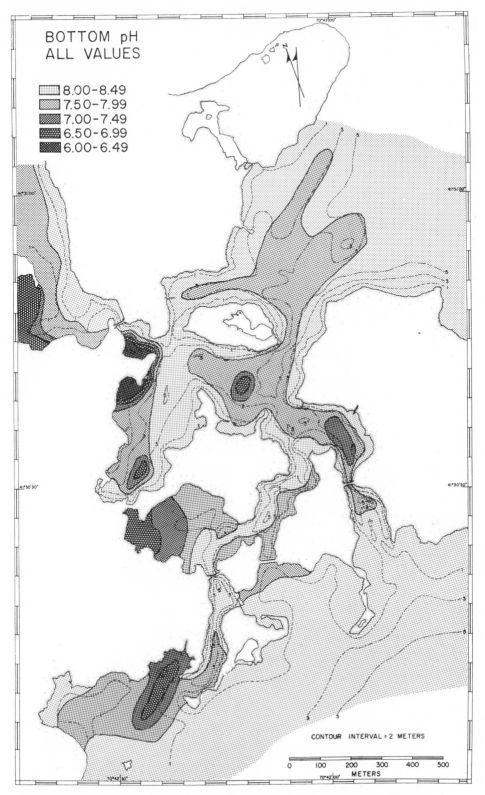

Fig. 29. Composite plot of all sediment pH values taken during the investigation.

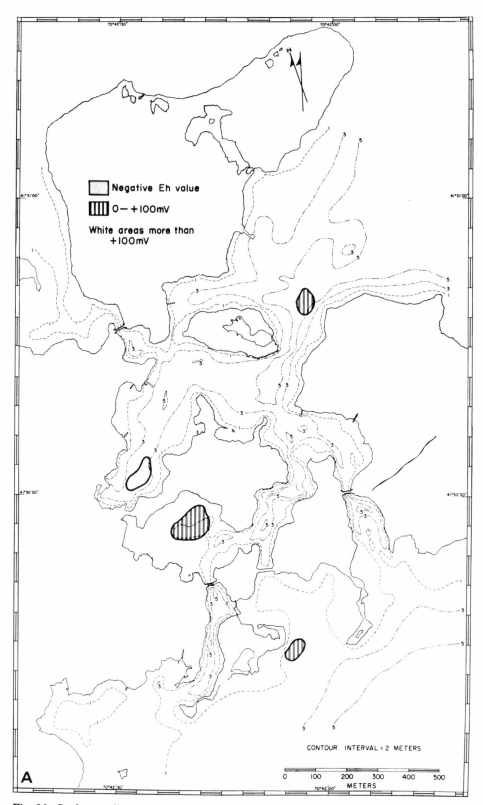

Fig. 30. Surface sediment reduction—oxidation potential (Eh) values plotted seasonally. A. Fall, 1964. B. Winter, 1964—65. C. Spring, 1965. D. Summer, 1965.

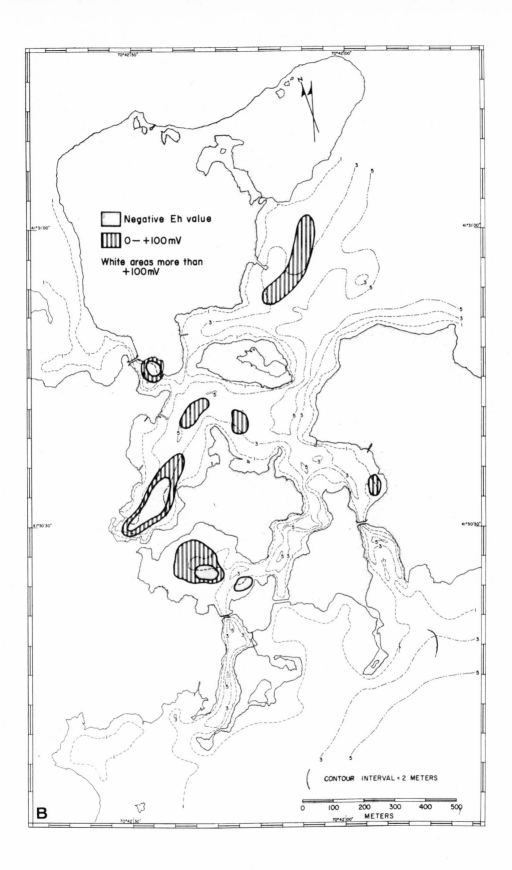

Negative Eh value

0 — +100 mV

White areas more than +100 mV

CONTOUR INTERVAL = 2 METERS

0   100   200   300   400   500
METERS

B

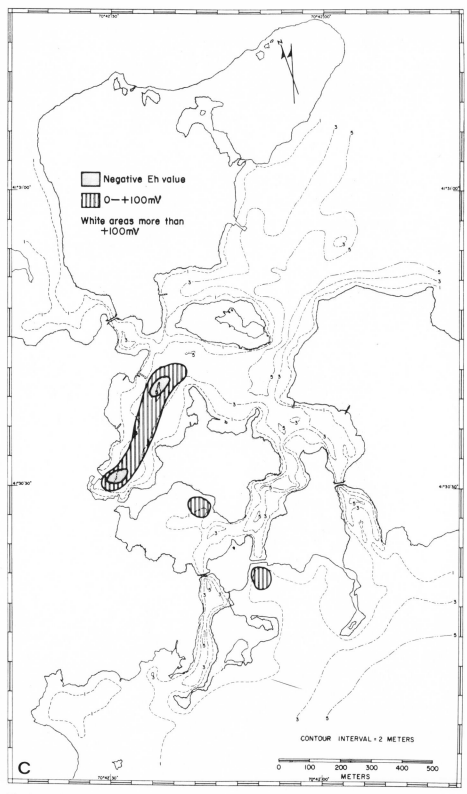

C

Negative Eh value

0—+100mV

White areas more than
+100mV

CONTOUR INTERVAL = 2 METERS

0   100   200   300   400   500
METERS

For legend see p. 62.

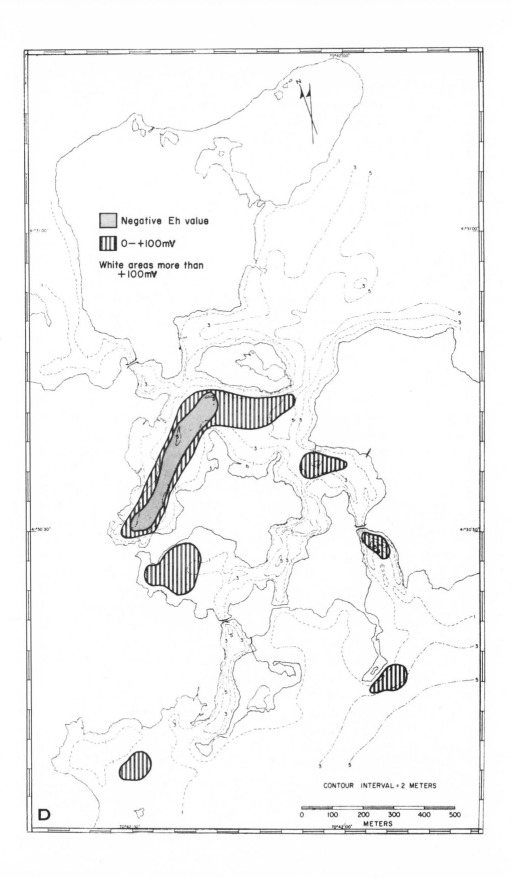

Negative Eh value

0 – +100mV

White areas more than +100mV

CONTOUR INTERVAL = 2 METERS

0   100   200   300   400   500
METERS

D

produce Eh values in the plus range, while sediments which have a high production of H_2S from microbial decomposition produce low or negative Eh readings. Little is known concerning the organic reactions taking place in sediments which may also be responsible for Eh values. In this study, Eh values were taken in the top centimeter of muds or in the water just at the water—sediment interface with long-lead electrodes. Also Eh was considered to be a measure of anaerobic conditions and thus a significant factor effecting the distribution of benthic animals.

As with pH values, redox-potential was plotted areally both seasonally and for the total period. All values indicated on the charts are corrected values standardized against a standard hydrogen electrode (i.e., 249 mV were added to readings obtained on the Radiometer pH meter used to take the measurements). Plots for the four seasons are shown in Fig. 30A—D, and although not as striking as pH, the Eh's also changed with the seasons. Reducing conditions developed towards the end of fall and were at their lowest values in the winter in Inner Harbor for both years. During the spring, values were all in the oxidizing range with the exception of one hole in the Inner Harbor which appears to have permanent reducing conditions. Low Eh values were usually found in Grassy Pond, although very low values were noted only in midsummer, associated with high temperatures and the presence of excessive organic matter. Measurements above 100 mV were typical of sediments of the gutters and harbor entrances and Eh's were always highest during the spring months.

An indication of the degree of seasonality of the redox-potential values is revealed by the trimonthly averages of the values obtained at the biological stations. The average for spring, 1964, was +235; for summer, 1964, +173; for fall, 1964, +218, and for winter, 1964—65, +128. These values show that summer and winter months are characterized by low Eh conditions, while spring and fall have high oxidizing conditions. On the other hand, measurements in 1965 differed considerably from those in 1964 for the same months, showing that conditions related to Eh were also unusual for 1965. Spring Eh values for 1965 averaged only +157 (versus +235 in 1964), and summer, 1965, averaged only +29, almost an order of magnitude lower than the value of +173 a year before. No explanation can be proffered for these yearly changes in Eh, although the seasonal ups and downs during a normal year can be explained by two phenomena. The low summer values, at least in Inner Harbor, can be explained by a sharp thermocline which developed as a result of little or no movement of water in and out of the harbor. The Inner Harbor is normally an anchorage for a large number of pleasure boats in the summer which throw overboard a considerable amount of sewage and wastes, thus adding to the existing abundant organic matter and organic decomposition. As there was virtually no mixing from surface to bottom, the

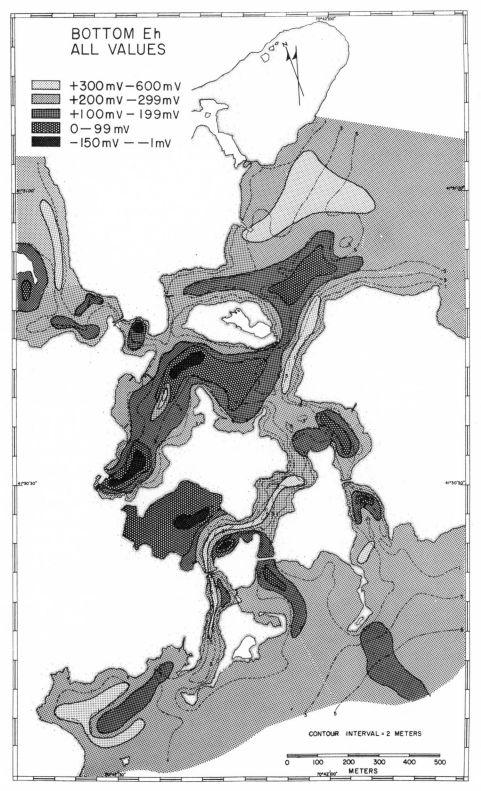

Fig. 31. Composite plot of all Eh values taken in the sediments during the study.

bottom oxygen was gradually used up and H_2S accumulated both in the sediments and in the water with little chance to escape until the fall overturn. Very low values also developed in the Inner Harbor in midwinter, because ice formed solidly in it for about a month and sometimes longer. Once again, there was restricted vertical mixing. From the appearance of sediment samples taken during the winter months, it seems that much of the eel grass that died down in the fall was torn off the bottom by fall and winter storms and swept into the Inner Harbor where it decayed, producing much the same Eh conditions that prevailed during midsummer. Waters throughout the Complex were well-mixed during the spring and fall periods; consequently Eh values were relatively high almost everywhere, averaging above +200 mV.

Contours were drawn for plots of all Eh values taken during the two years of the study and the areal picture shown on Fig. 31 resulted. With the exception of a portion of Grassy Pond, reducing conditions occurred primarily in the deeper basins. At times, during both summer and winter, quantities of organic matter which eventually decomposed sufficiently to produce reducing conditions were swept into Grassy Pond. As would be expected, highest oxidizing conditions developed in areas of highest current and wave activity. Intermediate oxidizing conditions, ranging from corrected values of +100 to +200 mV, occurred in areas of relatively high concentrations of living eel grass and currents of intermediate velocities. The large amounts of living eel grass probably contributed to the high oxidizing conditions by giving off oxygen during nocturnal respiration. By comparing Fig. 12 through 31, it can be seen that there is indeed a strong interdependence between all of the previously discussed environmental factors, especially pH, and reduction—oxidation potential. The fact that they are strongly correlated emphasizes the importance of making measurements of these factors during any marine benthic ecological study.

SALINITY

The one ecologic variable always measured during marine ecological studies has been that of salinity or chlorinity of the waters in which the animals were living. The Hadley Harbor study was no exception. Over 1500 salinity values were obtained during the two years of the investigation. Unlike the variables discussed on the past few pages, there was little to correlate with salinity, other than seasonal changes in temperature. Total variation in salinity was less than 2‰ throughout the year, and at times there was a greater difference between salinity values on the Buzzards Bay side of the Complex and those of the Vineyard Sound side than there was from one season to the next. Salinity values were measured or read to 0.01‰ throughout the investigation, although accuracies cannot be guaranteed to more than 0.05‰. The lowest values obtained were just under 31‰ and the highest just over 33‰.

Salinity values were used to identify the movement of water masses throughout the Complex. Although very slight, and possibly non-significant statistically, there appeared to be a difference in salinity between the waters of Buzzards Bay and Vineyard Sound. This was tested at a pair of stations sampled at the same time every week throughout the year; one was at the entrance to Buzzards Bay at Northwest Gutter (Physical Station 6) and the other at the entrance to Vineyard Sound off the West Gutter (Physical Station 24). Temperature—salinity ratios (T/S) were calculated for both sets of stations and plotted together as shown in Fig. 32. With the exception of three values out of 27, the Buzzards Bay T/S values were always higher than the Vineyard Sound ones. This slight difference between the two sides of Hadley Harbor Complex may be explained as follows. Most of the runoff and ground water from Cape Cod runs southward into Vineyard Sound, as the Cape's high ridges are close to shore on its west and north sides. Most of the runoff for the rest of southeastern Massachusetts (New Bedford to the town of Buzzards Bay) empties into Buzzards Bay on the west side. It also appears that higher-salinity Atlantic Ocean water comes into both Vineyard Sound and Buzzards Bay along the east side (i.e., along shore of Martha's

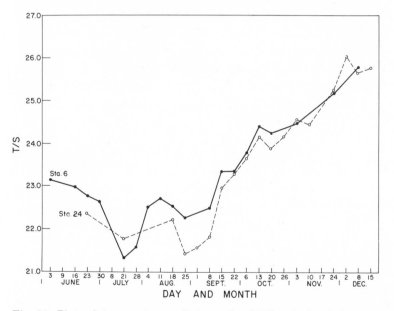

Fig. 32. Plot of temperature—salinity ratios (T/S) calculated from salinity and temperature values measured at Physical Station 6 (Buzzards Bay) and Physical Station 24 (Vineyard Sound) for a period of seven months in 1964.

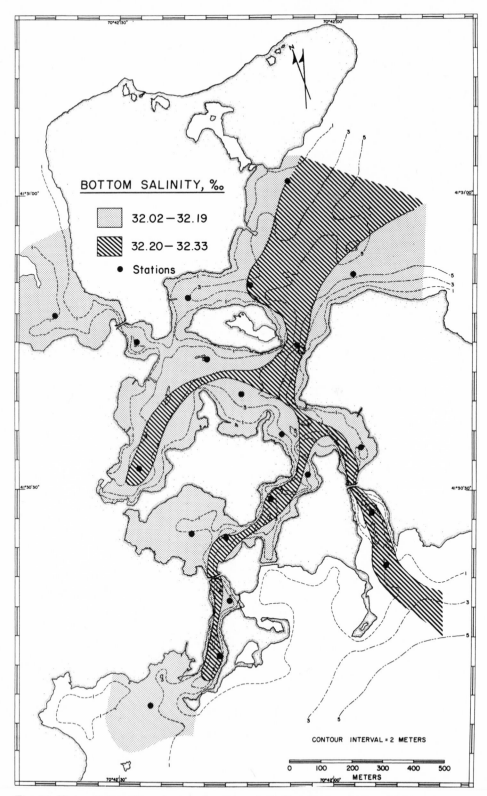

Fig. 33. High-salinity salt wedge moving through Hadley Harbor during tidal movement of water from Buzzards Bay to Vineyard Sound. All values were measured within three hours.

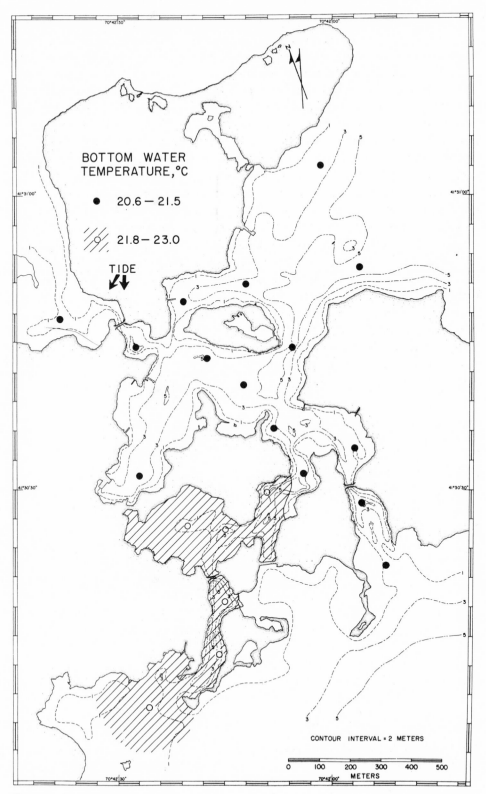

Fig. 34. Encroachment of higher-temperature bottom water into Hadley Harbor from Vineyard Sound during one morning's observations, 8 August 1964. Note that water is actually flowing from north to south.

Vineyard and along the Elizabeth Islands Chain). On the other hand, the runoff and slightly lower-salinity water seems to flow into the Atlantic along the west sides of these two bodies of water (i.e., the Vineyard Sound side of the Elizabeth Islands and along the New Bedford side of Buzzards Bay). The two water masses would be most distinct at Woods Hole, the first place along the coast where mixing could occur. The surface area of the Elizabeth Islands do not furnish enough ground water or runoff to reduce salinities permanently on the Vineyard Sound side, although some fresh water collects in a low marsh near Southwest Gutter. It was observed many times during synoptic observations, from one end of the Complex to the other, that salinity would generally be about 0.1—0.5‰ higher and temperature 1—3°C lower on the Buzzards Bay side and, depending upon the state of the tide, decreasing southward into Vineyard Sound (Fig. 33,34). Plots of weekly salinity variations for eight months between three contrasting habitats within the Complex are shown on Fig. 35.

Salinity values were particularly useful for verifying the movement of bottom water masses through the Complex. At no time did the slightly lower Vineyard Sound bottom water penetrate into the Buzzards Bay side, while the Buzzards Bay water mass frequently could be detected out into Vineyard Sound (Fig. 33).

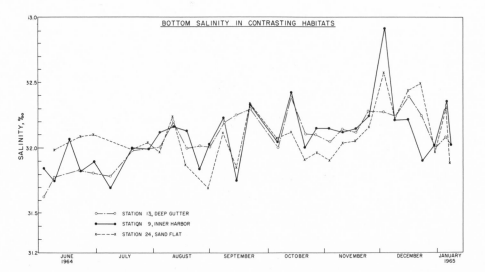

Fig. 35. Plot of bottom salinity measured in three contrasting habitats from June, 1964, through January, 1965.

WATER TEMPERATURE

Water temperature is the easiest physical measurement to make in the marine environment, and it was the most consistently measured factor during this study. As to be expected, water temperature showed more significant variation seasonally than areally. It was well correlated with salinity and density (T/S relationships), and it was necessary for computing electronic measurements of dissolved oxygen and for computing salinity from conductivity measurements. Seasonal variation in water temperature for the Woods Hole region is illustrated in the measurements taken in the Marine Biological Laboratory salt water system by Carriker and Van Zandt (Fig. 28). Maximum sea water temperatures occurred in early September, 1964 (21.3°C) and in late August, 1965 (23.0°C), while minimum temperatures were attained at the end of January, 1964 (+0.6°C) and in early February, 1965 (+0.7°C). The steady rise in temperature begins in the middle of March and reaches the summer plateau in late July, while the orderly decrease in temperature be-

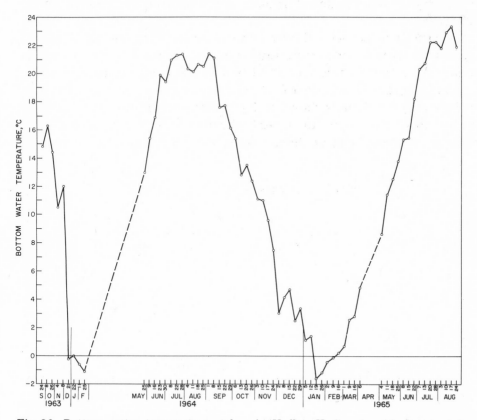

Fig. 36. Bottom water temperatures taken in Hadley Harbor (weekly averages) from September, 1963, through August, 1965.

gins in early September and reaches the winter plateau in early February. Temperatures below 0°C were not recorded from the Laboratory sea water system, as the water is kept in large holding tanks and distributed through the building, thus warming it slightly above the normal freezing which occurs in the open waters of the Woods Hole region.

Weekly averages of bottom temperature (from the biological stations only) for the Hadley Harbor Complex were plotted from September, 1963, to the end of August, 1965 (Fig. 36). In general these figures correspond closely to Carriker's and Van Zandt's (Fig. 28) for the same period, except that their rises and falls are much smoother than ours, and our extremes are greater between summer and winter. Note that a double summer peak with a maximum of 21.4°C occurred in 1964, and a single high peak at 23.3°C took place in 1965. Below-zero temperatures occurred steadily for a month-long period (part of January and February) in both 1964 and 1965. The total range of bottom temperature in the Hadley Harbor region was 25°C. This wide range has been characteristic of this region and may possibly be the widest range of water temperature along the Atlantic and European coasts in high latitudes.

The difference between the two "water masses" representing Buzzards Bay and Vineyard Sound is more striking in terms of water temperature than salinity. An areal synoptic picture of bottom water temperatures observed on August 8, 1964, but typical of values during any summer southward moving current pattern, is shown on Fig. 34. The colder Buzzards Bay water (20.6—21.5°C) moved into the Inner Harbor and only along the East Gutter, while the warmer Vineyard Sound water (21.8—23.0°C) remained in the

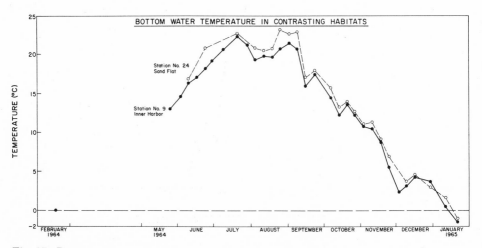

Fig. 37. Bottom water temperatures measured simultaneously at Station *9* in the Inner Harbor and Station *24* in Lackey's Bay.

West Gutter. The contrast between the two "water masses" is better shown as a 9-month plot of bottom water temperatures from the same stations, Station 9 (Inner Harbor) and Station 24 (Vineyard Sound) from May, 1964, to January, 1965 (Fig. 37). Inner Harbor water temperatures were consistently lower than Vineyard Sound values, except for one value in February of 1965.

CHAPTER 4

RESULTS OF THE BIOLOGICAL INVESTIGATIONS

A major problem with the biological portion of the Hadley Harbor study was interpretation of the mass of data collected. In studies involving only the megafaunal elements of marine communities, it is usually possible to define both the composition and areal extent of these communities by plotting the distribution and abundance of a few so-called dominant species. This was the approach of Petersen (1913, 1914, 1915), Sanders (1956, 1958, 1960), Thorson (1957), and others, who examined marine benthic communities in detail. However, for the most part, previous workers have sampled broad geographic areas of relatively uniform sediment and physical—chemical characteristics.

The Hadley Harbor study was unusual in that, although a small area of sea bottom was selected for investigation in a detailed way, this area exhibited great variability in the number and size of habitats available for benthic organisms. As the previous discussion of physical factors indicated, entirely different chemical and physical conditions existed within a few meters of each other; consequently, it might be expected that the fauna also would change across similar distances. For most major taxa represented in Hadley Harbor this patchiness of species populations and complete change in community composition over short distances held true.

Nearly 350 different species of invertebrates have been identified from the Hadley Harbor Complex. A conservative estimate of the number of species to be identified from those groups not critically examined (hydroids, nematodes, oligochaetes, about one-third of the polychaetes, and copepods) would be another 130—150 species. The number of individuals for each species ranged from 1 or 2 to 5,000 per station, and the average number of station occurrences for the abundant species was about 50—60 stations. From these rough numbers, and the fact that the average count of animals per station was between 1,700 and 2,500 individuals, it is easily seen that over one million individual occurrences of organisms must be put into proper context to prove or disprove the variability, and even existence, of real marine benthic communities. First, the results will be discussed as they have appeared from a partially subjective treatment of the data, handled in a more or less classical sense. The second half of the discussion of these results will be based primarily upon a statistical evaluation of the data carried out through computer analysis.

DISTRIBUTION PATTERNS OF INDIVIDUAL SPECIES

Mollusca

Before any conception of the existence of benthic communities and their boundaries can be realized, it is first necessary to examine in some detail the distribution and abundance of the individual species which comprise this complex of animals and plants. Even within the first few months it was possible to tell that there were several broad habitats or environments within the Hadley Harbor Complex characterized by distinctly different faunas. As the mollusks were the easiest to identify and also the largest most readily apparent organisms of the benthos, they proved to be the first recognized indicators for the various habitats intuitively observed. Since there was little trouble in recognizing mollusks at the species level, these were the first forms to be completely identified and plotted areally.

A series of areal distribution maps of the abundant or predominant species of mollusks and other organisms will serve to demonstrate that there are indeed separate environments for communities as well as habitats for individual species. Altogether, 43 species of gastropods, 1 chiton, and 33 species of pelecypods — or 77 species of mollusks — were collected during this study in contrast to over 900 species of mollusks identified from an equivalent number of stations taken in the Gulf of California (Parker, 1964a). Of these, only 14 species of gastropods and 12 species of pelecypods were abundant enough to reveal critical ecologic relationships. Eight of the 14 species of gastropods can be referred to as indicator species. Of the other 6 more or less abundant species, 3 were attaching forms (*Crepidula*), dependent upon a shell or gravel bottom, and were confined to the constricted high-current portions of the gutters. The other 3 species were not limited in their distribution, although maximum concentration of two anachids, for example, seemed to correlate well with the eel grass flats.

The distribution maps of the other 8 abundant species of gastropods are illustrated and discussed here. Two species of gastropods were abundant enough and occurred at enough stations to serve as index species for the silty sediments of the Inner and Outer Harbors. Fig. 38 shows the distribution of *Retusa canaliculata*, an opisthobranch, which with relatively few exceptions is confined to the clayey silts, low Eh, and slightly higher-salinity bottoms of the Inner and Outer Harbors. A second and closely related species, with an almost identical distribution pattern, is the opisthobranch *Cylichna oryza*, whose distribution is shown on Fig. 39. Within the range of this species in Hadley Harbor, the maximum populations were located in the center of the area in which it was found alive and probably represented the center of dispersal for that species within Hadley Harbor. No other species of gastro-

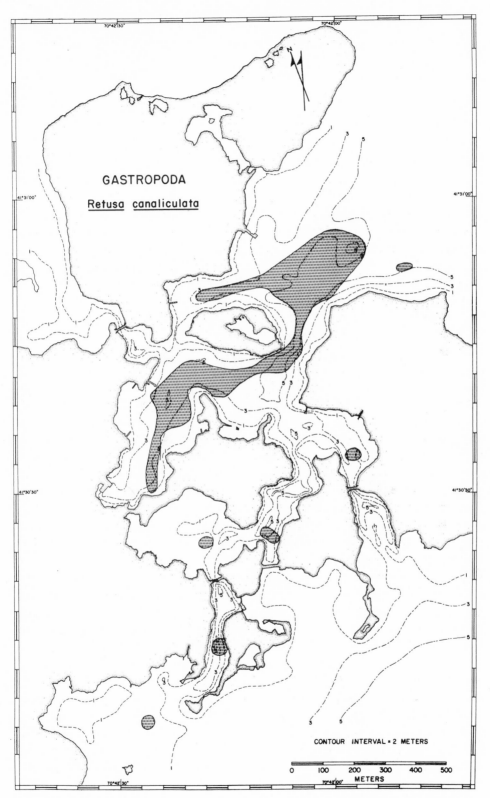

Fig. 38. Distribution of the opisthobranch gastropod *Retusa canaliculata*, typical of Inner Harbor muds.

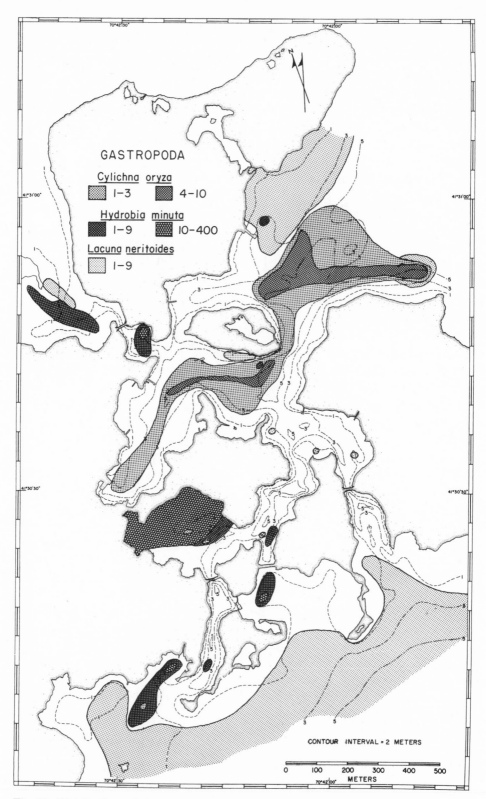

Fig. 39. Distribution of three common gastropods: *Cylichna oryza*, Inner Harbor, *Hydrobia minuta* and *Lacuna neritoides* (also *L. vincta*), Sand Flats, as derived from all biological stations.

pod occurred in this environment in any abundance, and, in fact, gastropods of any kind were lacking from the majority of samples taken in the southern portion of the Inner Harbor. In contrast to the opisthobranch distribution were the locations of the populations of *Hydrobia minuta* and *Lacuna neritoides*, shown on Fig. 39. *Lacuna* occurred primarily and almost exclusively on the wave-influenced sand flats where eel grass cover was at a minimum. Another species of *Lacuna*, *L. vincta*, also occurred in the same micro-habitat. Intermediate sizes of both species were almost indistinguishable and both species occurred at the same station, which suggests that there was really only one species in the Complex. The other species of gastropod found primarily on the outer entrance sand flats, but not simultaneously with *Lacuna*, was *Hydrobia minuta*. Its distribution is also shown on Fig. 39 and illustrates that little overlap existed between the occurrences of *Cylichna*, *Hydrobia*, and *Lacuna*. Although the area of occurrence of *Hydrobia* seems small, its numbers were exceedingly high when they occur at all, upwards to $16,000/m^2$. This species occurred in much higher concentrations on the sand and mud flats of Barnstable Harbor (Sanders et al., 1962) and in Sagadahoc Bay, Maine (Bradley, 1957). Its distribution differed from that of *Lacuna* in that it occurred in much more protected shallow flats, particularly Grassy Pond, off West Gutter, and the small coves on the Vineyard Sound side of the Complex. Both *Hydrobia* and *Lacuna* were seasonal, occurring only in the warmer months; they were completely absent from December—March sample collections. *Retusa* and *Cylichna*, on the other hand, were found throughout the year in Inner Harbor.

Three gastropod species with nearly identical distributions were *Caecum pulchellum*, *Mitrella lunata*, and *Turbonilla interrupta*. Of the three, *Caecum* had the most restricted distribution, and, as can be seen on Fig. 40, it was only found in areas of strong currents. Correlative with the strong current as a factor is that the sediments were generally coarse sandy or shelly gravel, and poorly sorted. Redox-potentials were always high. The other two species whose distributions are figured here, *Turbonilla interrupta* and *Mitrella lunata*, were typical of high-current, coarse sediment areas, but were also found in moderately dense stands of eel grass. The two species of *Anachis* (related to *Mitrella*) and another species of *Caecum* (*Caecum cooperi*) also had roughly the same distributional patterns. The distribution of *Turbonilla interrupta* is shown on Fig. 41. This species did occur in the Inner Harbor, but only on the shallow sides and the open portion towards the east.

The majority of pyramidellid gastropods previously investigated have been shown to be parasitic on echinoderms or polychaetes. However, Sanders (1960) states that what might be this same species, and the 8 most common species of the *Nephtys—Nucula* community of Buzzards Bay, is probably a deposit feeder, using its buccal pump to draw in the flocculent layer on the

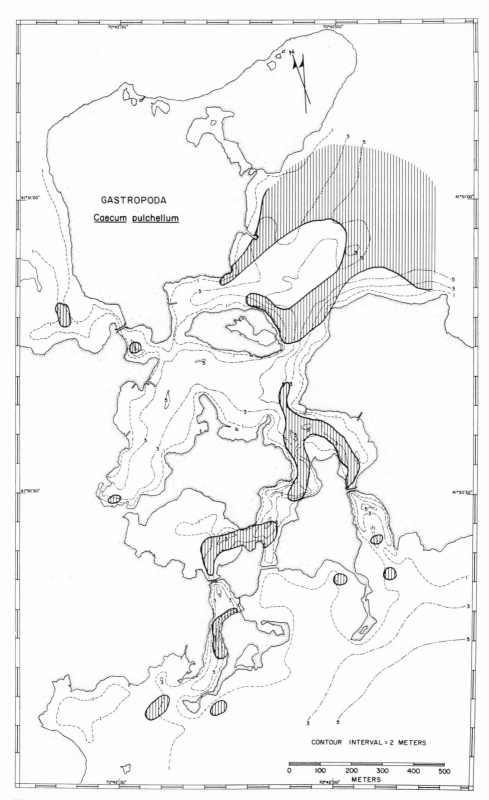

Fig. 40. Distribution of the small gastropod *Caecum pulchellum*, typical of the channels in Hadley Harbor, Massachusetts.

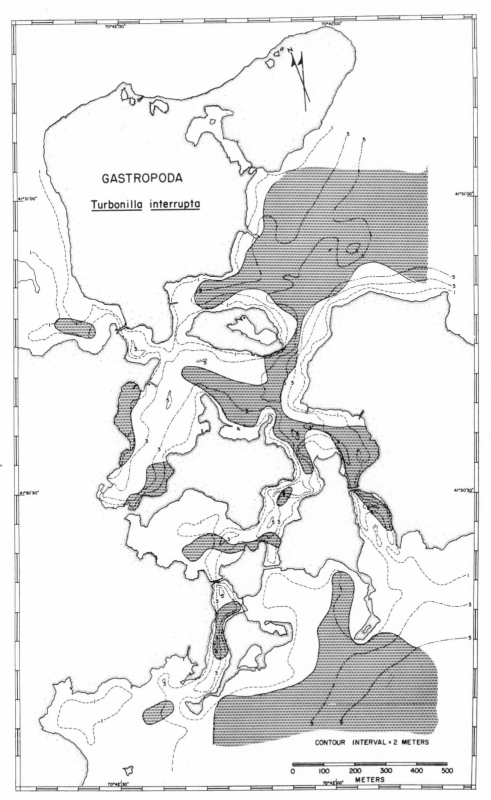

Fig. 41. Distribution of the opisthobranch gastropod *Turbonilla interrupta*, characteristic of channels and eel grass beds.

surface of the sediment. The distribution of this species within the Hadley Harbor Complex does not suggest any commensal or parasitic relationship with any specific animal. It occurs in rather large numbers at many stations, as many as $625/m^2$ and an average of $200-300/m^2$, actually larger populations than Sanders (1960) found at Station "R". This is not the sort of distribution that one would relate to a parasitic or commensal animal unless its host was also very abundant. No other organisms which could be construed as hosts for *Turbonilla interrupta* occurred consistently at the same stations in the proper numbers to support this gastropod. On the other hand, its virtual avoidance of the clayey silt bottoms typical of the Station "R" sediments of Sanders suggests that this species may not be the same as Sanders' *Turbonilla* sp., and that it may not be a deposit feeder in the same sense as described above.

The distribution of *Mitrella lunata* (and for all practical purposes *Anachis translirata* also) is shown on Fig. 42. In a broad sense, this gastropod occupied about the same habitat as *Turbonilla* and to a lesser extent *Caecum*. The major exception was the occurrence of *Mitrella* at a number of stations taken on the fine clayey silt bottoms of the Inner Harbor and Outer Harbor. Considering that *Mitrella* was one of the common associates of the eel grass community (determined by J.S. Nagle, 1968), it is surprising that it was found in areas where eel grass did not grow. From the distribution of *Mitrella* and the other two anachids in the Hadley Harbor Complex, it would appear that these columbellids probably feed on the diatoms and epiphytic algae associated mostly with eel grass blades.

One gastropod species was definitely associated with the eel grass and occurred in dense concentrations, both on the bottom between the plants and on the plants themselves. This was the cerithiid *Bittium alternatum*, the distribution of which is shown on Fig. 43. This species was by far the most abundant mollusk in the Hadley Harbor Complex, in which half a dozen stations contained over $10,000/m^2$ and averaged $2,500/m^2$ over the entire Complex. It also occurred in over three quarters of all samples taken in the Complex. As can be seen on Fig. 43, the only areas where *Bittium* did not occur were the very fine bottoms of the Inner and Outer Harbor and the center of the channels where currents were too high for eel grass to grow. The distribution of this species correlated directly with eel grass concentrations and with amphipod species which also seemed dependent upon eel grass.

In general, distributions of the pelecypod mollusks were more restricted than those of the gastropods, probably because gastropods are more motile than pelecypods. Certain pelecypods, however, proved to have distribution patterns identical with those of certain gastropods. There were no pelecypod species restricted to the eel grass beds, although one (*Solemya velum*) was

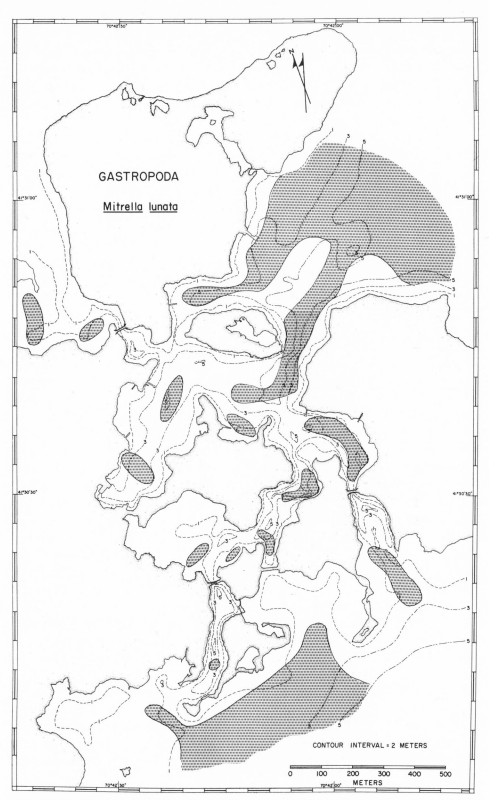

Fig. 42. Distribution of a small columbellid gastropod, *Mitrella lunata*, found primarily on eel grass and clayey-silt sediments.

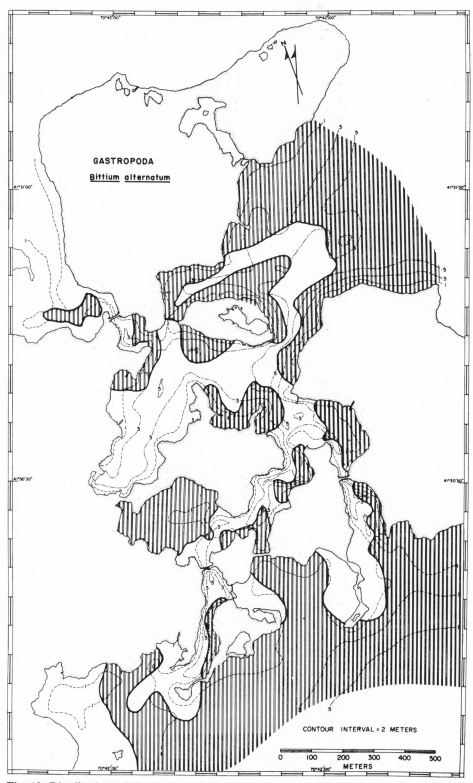

Fig. 43. Distribution of the gastropod *Bittium alternatum*, commonly associated with eel grass.

common there. Seven species have been chosen to demonstrate the selectivity of habitats.

The first pelecypod species to be discussed which demonstrated a preference for the silty substrates of Inner and Outer Harbors was the deposit-feeding protobranch *Nucula proxima*. As shown on Fig. 44, *Nucula* was found primarily on the Buzzards Bay side of the Complex and seemed to be derived from the *Nephtys—Nucula* community of Sanders (1960) found on the soft bottoms nearby in Buzzards Bay (Rhoads and Young, 1970). Maximum populations of *Nucula* were found in the center of the Inner Harbor and the soft-bottom portions of the Outer Harbor. Occasional specimens also were taken in the deeper muddy portions of the gutters. Only two specimens were taken from the Vineyard Sound side. The predominantly sandy bottom of the Vineyard Sound entrances may exclude *Nucula*. It was not, as will be shown later, a predominant member of the unique assemblage of the Inner Harbor habitat.

Another protobranch pelecypod, *Yoldia limatula*, also demonstrated the preference of these deposit-feeding forms for the low-energy soft bottoms. The influence that this organism has upon sediment stability and community trophic structure is discussed at length by Rhoads and Young (1970). Fig. 45 illustrates not only restriction of *Yoldia* to the Inner and Outer Harbor muds, but also the fact that the high populations occurred only in muds with the lowest Eh's. The only two occurrences of *Yoldia* outside of the Inner Harbor type habitat were in the only other areas where low Eh's also occurred — Grassy Pond and the deep backwater hole in West Gutter. Although analyses of organic matter of the sediments were not made, it was easy to discern that sediments, in which *Yoldia* and *Nucula* were taken, were exceedingly rich in decomposing organic matter. Whether or not this organic matter can be assimilated by these pelecypods is questionable, since it is primarily cellulose from the decomposition of eel grass washed in from surrounding eel grass beds.

Two pelecypod species occurring in the same habitat as *Yoldia* and *Nucula*, but of a totally different order (Eulamellibranchia), were *Mulinia lateralis* and *Macoma tenta*. *Mulinia lateralis* showed the greatest restriction to Inner—Outer Harbor muds (Fig. 46), and of all species of invertebrates occurring in this habitat *Mulinia* was the most persistent throughout the lowest-reducing conditions. Considering that *Mulinia*, a mactrid, is essentially a suspension feeder and possesses a short inhalent siphon, it is somewhat of a paradox to find it representative of an organic-rich detritus bottom. This species was also an indicator species of similar habitats in the coastal waters of the Gulf of Mexico where Parker (1956) demonstrated that its abundance was highly correlated with the exceedingly fine silty clays of the Pro-Delta front environment of the Mississippi Delta. It was also the predominant

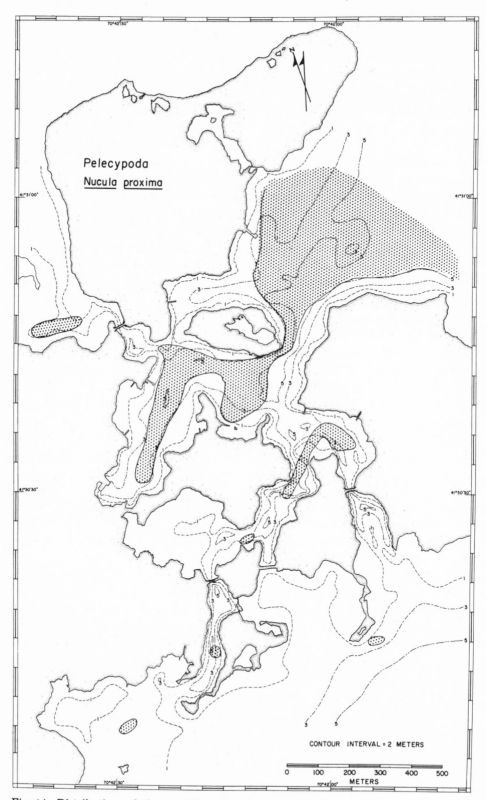

Fig. 44. Distribution of the protobranch pelecypod *Nucula proxima*, characteristic of clayey-silt sediments in the Inner Harbor and Outer Harbor.

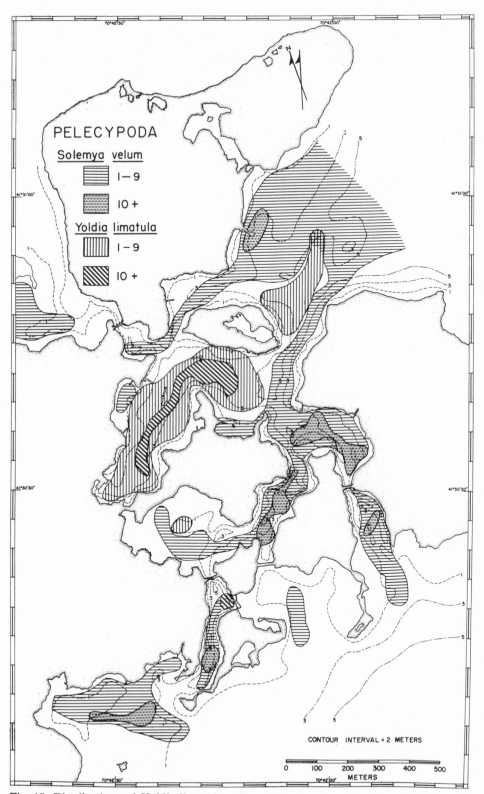

Fig. 45. Distributions of *Yoldia limatula*, a deposit feeder, found on the soft bottoms in the Complex, and *Solemya velum*, a suspension feeder, found in the channels and eel grass beds.

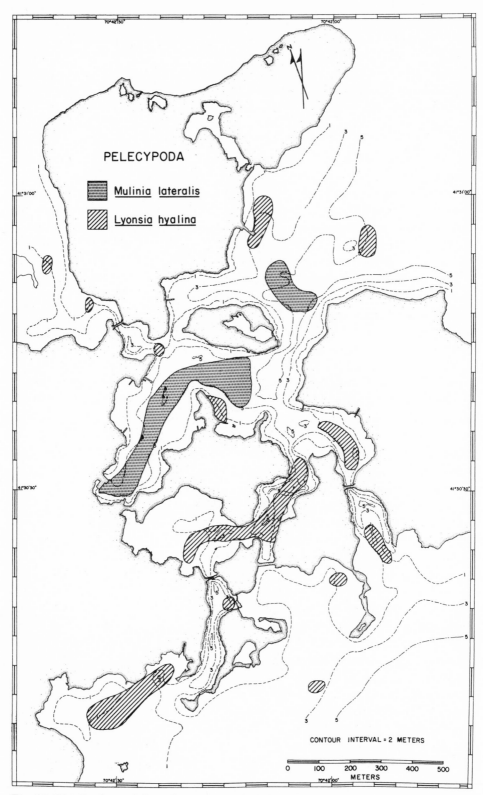

Fig. 46. Distributions of the pelecypods: *Mulinia lateralis,* typical of Inner Harbor habitat reducing muds, and *Lyonsia hyalina,* found in the channels.

mollusk in the silty clay bottoms of Aransas and San Antonio Bays, Texas (Parker, 1959). On the other hand, it was virtually the only molluscan species surviving in the extreme hypersaline portions of the Laguna Madre, where sediments were predominantly sand. A closely related species of *Mulinia* also was taken on the fine clayey bottoms of the shallow shelf of the Gulf of California (Parker, 1964a). Actually, *Mulinia lateralis* is extremely hardy, occurring from Prince Edward Island, Canada, to Yucatan, Mexico, in virtually every kind of sediment and in salinities ranging from 5‰ to 80‰. However, this species never attains large numbers in areas where other species and numbers of invertebrates are abundant. For this reason, *Mulinia* was considered as an indicator of environmental adversity. It may be extremely sensitive to competition and can only become abundant when nothing else can survive. A few preliminary experiments in the laboratory indicated that this species may actually be a deposit-feeding suspension feeder. It seems to use its exhalent siphon to stir up the flocculent layer so as to throw the organic matter into suspension just over the bottom. These suspended organic particles are then drawn out of suspension in the normal manner of a filter feeder.

The other eulamellibranch pelecypod with a distribution restricted to mud bottom of the Inner—Outer Harbor was *Macoma tenta*. Its distribution is shown on Fig. 47. The only exception to its occurrence in the Inner—Outer Harbor habitat was in the deep, muddy hole in the north end of West Gutter, a habitat not unlike that of the Inner Harbor. It is not surprising that *Macoma tenta* occurred in this habitat, as it is definitely a deposit feeder, using its exceedingly long prehensile siphon to draw up organic particles from the surface sediments. This same species was also characteristic of the same environment along the Gulf of Mexico coast (Parker, 1956, 1959). Another tellinid pelecypod, *Tellina agilis*, also was taken in large numbers within the Hadley Harbor Complex. Although it was a common inhabitant of the Inner Harbor sediments, it also was found in almost every part of the Complex, being one of the few really ubiquitous mollusks of the area. Two forms of this species can be recognized on the basis of color and shape, but, because they co-occurred at many of the stations and could not be separated ecologically, they have been considered in the text as one species. Boss (1968) records difference in color locally within its range, but considers them all one species. When counts were first made and entered onto the IBM data cards, this population was separated into *Tellina agilis* and *T. versicolor*. A comprehensive study of the autecology of *T. agilis* in the Woods Hole region has been completed by Gilbert (1970).

One of the pelecypod species whose distribution coincided with that of the gastropods *Hydrobia* and *Lacuna*, was the venerid clam *Gemma gemma*, the distribution of which can be seen on Fig. 47. This is a small clam which

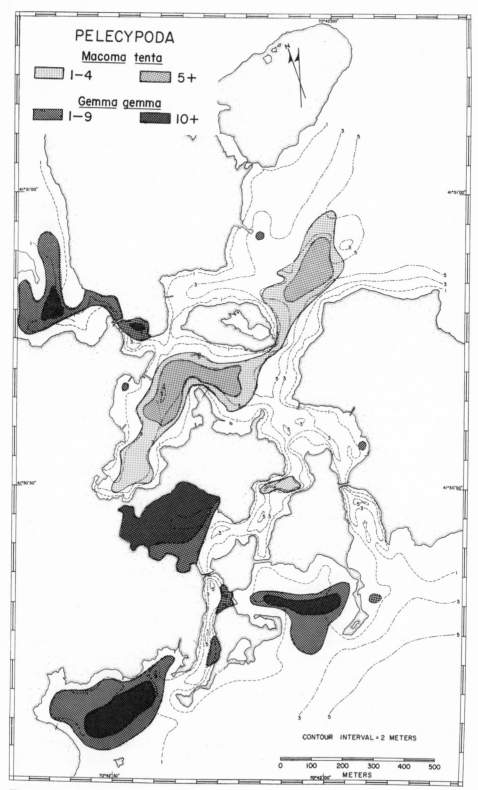

Fig. 47. Distribution of the small pelecypods: *Macoma tenta*, typical of the Inner Harbor habitat, and *Gemma gemma*, characteristic of the Sand Flats.

in Hadley Harbor attains a maximum size of only a few millimeters. Under optimum conditions, it is also one of the most abundant mollusks in the world. Hundreds of thousands of individuals were counted per square meter in Barnstable Harbor (Sanders et al., 1962; and Green and Hobson, 1970), Sagadahoc Bay, Maine (Bradley, 1957, 1959), and on a coastal area in New Jersey (Sellmer, 1959, 1967). It is primarily Boreal in its geographical distribution and typical of broad, enclosed tidal sand flats. Tidal sand flats were of rather small extent in the Hadley Harbor Complex, hence this species did not attain the high concentrations found elsewhere. Even so, counts of over $11,000/m^2$ were recorded in the Hadley Harbor area, and the average of all samples was about $1,500/m^2$. It was seasonal in its occurrence, being absent from samples during the coldest portion of the winter months. A comprehensive discussion of this species can be found in a paper by Sellmer (1967) and a more recent paper on its population dynamics by Green and Hobson (1970).

Two more species of pelecypods were selected to demonstrate restrictive distributional patterns. The protobranchiate suspension feeder *Solemya velum* demonstrates adequately the relationship between a strictly suspension-feeding animal and high kinetic energy bottoms. As shown on Fig. 45, *Yoldia limatula* and *Solemya velum* were mutually exclusive in that there was only one station at which both occurred simultaneously. *Solemya* perhaps was the only species which did occur in high numbers within the eel grass beds, although it attained its greatest concentrations in the high-current-scoured, shelly-gravel channels. As observed by us in the laboratory, *Solemya* is a highly motile species for a pelecypod, and can even dart about freely in the water, using its "velum" as an umbrella-like siphon. This may partially explain its success in the high-current areas. This species was also relatively abundant, attaining populations of almost $1,500/m^2$ and averaging $250/m^2$.

The final pelecypod species used to illustrate restrictive distributional patterns was *Lyonsia hyalina*, which was confined entirely to areas of high current, and high but seasonal eel grass concentrations (Fig. 46). This species is considered a nester and secretes sand grains on its rather bristly or sticky periostracum. Its feeding habits are not well known, but it is assumed to be a modified suspension feeder. *Lyonsia* was not an abundant species, normally occurring as single adults per station, and its highest concentration of about $200/m^2$ was made up exclusively of small juveniles.

A number of other pelecypod species were considered abundant enough to examine their distributions. Of these, only *Tellina agilis* was found in the Inner—Outer Harbor muds. Two cardiids, *Laevicardium mortoni* and *Cerastoderma pinnulatum*, were confined entirely to the deep channels of the Buzzards Bay—Woods Hole side of the Complex but, as will be shown later, were not a predominant part of the unique channel community. The quahog *Mercenaria mercenaria* occurred in dense beds in certain portions of the Complex. It did not show any extreme habitat preference, being found in both the Inner Harbor and in the gutters. It was, however, partially restricted to a horizontal narrow band just subtidally along the margins of the Complex. *Tagelus divisus* and *Ensis directus*, although relatively uncommon, were both found only in the deeper portions of the gutters, but for some un-explained reason were absent throughout all of 1965.

Amphipoda

As a major taxon, the Amphipoda were the most abundant identified organisms in the Complex and could thus be studied in sufficient detail to derive specific ecological implications. With the exception of those taken in the last few "repeat" stations in August, 1965, all amphipods were identified to species, size, sex, and stage of development. This tremendous task was undertaken by J.S. Nagle, formerly associated with this Program. Many of the identifications were further checked by Dr. E. Bousfield of the National Museum of Canada, who published a thorough revision of the systematics of the New England Amphipoda (Bousfield, 1973). At least 62 species of am-phipods, of which 26 occurred at enough stations to ascertain habitat prefer-ences, were identified from this small area. For the most part, amphipods are epifaunal and thus showed preferences for epifaunal habitats, particularly eel grass beds in the channels. Nagle (1968), using data obtained on this project, carried out a special study of this eel grass epifaunal community. One of the more revealing aspects of amphipod ecology was the distribution of so-called "sympatric" species — several species of the same genus apparently living in the same habitat. Nine genera of amphipods were represented by two or more species per genus, and five of the genera had at least three species occurring in the Complex. Before demonstrating habitat specificity for the amphipods, we will examine the problem of multiplicity of species within the same genus in apparently the same habitat.

The most interesting distributional patterns derived from the distribution of several species within the same genus are those of the genus *Ampelisca*. Three species (possibly four), based upon recent revisions by Mills (1964, 1967), are now recognized in the Hadley Harbor region. Prior to Mills' study, the presently named three species were considered one or possibly two spe-cies, and were known to occur in the same habitat. If one looks at the total distribution of ampeliscids in Hadley Harbor (Fig. 48), it can be seen that they occurred almost everywhere except on the wave-influenced sand flats. It is also one of the few amphipod genera which were taken frequently within the Inner and Outer Harbor silts. However, examinations of the distri-

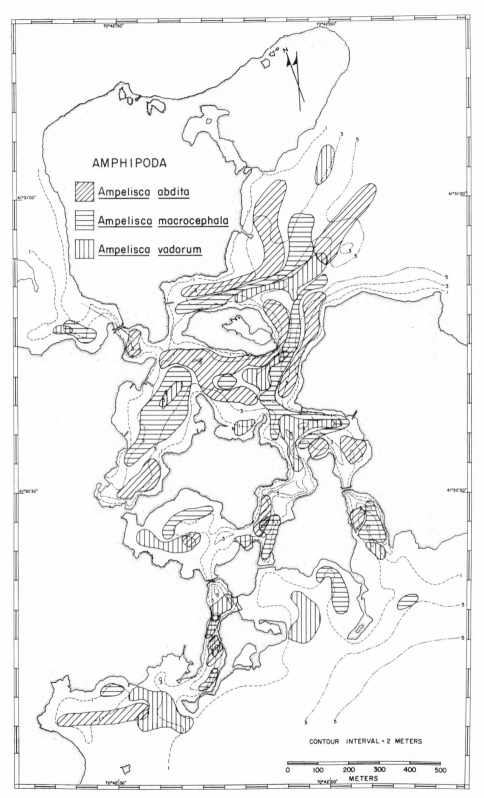

Fig. 48. Distributions of three closely related amphipods: *Ampelisca abdita*, *A. macro-cephala*, and *A. vadorum*, each of which occupied a separate niche within the Hadley Harbor Complex.

butional patterns of individual species of *Ampelisca* discloses a rather remarkable case of species exclusion or specificity for habitat. Overlap of two
species (never three) occurred at only seven stations out of the total of 350
stations at which the genus *Ampelisca* was taken, or a little over 1% of the
total population. *Ampelisca abdita* was a species of shallow water, slightly
sandy mud bottom, and occurred closest to shore, probably associated with
detritus in the larger eel grass beds. *A. macrocephala*, now considered *A.
verrilli* (see Mills, 1967), on the other hand occurred on the finest mud
bottoms and lowest-Eh areas, showing perhaps a greater preference for organic-rich bottoms. Its only occurrences on sand bottom were associated
with high eel grass concentration (and associated detritus) during the fall. *A.
vadorum* was intermediate in its requirements, occurring in the same habitats
as the other two, but not at the same stations, and also not at the same
season.

Sanders (1960) indicates that two species of *Ampelisca*, *A. spinipes* and *A.
macrocephala*, occurred at Station "R" in Buzzards Bay, which was primarily a clayey-silt bottom. The later revision by Mills (1964) revealed that what
Sanders had included under the term "*A. spinipes*" was in reality *A. abdita*
and *A. vadorum*. At Station "R" then, *A. abdita* was the most abundant
crustacean (although 54th in rank of abundance of all species), and *A.
macrocephala* was relatively rare. Sanders (1958), in an analysis of all of his
Buzzards Bay stations, found that two different species occurred simultaneously at his Station "P". *A. macrocephala* was the predominant one of the
two, and *A. vadorum* was also abundant (H.L. Sanders, personal communication, 1965). The sediments at Station "P" were fine, fairly well-sorted sand.
According to Sanders' findings, *A. macrocephala* and *A. vadorum* are considered fine-sand bottom species and *A. abdita* a silt or clayey-silt bottom
species.

Within the Hadley Harbor Complex, there seemed to be a reversal of
preferences. *A. abdita* was more common on the well-sorted, fine-sand bottom, while both *A. macrocephala* and *A. vadorum* were more abundant on
the clayey-silt sediments. If the distributions of the three ampeliscids
(Fig. 48) are compared with the charts of median diameter (Fig. 20) and
sorting coefficients (Fig. 21), it can be observed that, in general, *A. abdita*
was associated with coarse silt which is well sorted; *A. macrocephala* occurred mostly on fine silt and clay, which was medium well sorted; *A. vadorum* was found primarily on well-sorted, very fine to fine sand. Reasons for
the discrepancy between the results of Sanders and of this study may be
partly attributable to problems concerned with the systematics of the local
species. On the other hand, Sanders' investigations were carried out in relatively large homogeneous areas of similar environmental characteristics. The
Hadley Harbor Complex was highly variable in both habitats and environ-

mental factors, with few homogeneous areas of more than a few hundred square meters in size. Because of the small size and close proximity of highly variable habitats, different competitive relationships may be set up between related species of organisms.

A rather different picture was obtained on intraspecific competition from the distribution of the amphipod genus *Corophium*. Six species were taken, all in the same habitat, with the three most abundant species almost always occurring at the same stations. Because of the complexity of depicting six distribution maps of nearly the same patterns on one illustration, those data are not given visually. Individuals of the genus *Corophium* preferred dense beds of eel grass in the high-energy channels and sand flats. They avoided the fine sediments and low Eh's of Inner Harbor and Grassy Pond. The most consistently abundant species was *Corophium acutum*, which showed strong seasonal abundance on the eel grass of the shallow sand flats. The species of *Corophium* with the densest populations per unit area was *C. insidiosum*, averaging over 7,500 animals/m^2. This species was also a member of the eel grass epifaunal community, but was more abundant on the Vineyard Sound side than in Buzzards Bay. The other four species occurred at fewer than 20 stations. *Corophium bonelli*, taken at 16 stations, had one of the highest counts (25,000/m^2) of any species. This species preferred the channel eel grass beds to those on the outer sand flats. The other three species, *C. acherusicum*, *C. tuberculatum*, and *Corophium* sp., occurred at the same stations in the channels in relatively low eel grass concentrations. It is impossible to state that any of these *Corophium* species is mutually exclusive of the other five (Nagle, 1968). There is some indication that each has a separate and specific breeding period and that no one overlaps the other. This means that the periods of peak abundance (juveniles, primarily) of each species are temporarily separate from any other. Therefore, when two or three species were found in the same niche, only one species was predominant, while the others were the remnants of the previous peaks of abundance.

Three species of *Paraphoxus* were taken in the same channel eel grass beds as *Corophium*. Both *Paraphoxus epistoma* and *P. spinosus* occurred at the same stations, while *P. oculatus* occurred at completely different stations, but in exactly the same kind of niche and usually only a few meters away from the other two species. *P. oculatus* was the most abundant (1,500/m^2), found at about 50 stations. All three species were more characteristic of the Vineyard Sound side of the Complex and appeared to invade or be recruited from Vineyard Sound rather than from Buzzards Bay. The ampeliscas, on the other hand, seemed to be derived primarily from Buzzards Bay. The *Corophium* species showed no particular trend towards either Buzzards Bay or Vineyard Sound.

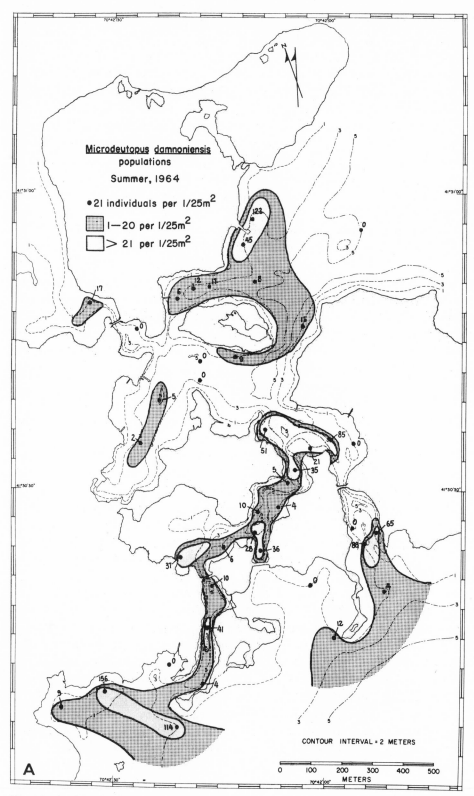

Fig. 49. A. Distribution of *Microdeutopus damnoniensis* during the summer of 1964, concentrated in deeper waters of the channels and Outer Harbor. B. Distribution of

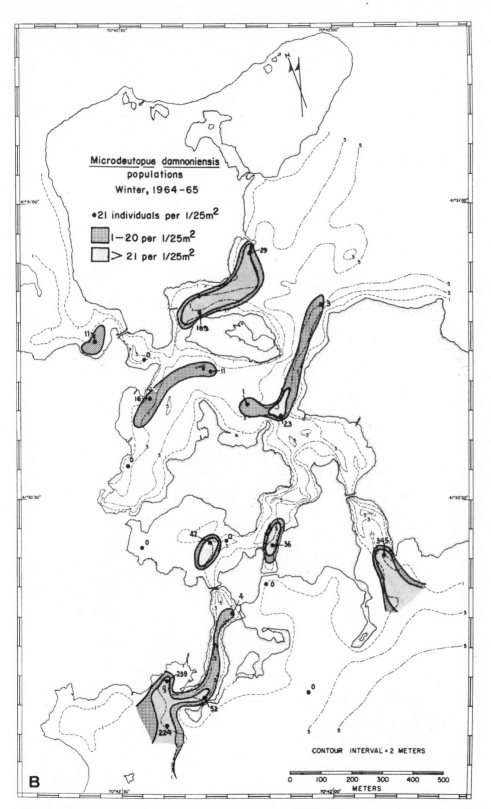

Microdeutopus damnoniensis during the winter of 1964—65, now concentrated on the shallow flats and near the edges of channels. (Illustrations modified from Nagle, 1968.)

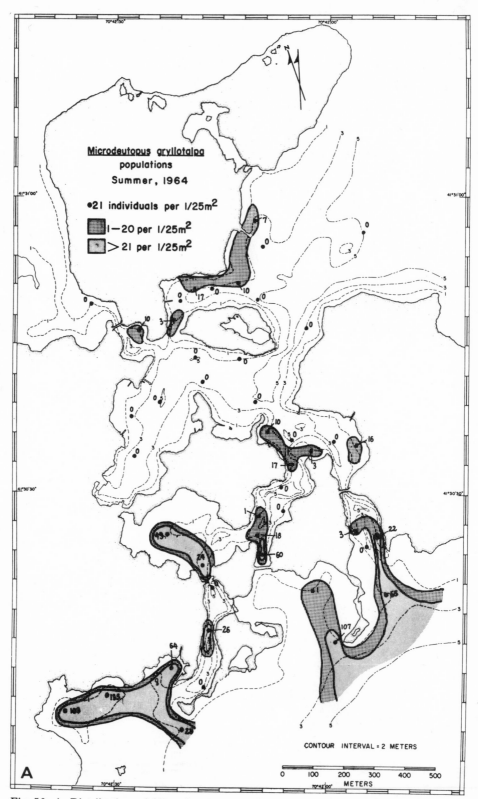

Fig. 50. A. Distribution of *Microdeutopus gryllotalpa* during the summer of 1964, occupying the shallow eel grass beds almost exclusively. B. Distribution of *Microdeutopus*

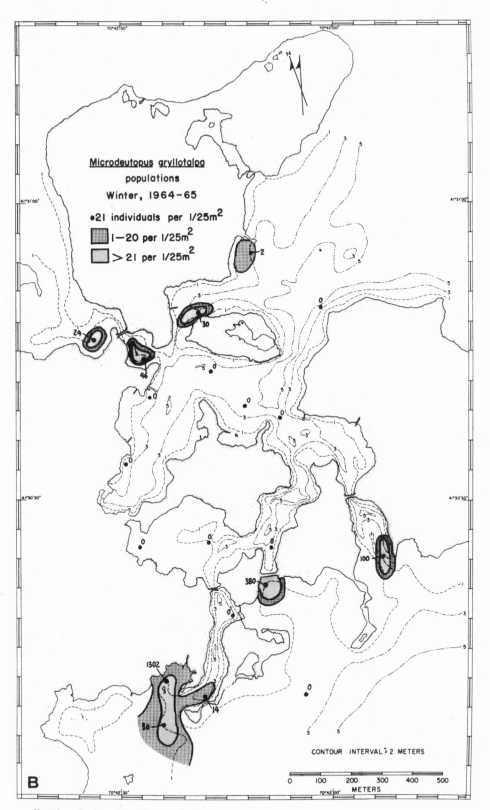

gryllotalpa during the winter of 1964—65, now occupying channels and protected coves. (Illustrations modified from Nagle, 1965).

There were three more amphipod species pairs within the Complex, of which two pairs demonstrate the principle of mutual exclusion for members of each pair. *Microdeutopus* was another genus represented by a species pair, although it was taken at more stations than any other species of mega-invertebrate. The two species, *Microdeutopus damnoniensis* and *M. gryllotalpa*, were part of a special study carried out by J.S. Nagle. Some of his preliminary results are presented here. Details of this study are discussed at length in Nagle (1968). If all occurrences of the two species of *Microdeutopus* are plotted on the same chart, they nearly always occur together and in roughly the same abundance. Nagle (1965, 1968) examined their distribution as separate entities through time, and depending upon the season found striking differences in the distribution of the two. For instance, it can be seen on Fig. 49A,B that during the summer the two species occupied different areas. *Microdeutopus gryllotalpa* attained its predominance in Grassy Pond and the other large shallow eel grass area in Lackey's Bay. Few specimens were taken in the Inner and Outer Harbor or in Northwest Gutter. On the other hand, during the same period of the summer, *M. damnoniensis* attained its greatest concentration in the Outer Harbor and deeper portions of the Inner Harbor and gutters. It was scarce in the shallow sand flats in Vineyard Sound and Grassy Pond. A few preliminary experiments on heat tolerances indicated that the thermal death point of *M. damnoniensis* was close to or at the temperatures found during the warmest period of the summer on the shallow sand flats. In the winter, *M. damnoniensis* was found in the shallow areas, while *M. gryllotalpa* was found in the deeper portions of the Complex (Fig. 50A,B). Fig. 51 indicates the areas of maximum abundance and breeding periods of the more common amphipods.

The other two sympatric species pairs within the same genus pose no problem of mutual exclusion or competition. One of the members of each pair attained large populations of great areal extent, and the other species of the pair was present only at three stations. In the case of *Listriella barnardi* and *Listriella clymenella*, *L. barnardi* was very common but restricted entirely to the east side of the Complex, following the continual channel from Buzzards Bay (the Woods Hole portion) to Vineyard Sound; largest populations occurred in the deeper portions of the gutter. *L. clymenella* was taken only at three stations (with the polychaete *Clymenella*), and its distribution was apparently restricted by its commensal association in the tube of the polychaete. *Clymenella* was uncommon in our collections, thus, it is not surprising that the commensal amphipod was also rare. *L. barnardi*, on the other hand, was not associated with any other invertebrate, was relatively abundant, and was apparently a free-living benthic form. The other genus is *Microprotopus* and comprises two species. Like *Listriella*, one species, *Microprotopus ranei*, was common, was also associated with eel grass, and was

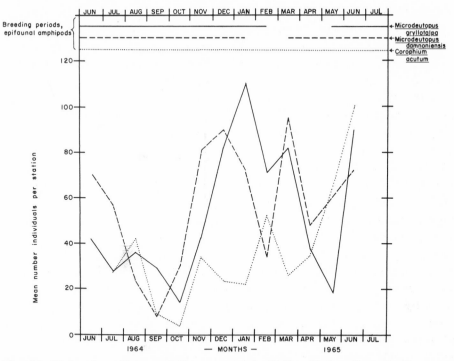

Fig. 51. Plots of weekly population averages in Hadley Harbor throughout an annual cycle for the amphipods *Microdeutopus damnoniensis*, *Microdeutopus gryllotalpa*, and *Corophium acutum*. Shown also are breeding periods of all three species. (Based on data supplied by J.S. Nagle.)

found primarily on the Vineyard Sound side of the gutters. *M. maculatus* occurred at only three stations, all in Vineyard Sound (Lackey's Bay), and never at any of the *M. ranei* stations.

Habitat specificity is not characteristic of the amphipods, presumably because of their relatively high motility. The majority of the mollusks, which are much larger, showed restricted species patterns, while the amphipods as a whole encompassed broad areas of distribution, or else were found as small patches with no particular habitat preference. Even so, there were portions of the Hadley Harbor Complex which were optimal habitats for each species of amphipod and, for most of the species, certain areas which each species avoided. Twenty-six species occurred at enough stations to suggest habitat specificity. The number of characteristic species increased from two in the adverse environment of the Inner Harbor to sixteen in the optimal amphipod habitat of the channel eel grass beds.

Within the fine-mud bottom of Inner Harbor and Outer Harbor, only three species were relatively abundant, and one of these, *Jassa falcata*, was more or less restricted to this habitat. According to Nagle (1968), *Jassa* is a suspension feeder and tube builder, requiring quiet waters for feeding. The largest amphipod collected, *Jassa falcata*, was an exclusive inhabitant of the quieter clayey-silt bottoms, and as is usually the case with larger organisms, small numbers (for amphipods) were taken at most stations. *Ampelisca macrocephala* was another species of the Inner—Outer Harbor fine-mud bottom, although it occurred also in some of the finer sediments in the outer flats. The other species which occupied a portion of the Inner—Outer Harbor niche (but only the oxidizing part) was *Batea catherinensis*. This species spread from the deep Inner—Outer Harbor area into the deep channels of the West—East Gutter Complex and so might also be called a channel species. *Batea* appears to be a true infaunal amphipod, and was seldom found epifaunally on eel grass. It thus resembles the only other two Inner Harbor species of amphipods which were also infaunal species.

The outer shallow, wave-influenced sand flats were characterized by five species of amphipods, only one of which was entirely restricted to them. *Acanthohaustorius millsi*, a recently described species (Bousfield, 1965), showed a narrow but consistent distribution related to the very well-sorted clean sand flats. It was consistently taken in numbers averaging about $4,000/m^2$ at Physical Station *24*, on the sand flat outside of the entrance to West Gutter in Vineyard Sound. It was rare or absent during the winter months, attaining its maximum population density in May, June, and July as shown on Fig. 52. Another species of amphipod characteristic of the sand flats on the Vineyard Sound side of the Complex was *Elasmopus laevis*. This species occurred at every station taken in Lackey's Bay and surrounding portions of the Vineyard Sound side. A few specimens also were taken in the northern entrance to East Gutter and the sand area of the Outer Harbor. The occasional records of this species found living off the sand flats are limited to one specimen per station, while an average of 9 specimens per station or $225/m^2$ occurred in the shallow sand flat habitat on the Vineyard Sound side. *Ampelisca vadorum* already has been discussed as an inhabitant of the fine, well-sorted sand bottoms, and its distribution as shown on Fig. 48 verifies its relationship to the outer, wave-influenced sand flats. The two other species found in large numbers on the sand flats, *Corophium acutum* and *Paraphoxus oculatus*, were not nearly as restricted to this habitat as the other three species. *Paraphoxus oculatus* (an infaunal species) not only attained its greatest concentration on the sand flats at all Complex entrances, but also was found in the sandy shallow edges of the gutters. *Corophium acutum* was taken in all habitats, including the Inner Harbor muds, but tended to be densest on the sand flats. J.S. Nagle (1968, and personal communication) found a marked seasonal abundance of this species on the sand flats, although it apparently breeds the year round. The seasonality of this epifaunal species can be attributed to fluctuations of either temperature or

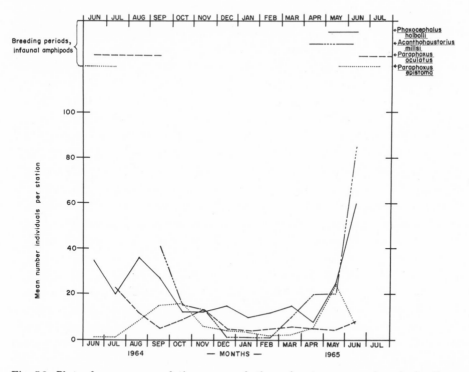

Fig. 52. Plot of average population per week throughout one annual cycle for the sand flat amphipod *Acanthohaustorius millsi*, showing peak abundance in summer and absence in winter on the sand flats. Also shown are weekly polulation averages for three more infaunal amphipod species found primarily on the sand flats and in the channels, as well as breeding periods for all four species.

eel grass. The five species of amphipods given here were not the only ones found in this habitat in large numbers. Virtually every epifaunal species of amphipod found in this study was taken on the eel grass covered portions of the sand flats, but only five species had their greatest concentration there.

The next habitat, the deep, strong current-dominated channels, contained the largest number of characteristic species of amphipods (16) with 9 species which were more apt to be found there than in other portions of the Complex. The amphipod which was most restricted to the channel eel grass, particularly the deeper portions, was *Listriella barnardi*, which like most of the channel species was almost entirely restricted to the eastern and southern side of the Complex. There were no occurrences in the Inner Harbor or Northwest Gutter, and it would appear that this species followed the primary circulation from the Woods Hole to Vineyard Sound. *Listriella barnardi* was never an abundant species, an average of only 4 or 5 specimens per station or about 100/m². A species with almost the same distribution pattern as *Listriella* was *Microprotopus ranei*, which was confined entirely to the channels. It, too, was not very abundant at any one station, averaging only 4 per station or, again, 100/m². The most abundant species with an apparent preference for the channel habitat was *Lysianopsis alba*, which was taken at over 100 stations and averaged between 50 and 100 per station or 2,500/m². It is likely that this species is more of an eel grass community species than a channel species, since its distribution most parallels that of *Phoxocephalus holbolli*. One other species restricted to channels and which was relatively abundant was *Cymadusa compta*; it occurred at about 55 stations and averaged about 10 per station or 250/m². It occurred at only 8 stations outside the gutters, and at these were represented only by single specimens. *Corophium bonelli, C. acherusicum, Paracaprella tenuis,* and *Elasmopus laevis* also were characteristic of the channels. None of these species was abundant at any one station, nor did they occur at many stations. All were scattered throughout the deeper portions of the channels and one or two specimens were found in the other major habitats. There is no concrete evidence as to which of these channel species are epifaunal or infaunal. *Leptocheirus pinguis* also is a characteristic channel species; whereas most of these have their maximum concentrations on the Vineyard Sound side of the gutters, *Leptocheirus* was almost exclusively found in the deep channel leading from the Outer Harbor into the wide area of the Inner Harbor where West and East Gutters converge from their separate Vineyard Sound entrances. Only three specimens were taken south of the Goats Neck entrance to West Gutter. This species was plainly derived from Woods Hole or Buzzards Bay via Woods Hole, and cannot get through to Vineyard Sound. From its distribution, it can be assumed to be an infaunal species, preferring a silty sand, or, in terms of other sedimentary parameters, a poorly-sorted medium sand. Recent research on *L. pinguis* autecology has been carried out by Michael (1971).

The final habitat which was distinct for certain of the amphipods was the shallow eel grass beds. This habitat supported the largest populations of amphipods, most of which were epifaunal. Nine species were characteristic, although none were restricted to the shallow eel grass beds. The two species which were most abundant upon eel grass were discussed previously. These were *Microdeutopus damnoniensis* and *M. gryllotalpa*. Their presence and concentration on eel grass was seasonal and could be related to grass growth and breeding cycles. Both species had their greatest concentration associated with the eel grass on the Vineyard Sound side of the Complex, although *M. damnoniensis* also frequently occurred on the Buzzards Bay side. Both species approached populations of 30,000/m². *Phoxocephalus holbolli* is also an eel grass epifaunal species, although its primary centers of distribution were in the gutters, principally on the tall eel grass clumps in the shallower portions of the channels. When found associated directly with eel grass in the shoaler areas, populations averaged about 25 per station or about $275/m^2$. In the smaller stands of eel grass or relatively bare portions of the bottom, counts ran only 1 or 2 per station. *Corophium insidiosum* was the most abundant of the genus and also the species most closely associated with eel grass. It avoided areas where eel grass did not grow and attained its highest populations of 4,000 per station, or $100,000/m^2$, in areas of high summer eel grass growth. *Caprella geometrica* is clearly an associate of the eel grass, which is borne out by its peculiar shape resembling the epiphytic algae living on eel grass blades. Its seasonal distribution is centered around that of eel grass beds in the channels, with an average population of about 8 per station or $200/m^2$. It was far more common on the Vineyard Sound side of the Complex than on the Buzzards Bay—Woods Hole side. *Ampelisca abdita* is an infaunal species, but, as shown on Fig. 46, it prefers the substrate in and around the eel grass beds. *Ampithoe longimana* and *Dexamine thea* also are associates of the eel grass beds but were somewhat less abundant than the other species. *Ampithoe* was the more abundant, while only one or two individuals of *Dexamine* occurred at each station. The remaining 35 or so species of amphipods were found at less than 10 stations and were mostly associated with epifaunal communities. One interesting fact arising from this study was the apparent strict vertical zonation of amphipod species on eel grass blades and algae fronds (Nagle, 1968). Vertical distribution could be closely correlated with feeding types.

Ostracoda

Of the fully identified taxa collected during this study, the Ostracoda constitute the next most abundant group. Over 30 species were identified by Dr. N.C. Hulings. Two of the species occurred at nearly every station and, in some instances, there were over $25,000/m^2$. *Parasterope pollex* was by far the most abundant, and it was also ubiquitous. This species was taken at all but three stations in the Inner Harbor, two stations in Grassy Pond, and two stations in the Outer Harbor (Fig. 53). Comparative abundances were more indicative of habitat preference than just presence or absence in this case. Note on Fig. 53 that *Parasterope* occurred in concentrations of over 100 per station in the channels and on the densest eel grass beds. This distribution chart suggests that, although ubiquitous, *Parasterope* was a predominant member of the channel eel grass community. A comprehensive discussion of the ecology of this species in Hadley Harbor is given in Hulings (1969).

The next most abundant species of ostracode was *Propontocypris edwardsi*. Distribution maps of this species and the other ostracodes are not given, as they either duplicate that of *Parasterope* or are so patchy that they do not demonstrate habitat specificity. *Propontocypris* was also ubiquitous, occur-

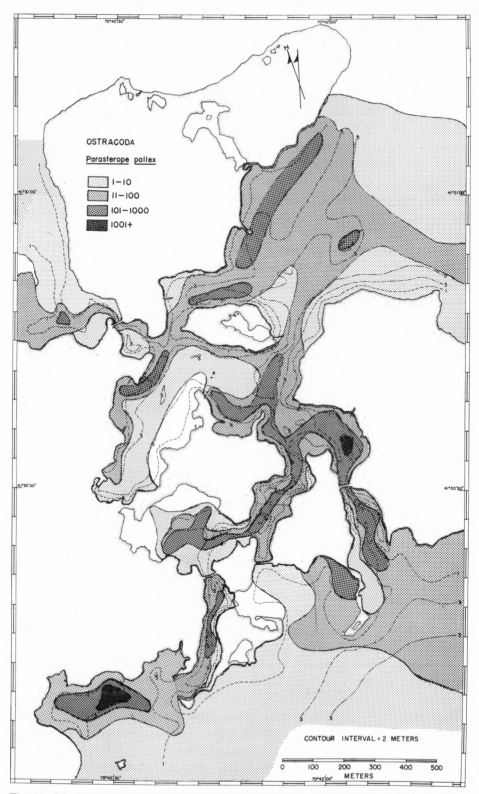

Fig. 53. Distribution of the ostracod *Parasterope pollex*, ubiquitous within Hadley Harbor, Massachusetts. High concentrations show it had a preference for eel grass beds within the channels.

ring at over three-quarters of all stations taken. It was missing or rare in the Inner Harbor, the margins of Grassy Pond, bare sand flats, and on the fine silt bottom of the Outer Harbor. Like *Parasterope*, it was confined to channel areas with high eel grass growth. The *Propontocypris* populations were just as high as those of *Parasterope*, attaining concentrations of $37,500/m^2$ and occurring in maximum populations at the same stations as *Parasterope*.

Cythereis zostericola and *Sarsiella zostericola* also were relatively abundant ostracodes which, as their names suggest, were associated with eel grass in the channels, although *Sarsiella* occurred to a limited extent in the Inner and Outer Harbor and also on the sand flats. It was uncommon, only one or two individuals being taken at each station, compared to the other two species of ostracodes. As most of the stations where *Sarsiella* was found were in eel grass areas, it is a part of the eel grass community. It is not known whether these animals fed on the attached epiphytic algae, the diatoms, or the plant debris at the base of the eel grass.

Six more species of ostracodes were taken at sufficient stations to plot their distributions. *Cushmanidea echolsae*, *C. magniporosa*, *C. sandersi*, *Megacythere robusta*, and *Camylocythere laeva* were almost exclusive inhabitants of the sand flats and *Leptocythere paracastanea* was a channel species — all six apparently derived from Vineyard Sound. None of the species exceeded 10—20 individuals at a station, and most of their occurrences were limited to 1 or 2 individuals.

Smaller groups of Arthropoda

A number of smaller Arthropoda, representing rarer taxa, were taken in sufficient quantities in Hadley Harbor to warrant their discussion. The Cephalocarida were represented by the single species known from this coast, *Hutchinsoniella macracantha*. Previous records of this primitive crustacean indicated that it did not occur in less than 5—7 m and was restricted to soft bottoms of the Sanders Station "R" type (Sanders, 1956, 1958, 1960). Within Hadley Harbor, *Hutchinsoniella* occurred in almost every habitat from muds of Inner Harbor to eel grass covered sand flats. It did not occur on the bare, just sub-tidal sand flats but was found at a depth of less than 0.5 m in the eel grass beds (Fig. 54). Its greatest concentrations were found in the deeper portions of the channels, usually on a soft clayey silt substrate or on poorly sorted sediments. Many specimens were taken on a sandy substrate, but the animal is considered primarily infaunal and prefers a fine, organic-rich bottom (H.L. Sanders, personal communication, 1965). Although the usual number of *Hutchinsoniella* per station varied from 2 to $125/m^2$, it occurred in maximum concentrations of over $3,600/m^2$, much higher than hitherto reported by Sanders (1958, 1960). Puzzling is the fact,

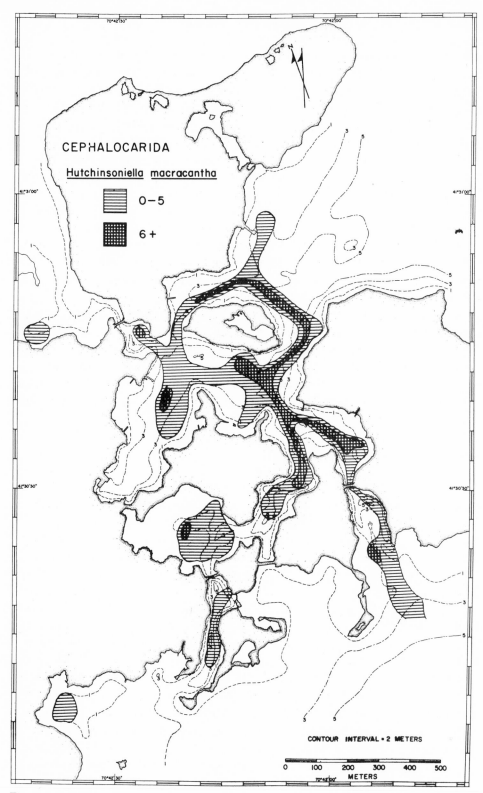

Fig. 54. Distribution of the cephalocarid *Hutchinsoniella macracantha*, occurring in areas of high currents and poorly sorted fine sediments. Majority occurrences in 1964.

however, that this species was found mainly in 1964. During the late spring, summer, and fall of 1964, it was taken at nearly every station sampled in the interior of Hadley Harbor. On the other hand, during the following year of sampling, from November 1964 to September 1965, only 15 specimens were taken, 11 of them at one station (Repeat Station *19* in Grassy Pond). H.L. Sanders (personal communication, 1965) also reported a scarcity of this animal in Buzzards Bay and Quisset Harbor in 1965, at localities where *Hutchinsoniella* usually had been abundant over the past 6—8 years. No explanation can be offered for the almost complete disappearance of the species in less than a year.

Another taxon (Acarina or mites) also was apparently represented by a single species in the Hadley Harbor Complex. Little is known concerning marine mites. They were taken in relatively large numbers and at about half of the stations. Dr. K. Hyland of the University of Rhode Island examined the collections and identified the single species as *Copidognathus* sp. The species itself was not named at the time of identification, although the genus was mentioned as occurring in the Woods Hole region by Hag (1965). The distribution map of *Copidognathus* sp. (Fig. 55), shows it to be ubiquitous, with no habitat preference, and present in almost as many Inner Harbor clayey silt stations as outer sand flat and deep channel stations. It is significant that the maximum populations of over $250/m^2$ coincided with those of amphipods and maximum growth of eel grass. It is not known whether the mites were associated directly with the eel grass, the high organic content of the sediments amidst the eel grass, or even commensal with the amphipods.

Even the class Insecta was relatively well represented within the Complex. A larva of the genus *Hydrobaenus* (Order Diptera, Family Chironomidae = Tendipedidae) occurred at 45 stations and averaged $50/m^2$. A number of specimens of adult Diptera (which could not be identified to Family) were also taken at 12 stations. Location of the adult Diptera close to shore suggests that these insects were derived from the shore or overhanging vegetation. *Hydrobaenus* sp. seemed to be entirely marine with a restricted distribution. All individuals were associated with strong currents in the narrow constricted portions of the gutters, and were found on poorly sorted fine to medium sands. There was no close association with eel grass, although these plants in varying amounts occurred at every station in which *Hydrobaenus* was taken.

A small and little-known group of crustaceans, the cumaceans, demonstrated nicely the restriction of habitat and separateness of the two predominant forms. Four species were identified within the Complex, but two of them from only three or four stations as apparent accidentals from the deeper waters of Buzzards Bay and Vineyard Sound. Two species, *Leucon americanus* and *Oxyurostylis smithi* (Fig. 56), were quite abundant, occur-

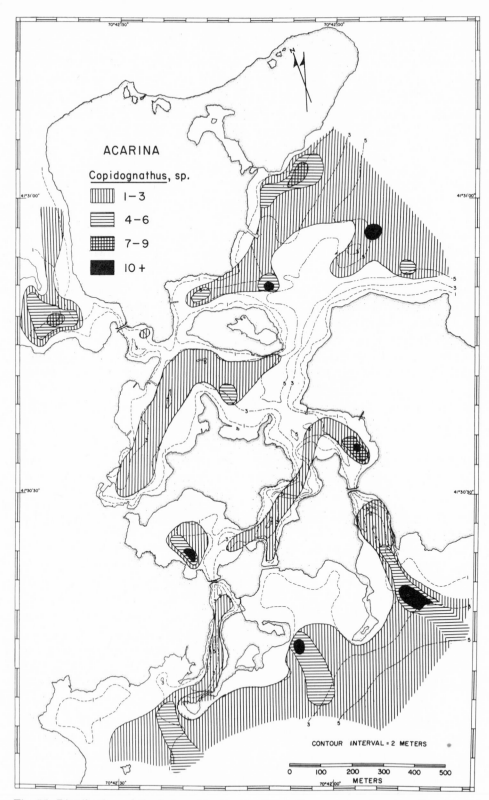

Fig. 55. Distribution of the halocarid mite *Copidognathus* sp., showing virtually no habitat preference, although highest concentrations were associated with eel grass.

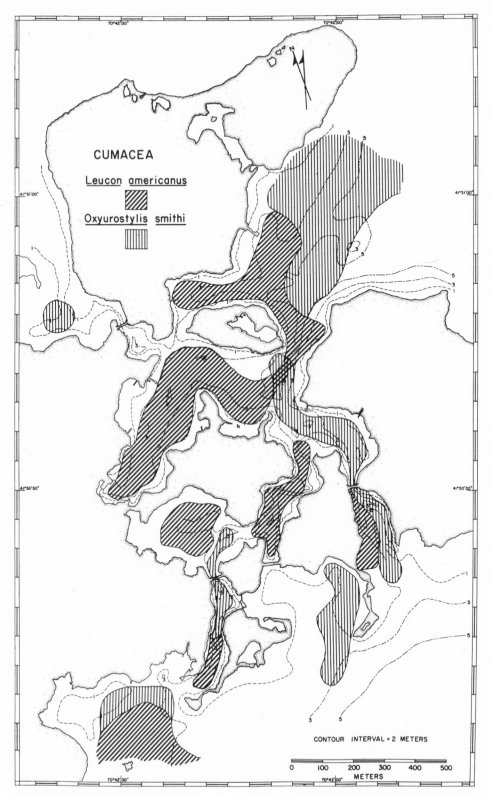

Fig. 56. Distributions of two species of cumaceans: *Leucon americanus*, associated with the Inner Harbor habitat, and *Oxyurostylis smithi*, a channel species. Overlap occurs at only one station.

TABLE I

Differences in the distribution of the cumaceans *Oxyurostylis* and *Leucon*

Oxyurostylis	*Leucon*
1. Greatest abundance in fall and winter	1. Greatest abundance in summer
2. Sands with median diameter of 175μ	2. Silts and sandy silts, median diameter of 89.5μ
3. High eel grass at 68% of the stations	3. Some eel grass at 50% of the stations
4. Occurrences at temperatures lower than average	4. Occurrences at temperatures higher than average
5. Average depth 8.6 ft., over wide range	5. Average depth 9 ft., preference for deeper waters
6. Over 72% of stations characterized by high currents	6. Most of the stations had little or no currents on the bottom

ring at 40 stations (*Oxyurostylis*) and 70 stations (*Leucon*), and at concentrations to 3,500/m^2. All specimens were identified by D. Solomon and checked by Dr. R. Wigley, as part of an unpublished Senior Project for Kalamazoo College (Solomon, 1965). *Leucon americanus* was a soft-bottom infaunal species, occurring on the silts of the Inner—Outer Harbor, Grassy Pond and the deeper, muddy portions of the channels (Fig. 56). *Oxyurostylis smithi*, on the other hand, occurred only on the sand and gravel bottoms, avoiding the fine silty sediments completely. The two species occurred jointly at only one station in the entrance to Inner Harbor, where all communities overlapped. These two cumaceans provide an excellent illustration of the principle of mutual exclusion of similar forms. Solomon (1965) has summed up the differences in their distribution, as shown in Table I.

Two more small crustacean groups, the Tanaidacea and Isopoda, were identified, and provided enough distributional evidence to ascertain habitat preferences. One genus of tanaids, *Leptochelia*, was represented by one very abundant species, *Leptochelia savignyi*. This was so abundant that plotting of the 60 stations (out of 350) at which it did not occur was more important than its presence. It was absent, or present as only one or two individuals, in those stations in which the eel grass was also absent. Unquestionably *Leptochelia* is an important member of the eel grass epifaunal community. Where eel grass attains its greatest growth, *Leptochelia* averaged 900/m^2, and approached 6,000/m^2. It was absent from the clayey silts of the Inner and Outer Harbor, the clean sand flats, and the deep gravelly portions of the gutters. Of the isopods, only *Erichsonella filiformis* occurred at enough stations to be considered a significant resident of the Complex. Another species, *E. attenuata*, was also taken, but in the same habitat as *E. filiformis*. Only 3 stations of the 17 at which *Erichsonella* was taken had more than two specimens of this species in the samples. All specimens were taken at eel

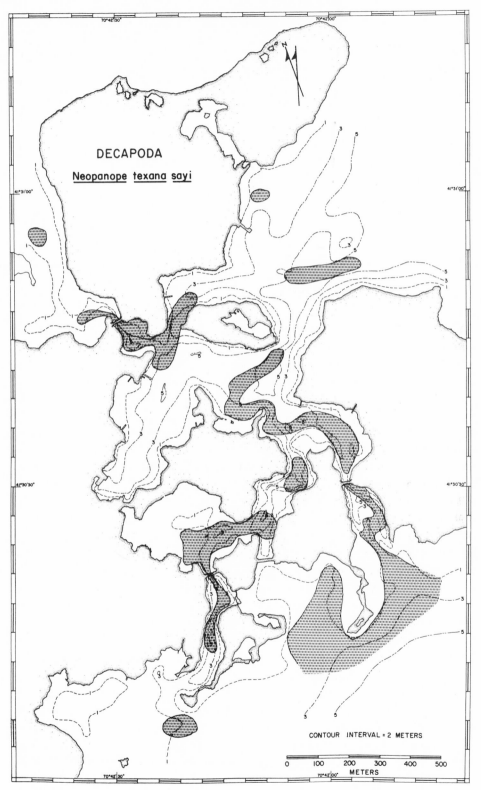

Fig. 57. Distribution of the decapod crab *Neopanope texana sayi*, typical of the channel community.

grass stations, indicating that this species, too, was an epifaunal resident of
the eel grass community. Its protective coloration and habit of clasping small
blades of grass or slivers of wood also supports this hypothesis. Eight occurrences of *Edotea triloba*, the largest isopod in the Complex, were all confined to eel grass beds very close to shore.

The largest crustaceans collected quantitatively were the decapods, which
included the mud crab *Neopanope texana sayi*; the pinnixid crabs *Pinnixa
chaetopterana* and *P. sayana*; the pagurid crab *Pagurus longicarpus*; and three
shrimp, *Crangon septemspinosus*, *Palaemonetes vulgaris* and *Hippolyte zostericola*. All three shrimp were definitely epifaunal in association with the eel
grass. *Pagurus longicarpus*, living in cast off gastropod shells, showed no
preferential distribution. *Pagurus* were sampled at as many stations in the
Inner Harbor type silts as on the outer sand flats. The two pinnotherid crabs
Pinnixa chaetopterana and *P. sayana* showed no special habitat preferences,
presumably because they are commensal on polychaetes or some other larger
invertebrates. All occurrences were on the eastern side of the Complex and
on the edges of channels. The most abundant decapod was *Neopanope texana sayi* (Fig. 57). This was an infaunal channel species, taken at 57 stations,
with an average of three individuals per station and a maximum population
of $850/m^2$. There was evidence to suggest that specimens could be separated
into two groups on the basis of their external morphology, a number of
them being identified as *Neopanope texana texana*. As specimens were not
separable ecologically, and two subspecies should not occur in the same
habitat in the same place, all specimens were considered as *Neopanope texana sayi*. The other subspecies has a presumed northern limit of Cape Hatteras
(Williams, 1965).

The only other identified arthropod occurring at more than five stations
was the pycnogonid *Callipallene brevirostris*. Three of its occurrences were
on the deep, gravelly bottom of the channels, two on the sandy sides of the
channel into the Inner Harbor, and three on the outer sand flats. None of the
stations were taken in eel grass beds, so it can be assumed that this species
was epifaunal on a hard bottom.

Meiofaunal groups

The most abundant of the small, infaunal soft-bodied animals in Hadley
Harbor were the kinorhynchs. Dr. R.P. Higgins formerly of Wake Forest
University identified two species. A third species, of a smaller size range than
encountered in this investigation, was collected by Higgins from the same
area after our sampling program had been terminated. The most abundant
kinorhynch was *Pycnophes frequens* (Fig. 58). It showed no habitat preference, although the greatest numbers per unit area occurred on the coarse to

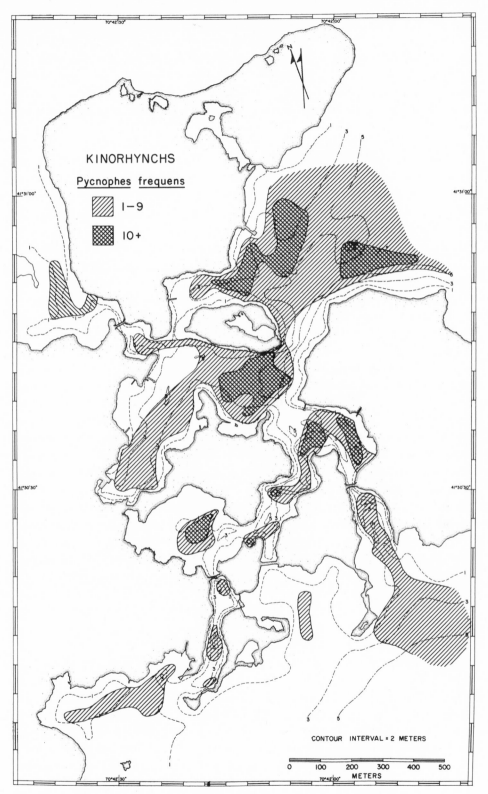

Fig. 58. Distribution of the kinorhynch *Pycnophes frequens*, an inhabitant of fine silty bottom, but showing no specific habitat preference.

fine silt sediments. It was generally absent from areas of dense eel grass and was restricted to the deeper portions of the Complex. According to R.P. Higgins (personal communication, 1966), *Pycnophes frequens* is one of the more abundant species in the Buzzards Bay muddy sand communities. The other species of kinorhynch collected as part of this study was *Trachydemus mainensis*, which was less common and had a more restricted distribution (Fig. 59). This species appeared to be a seasonal migrant into the Complex from Buzzards Bay, where it occurred in much larger numbers (Janice Czikowsky, former student at Wake Forest University, personal communication, 1965). During the spring of 1966 it was frequently collected in the Outer and Inner Harbor, but was absent by June and July. *Trachydemus* was also absent from our samples during the same months of 1964 and 1965. Its center of distribution was in the Outer Harbor, and it was virtually absent from the Vineyard Sound side of the Complex (Fig. 59). Except for a few specimens in a portion of the Inner Harbor, *Trachydemus* was found primarily on a fine to medium sand bottom in areas of moderate eel grass growth. It also occurred in much shoaler depths than *Pycnophes*. There were only a few stations at which *Trachydemus* was not found in company with *Pycnophes*.

The only other meiofaunal group which was studied in any detail in Hadley Harbor Complex is the Turbellaria. Knowledge of this group is limited, although Dr. L. Bush, associated with the Systematics—Ecology Program, is working on the difficult taxonomy and ecology of the Woods Hole species. Bush isolated some 15—20 species from the Hadley Harbor Complex. Two species of two genera were abundant enough for examination of their distributions (Fig. 60). A species of *Plagiostomum* was primarily associated with the deeper channels on the Vineyard Sound side. A representative of the genus *Austrorhynchus* occurred in the deeper channels on the Buzzards Bay side where there was more eel grass than at the stations with the other species. There was no overlap in the distribution of the species, suggesting different requirements for each. In general, *Austrorhynchus* sp. preferred coarser sediments associated with eel grass, while *Plagiostomum* sp. preferred finer and well-sorted sediments in the absence of eel grass. None of the other species of turbellarians was sufficiently abundant to consider their ecology.

Although considered microfauna, the Foraminifera also can be discussed under the present heading of small meiofauna. Only a suggestion of the foraminiferal distribution can be presented here, as the bulk of the samples taken for this specific phase of the study is still being analyzed by Dr. M. Buzas of the United States National Museum. Some of these data are discussed in a paper by Buzas (1968). A preliminary distribution map of the predominant species of Foraminifera shown on Fig. 61 was prepared by Buzas in 1964. Four separate groups of Foraminifera could be discerned:

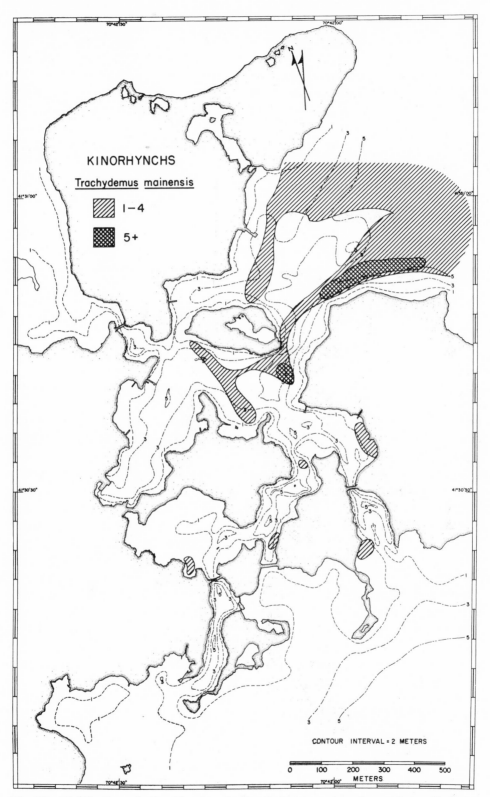

Fig. 59. Distribution of the kinorhynch *Trachydemus mainensis*, an Outer Harbor—Buzzards Bay form.

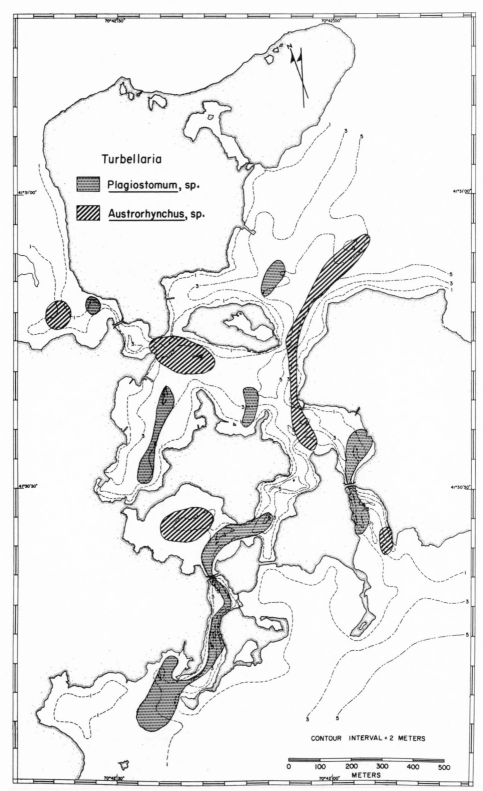

Fig. 60. Distributions of two turbellarians: *Plagiostomum* sp., a Vineyard Sound, deep-channel species, and *Austrorhynchus* sp., a Buzzards Bay channel species.

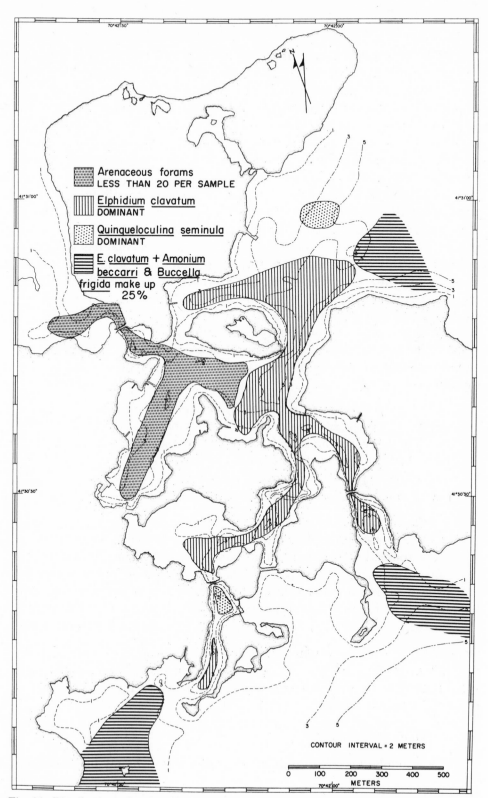

Fig. 61. Distribution of major foraminiferal assemblages in Hadley Harbor. (After Buzas, unpublished).

one, where arenaceous species made up less than 20% of the sample, limited to the Inner Harbor and Buzzards Bay entrance; two, where *Elphidium clavatum* was dominant, occurring in the high-energy channels and the deeper portions of the Outer Harbor; three, a *Quinqueloculina seminula* dominant assemblage, occurring as two isolated samples, one in the sand of the Outer Harbor and the other in a deep hole in West Gutter; and a fourth assemblage, where *Elphidium clavatum, Ammonium beccarri*, and *Bucella frigida* made up 25% of the sample, and which occurred only in the outer wave-influenced portions of the Complex. In general, foraminiferal distributions agree with those of the other major faunal elements of the Hadley Harbor communities. The fact that megafaunal, meiofaunal, and microfaunal animals all show somewhat similar distributions suggests that real communities exist in this small area. More recent accounts of Foraminifera assemblages were noted by Buzas (1966, 1968). In the first paper, Buzas (1966) found the number of species within the Inner Harbor to be sharply reduced as compared with the number in the outer portions of the Complex. No mention was made of community aggregations. In a later paper, Buzas (1968), having completed the analysis of the Foraminifera samples, reversed his previous opinions regarding the existance of Foraminifera communities. He states:

"No apparent simple relationship between the distribution of foraminiferal species and the environmental subareas outlined previously was found. That is, no simple assemblage characteristic of outer harbor, inner harbor, and gutter subareas can be defined. The only clearly discernible pattern is that most of the gutters and outer harbor subareas have Foraminifera whereas the inner harbor and northwest gutter do not ..."

"The Foraminifera are obviously not distributed at random but a more sophisticated classification than 'have' and 'have not' subareas is not warranted from the data of this study. If a more complex (several categories) multispecies distributional pattern can be defined geographically, it exists on a scale for which the sampling of this study is inadequate." (Buzas, 1968, pp. 9–10)

Only 24 stations were occupied during his first trip and 13 the second, thus, it is not surprising that his final analysis did not result in area patterns of species aggregations which resembled those of the larger invertebrates, based on several hundred stations.

Uncommon megafaunal species

A few echinoderms were taken in this study, although only one species in sufficient abundance to consider its habitat preference. The most abundant echinoderm, sampled by the small grab, was the holothurian *Leptosynapta* sp. This is a very small undescribed species with a maximum size of only a couple of centimeters, and apparently sexually mature at sizes below this. It is a member of the wave-influenced outer sand flat community, occurring in every biological sample taken at Physical Station *24* in Lackey's Bay. It was also relatively abundant ($675/m^2$) at Station *6* on the sand flats in Northwest Gutter. Most of the occurrences were limited to other portions of the outer sand flats, with the exception of six in shallow sandy portions of the gutters. The ophiuroid *Amphipholis squamata* was almost always associated with *Leptosynapta*, but in smaller numbers. Its center of abundance was in the shallow sand flats of Northwest Gutter and the shallower sand portions of the Outer Harbor and the Vineyard Sound entrances to West and East Gutter. There were three records of *Amphioplus abditus*, a rare ophiuroid for this region but common in the Miami, Florida, region (H. Moore, personal communication, 1964). The type locality of this species is Hadley Harbor, but only three prior records of it are known since its description. All three collections of *Amphioplus* during this study were made in the deep channel which leads to the entrance of the West and East Gutters from Woods Hole.

One infaunal coelenterate, the solitary burrowing anemone *Edwardsia elegans* was taken in sufficient numbers to reveal its habitat preferences. *Edwardsia* was found in 18 samples, although no more than four individuals per station. All were present on sandy bottom where eel grass was present but not in large quantities. Most specimens were collected on the Vineyard Sound side of East and West Gutters, and none was taken in the fine silty bottom of Inner and Outer Harbor.

Some idea of the distribution of invertebrates too large to be taken in the small Van Veen grab was gained through the efforts of the Supply Department of the Marine Biological Laboratory. Messrs. J.J. Valois, P. Chave, and D. Graham plotted the distributions of the larger animals in general demand by biologists of the Laboratory; a portion of these data is given on Fig. 62. Large beds of *Aequipecten irradians* existed in Grassy Pond, the wider portion of Northwest Gutter and close to the Vineyard Sound entrance of West Gutter. The lobster *Homarus americanus* lived in the deep rocky portions of West Gutter and the deep channel leading out of the Inner Harbor into the Woods Hole. One large population of the echinoid *Arbacia punctulata* existed under the bridge across Northwest Gutter, and a much smaller population was found near the bridges of both West and East Gutters. The relatively large gastropod *Littorina littorea* was rarely taken as part of this study, but occurred in large numbers in the intertidal portion of the Complex. The largest invertebrates were patchy in their distribution and probably account-

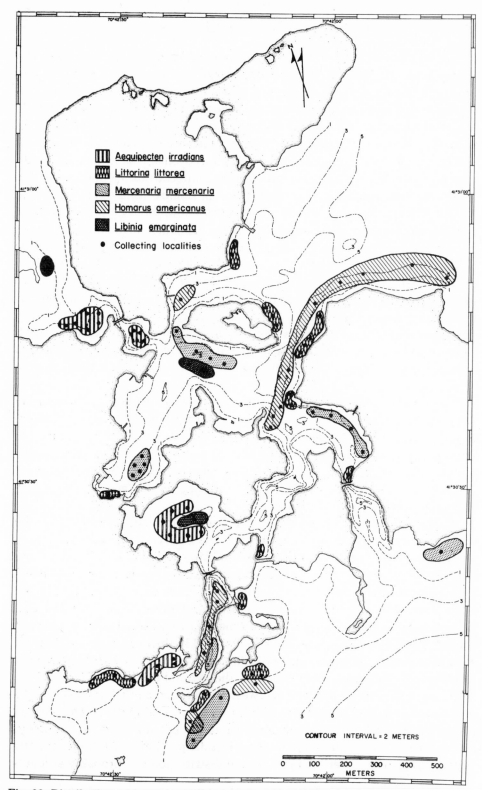

Fig. 62. Distribution of larger invertebrates collected by the Supply Department, Marine Biological Laboratory, Woods Hole, Massachusetts. (Based on a chart supplied by Messrs. Valois, Chave, and Graham, Supply Department, Marine Biological Laboratory.)

ed for less than 1% of the total population of the invertebrates in the Complex, especially if considered as numbers/m^2.

Data concerning distribution and habitat preferences of the polychaetes and oligochaetes are not completed as both groups have not yet been identified by specialists. Detailed information on the distribution and ecology of these two groups will be published subsequently. At least three-quarters of the specimens have been identified, and this provides enough evidence to indicate habitat preferences for the common species. It can be mentioned that little evidence of substrate preference within the polychaetes was revealed by plots of specimens identified thus far. This has been true of polychaetes in general, except that one of the dominant animals of Sanders' Station "R" community, *Nephtys*, is a polychaete with apparent substrate preference. According to Dr. J. Brinkhurst (University of Toronto, personal communication, 1966), most of the Oligochaeta are comprised of one species complex *Peloridex gabriellae* Marcus, the common species complex in the San Francisco Bay communities of Jones (1961). The cosmopolitan distribution of this species is re-enforced by the fact that the almost ubiquitous oligochaete species in Trinity Bay, Texas, is the same one (Parker et al., 1972; Williams, 1972).

Copepods, both harpacticoid and calanoid, were exceedingly common in the grab samples. Although no specific identifications of these animals were made, it was observed by J.S. Nagle that they occupied a specific niche on the eel grass blades, and their concentrations could be correlated with that of eel grass. The other group of meiofaunal and microfaunal invertebrates which cannot be discussed as to habitat preference are the nematodes. These animals were by far the most abundant taxa in the Complex. They were also the most difficult to identify as each specimen must be mounted separately on a slide. Dr. D. Hope of the U.S. National Museum, is working on the nematode fauna of the Woods Hole area (Hope, 1966), particularly that of the Hadley Harbor Complex.

PATTERNS OF COMMUNITY DISTRIBUTION

In the majority of studies on marine benthic communities occurring under uniform environmental conditions, the patterns of community structure are readily apparent from the nature of a relatively few samples taken over broad areas. Reports on the composition of these communities are usually based on a few large and predominant organisms, and community designations are based on the so-called (but misnamed) "dominant" species. Examples of this type of community analysis were published by Petersen (1913, 1914, 1915), Thorson (1957), Sanders (1958, 1960), Lie (1968), and Wade (1972). Clearly defined species predominance within benthic communities is adequately described and apparent in Boreal northern European waters and recognized, but not as clearly, in some cold to warm temperate waters of the Americas. No clear numerical dominance is exhibited in associations of animals in the tropics and subtropics as evidenced in some of the studies of Longhurst (1958), Parker (1964a), Hessler and Sanders (1967), and Wade (1972). Diversity and predominance of infaunal species are intimately tied together.

When studies deal with a wide range of sizes of benthic organisms, the question of "dominance" (based on predominant or most abundant animals) becomes a much more complicated one, and clear-cut communities are no longer evident if both meiofauna and megafauna are considered together. Sanders (1958, 1960) dealt with both the megafaunal and meiofaunal elements of the infauna but designated his communities on the basis of the larger abundant animals. The areal extent of these "communities" was not described, but their composition was clear cut (at least in the case of the *Nephtys—Nucula*, Station "R" community). The abundant animals were always abundant, either in replicate samples or seasonal samples within the same limited area encompassed by the sampling pattern. Sanders (1960) inferred that the areal extent of his communities would be delimited by the sediment types preferred by each community. Other environmental factors, temperature, salinity, light, etc., were not included in that they were all varying together with time and had little influence (as compared to sediment) on the areal limitations in such a stable environment as the broad level bottom of Buzzards Bay. Similar bodies of water were studied by Parker (1956, 1959, 1960), but rather than designating communities on the basis of dominant organisms, he devised associations of both living animals and shells which exemplified sedimentary environments. The samples used by Parker were not all quantitative, and no real expression of dominance could be given. The areal extent of these assemblages was emphasized in relation to the geomorphology of the shoreline. The magnitude of these assemblages was represented by the boundaries of multiple distribution maps of the more abundant species.

As there was practically no areal or temporal homogeneity within the extremely variable but small area of marine bottom of Hadley Harbor, the problem of community organization and designation is infinitely more complicated than those conceived by Petersen, Sanders or Thorson, or of Parker and perhaps Brett (1963). These workers, however, may have been investigating spatially heterogeneous environments occupied by homogeneous (in terms of larger organisms) assemblages of larger areal extent. Perhaps in large bodies of water, biotic interactions are not as restricted as they would be in small confined marine bottoms. It is probable that within Hadley Harbor 12 communities would have been described from only 12 samples, as each faunal analysis of these 12 samples would have been completely different. This is more or less the situation described by Buzas (1968) in searching for communities of Foraminifera with only 24 samples in Hadley Harbor. A similar situation is described by Lie (1968), who sampled only eight localities in Puget Sound, Washington. These same localities were sampled repeatedly. Species dominance was found, but each station could be designated as a separate "Thorson type" community. Even with data from over 300 stations, it is not possible to delineate communities in the true sense of the word, as, even in the same spot, no two samples were exactly alike, especially when taken at widely spaced intervals. A possible definition of a community (and there are as many definitions as there are community ecologists) is that it might consist of the total aggregation of living things within the ecosystem, each individual performing specific functions and making efficient use of the energy input to the system. No method has yet been devised whereby all the organisms in a specific habitat can be assigned specific functional roles in the marine ecosystem. Until this can be done, it will not be possible to more than approximate (as I have done) community boundaries and composition through assembling by various means, the individual boundaries and abundances of individual species into composite groups of organisms with some degree of homogeneity.

SUBJECTIVE ANALYSIS OF BENTHIC ANIMAL AGGREGATIONS

There were two methods which could be employed to synthesize the mass of data on distribution and abundance of individual species in order to distinguish aggregations of relatively homogeneous animals living together (implying biological interaction) and responding to a common set of environmental variables. One means is by matching the abundance and areal distribution of each animal to every other animal by continually superimposing their plots one over the other. Eventually patterns of groups of organisms which may or may not correspond to patterns of the environmental variables can be ascertained. The other method is to subject all data to a multivariate statistical analysis, emphasizing factor analysis, and utilizing computer techniques. The former method introduces considerable subjectivity, inasmuch as boundaries of individual species distribution and of the aggregations of species are drawn up at the discretion of the investigator. No matter how objective the investigator may think he is in contouring, a certain amount of intuitive subjectivity creeps into the process. On the other hand, when the data are processed by computer, the clustering and plotting are based primarily on mathematics, and some human subjectivity may be needed which unconsciously integrates hundreds of unrecorded variables.

The first method was employed rather successfully by the author in Hadley Harbor with a limited number of species. It was evident, even at an early stage of analyzing the areal distribution of these species, that certain ones occupied specific areas, and others were found in completely different areas. On the other hand, a number of species showed no specific habitat or areal specificity. Of the 300 species identified to date, about 100 were taken frequently enough to give a good idea of their areal distribution. Individual maps of the geographic distributions of individual species (discussed in previous sections) were drafted on a seasonal basis and for all station occurrences for the two years. The maps were semitransparent so that several could be superimposed one upon the other, and a major pattern of distribution be ascertained. Inspection of the maps of the 100 species revealed that there were at least four major composite patterns to which the common species could be relegated. No two species patterns were exactly alike, but there was sufficient similarity in related patterns to permit construction of one pattern which would envelop all the individual species patterns that seemed to occupy a specific portion of the Complex. Each of these four patterns was then superimposed upon the others to ascertain areas which were common to groups of organisms. However, areas common to certain species groups only, did not contain all occurrences of the species composing the group, as many of the species found there were found in other areas, too. These unique areas are important in that only here were certain species found in a particular combination, and no characteristic species from neighboring areas were taken with them. The areas of unique species combinations when compared with the areal distribution of physical—chemical variables, coincided with particular sets of environmental conditions. This in part may have influenced the composition of the fauna in these areas.

Inner Harbor, clayey-silt habitat

The first set of 10 species with similar distributional patterns was found in the clayey-silt habitat of Inner Harbor (Fig. 63). Although the composite pattern filled much of the Inner Harbor area, it also extended into the Outer Harbor, and reconnaissance sampling indicated that it was contiguous with the soft-bottom community in Buzzards Bay, via Woods Hole channel. The individual species patterns which make up this overall distributional pattern consist of the following species:

Mulinia lateralis (pelecypod)	*Retusa canaliculata* (gastropod)
Yoldia limatula (pelecypod)	*Cylichna oryza* (gastropod)
Nucula proxima (pelecypod)	*Ampelisca macrocephala* (amphipod)
Macoma tenta (pelecypod)	*Jassa falcata* (amphipod)
Trachydemus mainensis (kinorhynch)	*Leucon americanus* (cumacean)

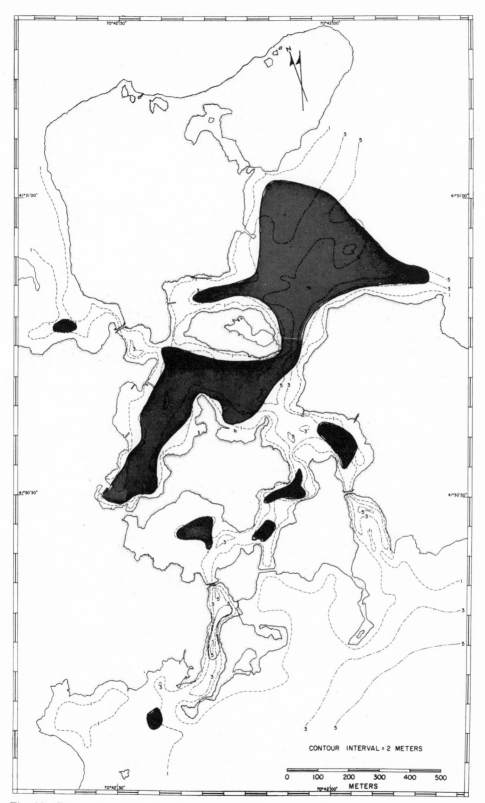

Fig. 63. Composite distributional pattern of 10 species of invertebrates characteristic of the Inner Harbor habitat, based on individual species plots.

TABLE II

Characteristic invertebrate species derived from computer sorting of stations from unique area plots

---

Inner Harbor habitat

Megafauna (34 species)

Littorina littorea	G[1]	*Nereis succinea*	PO
Polinices duplicatus	G	*Nephtys incisa*	PO
Anachis avara	G	*Nephtys* sp.	PO
Haminoea solitaria	G	*Glycera americana*	PO
Cylichna oryza	G	*Scolopus acutus*	PO
Retusa canaliculata	G	*Scolopus fragilis*	PO
Nucula proxima	P	*Scolopus* sp.	PO
Yoldia limatula	P	*Polydora ligni*	PO
Anadara transversa	P	*Streblospio benedicti*	PO
Pitar morrhuana	P	*Heteromastus filiformis*	PO
Macoma tenta	P	*Notomastus latericans*	PO
Mulinia lateralis	P	*Axiothella catenata*	PO
Petricola pholadiformis	P	*Clymenella zonalis*	PO
Lepidonotus squamatus	PO	*Maldanopsis elongata*	PO
Eteone lactea	PO	*Melinna cristata*	PO
Eteone sp.	PO	*Limulus polyphemus*	AR
Exogone dispar	PO	*Amphipholis squamata*	OP

Meiofauna (10 species)

New species "A" (Turbellaria)		*Parajassa pelagica*	AM
Cylindrostomidae (undescribed)	TU	*Tmetonyx nobilis*	AM
Scanorhynchus sp.	TU	*Ampelisca macrocephala*	AM
Phonorhyncus sp.	TU	*Leucon americanus*	CU
Hutchinsoniella macracantha	AR	*Cyprideis floridana*	OS

Sand flats habitat

Megafauna (23 species)

Lacuna neritoides-vincta	G	*Pygiospio elegans*	PO
Hydrobia minuta	G	*Spiophanes bombyx*	PO
Crepidula fornicata	G	*Capitella capitata*	PO
Crepidula convexa	G	*Clymenella* sp.	PO
Polinices immaculata	G	*Sabella microphtalma*	PO
Gemma gemma	P	*Polycirrus eximius*	PO
Macoma calcarea	P	*Callipallene brevirostris*	AR
Turtonia minuta	P	*Pagurus longicarpus*	AR
Nereis pelagica	PO	*Asterias forbesi*	AS
Paraonis fulgens	PO	*Leptosynapta* sp.	HO
Polydora ciliata	PO	*Saccoglossus kowalewskyi*	PR
Prionospio heterobranchia	PO		

Meiofauna (24 species)

Plagiostomum sp.	TU	*Cushmanidea ashermani*	OS
Phonorhynchus n. sp. "A"	TU	*Cushmanidea magniporosa*	OS
Phonorhynchus n. sp. "B"	TU	*Cushmanidea sandersi*	OS
Gnathorhynchidae, (Turbellaria)		*Haplocytheridea bradyi*	OS
Copidognathus sp.	AR	*Camylocythere laeva*	OS
Cytheretta sahni	OS	*Carinogammarus mucranatus*	AM

TABLE II *(continued)*

Loxoconcha granulata	OS	*Microdeutopus damnoniensis*	AM
Semicytherura elongata	OS	*Microdeutopus* sp.	AM
Acuticythereis multipunctata	OS	*Monoculoides edwardsi*	AM
Acuticythereis gigantea	OS	*Paraphoxus epistoma*	AM
Cushmanidea echolsae	OS	*Paraphoxus* sp.	AM
Megacythere robusta	OS	*Acanthohaustorius millsi*	AM

Channels habitat

Megafauna (37 species)

Caecum pulchellum	G	*Golfingia gouldi*	SI
Caecum cooperi	G	*Harmothoe imbricata*	PO
Niso sp.	G	*Sthenelais boa*	PO
Crepidula plana	G	*Eulalia viridis*	PO
Natica pusilla	G	*Phyllodoce arenae*	PO
Urosalpinx cinerea	G	*Brania clavata*	PO
Anachis translirata	G	*Exogone verugera*	PO
Odostomia sp.	G	*Sphaerosyllis hystrix*	PO
Pryamidella sp.	G	*Streptosyllis varians*	PO
Solemya velum	P	*Nereis arenaeceodonta*	PO
Mytilus edulis	P	*Nereis virens*	PO
Cerastoderma pinnulatum	P	*Nephtys picta*	PO
Mercenaria mercenaria	P	*Glycera capitata*	PO
Cumingia tellinoides	P	*Lumbrinereis tenuis*	PO
Arctica islandica	P	*Libinia dubia*	AR
Aligena elevata	P	*Neopanope texana sayi*	AR
Mysella planulata	P	*Amphipholis squamata*	OP
Ensis directus	P	*Heteromysis* sp.	AR
Lyonsia hyalina	P		

Meiofauna (44 species)

Austrorhynchus sp.	TU	*Caprella geometrica*	AM
Utelga heineckei	TU	*Paracaprella tenuis*	AM
Stylochus ellipticus	TU	*Oxyurostylis smithi*	CU
Elasmopus laevis	AM	*Cyclaspis varians*	CU
Listriella clymenellae	AM	*Leptochelia savignyi*	IS
Leptocheirus pinguis	AM	*Cyathura* n. sp.	IS
Microprotopus ranei	AM	*Hydrobaenus* sp.	IN
Microprotopus maculatus	AM	*Propontocypris edwardsi*	OS
Corophium acutum	AM	*Trachyleberis vineyardensis*	OS
Corophium acherusicum	AM	*Cytheromorpha warneri*	OS
Corophium bonelli	AM	*Leptocythere paracastanea*	OS
Corophium insidiosum	AM	*Sarsiella angusta*	OS
Corophium tuberculatum	AM	*Sarsiella tubipora*	OS
Corophium sp.	AM	*Callistocythere* sp.	OS
Ampithoe longimana	AM	*Hirschmania viridis*	OS
Cymadusa compta	AM	*Pterygocythereis* sp.	OS
Dexamine thea	AM	*Loxoconcha impressa*	OS
Batea catherinensis	AM	*Puriana* sp.	OS
Paraphoxus oculatus	AM	*Aurila amygdala*	OS
Paraphoxus sp.	AM	*Pseudocythereis*	OS

TABLE II *(continued)*

Lysianopsis alba	AM	*Parasterope pollex*	OS
Ampelisca vadorum	AM	*Propontocypris edwardsi*	OS

Eel grass habitat

Megafauna (28 species)

Chaetopleura apiculata	CH	*Harmothoe extenuata*	PO
Bittium alternatum	G	*Eumida sanguinea*	PO
Mitrella lunata	G	*Parapionosyllis longicirrata*	PO
Lora cancellata	G	*Platynereis dumerilii*	PO
Odostomia bisurturalis	G	*Scolopus robustus*	PO
Odostomia seminuda	G	*Aricidea jeffreysi*	PO
Turbonilla interrupta	G	*Cirratulus grandis*	PO
Acteon punctostriatus	G	*Clymenella torquata*	PO
Diaphana debilis	G	*Praxiella* sp.	PO
Aequipecten irradians	P	*Pista palmata*	PO
Laevicardium mortoni	P	*Polycirrus medusa*	PO
Tagelus divisus	P	*Crangon septemspinosa*	AR
Abra aequalis	P	*Hippolyte zostericola*	AR
Psudopythina sp.	P	*Pinnixa sayana*	AR

Meiofauna (14 species)

Pycnophes frequens	K	*Ampelisca abdita*	AM
Trachydemus mainensis	K	*Erichsonella filiformis*	IS
Listriella barnardi	AM	*Sarsiella zostericola*	OS
Listriella sp.	AM	*Cythereis zostericola*	OS
Eurystheus sp.	AM	*Paradoxostoma delicata*	OS
Microdeutopus damnoniensis	AM	*Parasterope pollex*	OS
Microdeutopus gryllotalpa	AM	*Cytherura* sp.	OS

[1] Letter key to taxa:

AM = Amphipoda; AR = larger Arthropoda; AS = Asteroidea; CH = chiton; CU = Cumacea; G = Gastropoda; HO = Holothuroidea; IS = Isopoda; IN = Insecta; K = Kinorhyncha; OP = Ophiuroidea; OS = Ostracoda; P = Pelecypoda; PO = Polychaeta; PR = Protochordata; SI = Sipunculida; TU = Turbellaria.

These 10 were the most consistently abundant species identified in the area. At least another 34 species can be considered typical of the stations unique to the Inner Harbor habitat (Table II). Difficulties in the systematics of oligochaetes, polychaetes, and nematodes, easily the dominant taxa there, prevented the naming of more species and preparation of their distribution maps. It is significant that most of the species making up this aggregation are of megafaunal size (Table II), and feed on detritus often in suspension. The Inner Harbor was rich in detritus and should favor animals with a taste for organic matter. A complete list of animals taken in all samples from the stations comprising the Inner Harbor group can be found in Table III. A special computer search program was devised to find all occurrences of all species at a designated set of stations, as an aid to mechanical sorting of data.

Outer Harbor, shallow sand flat habitat

A second distinct set of overlapping distribution maps was used to construct the composite map representing an aggregation of species found on the shallow sand flats of the Outer Harbor (Fig. 64). Occupied areas correspond rather closely to those of the fine well-sorted sand flats, except for one section in the small pond off West Gutter which, although shallow, is not sandy. Relatively few invertebrate species maps were used to obtain contours enclosing the sand flats habitat. Although Inner Harbor was an area of environmental stress in terms of certain physical—chemical factors, the shallow sand flats were probably even more so. In the winter, they sometimes completely freeze over, with only a thin layer of salt water between ice and sediment. In the summer, temperatures rose far above the normal temperatures of the surrounding deeper waters of Buzzards Bay and Vineyard Sound. As the sediment was composed of very well-sorted fine sand, there was little space between the sand grains for the accumulation of organic matter needed to sustain a large population of deposit feeders. Wave action was almost always effective to the bottom, consequently turbulence was also an adverse factor, especially for those forms trying to settle there. For these reasons the number of species confined to the sand flats was quite small, although these species attained very dense populations, in part because of lack of competition. Species distributions used to create the composite pattern shown on Fig. 64 (p. 144) are of the following:

Lacuna neritoides (L. vincta) (gastropod)   *Ampelisca vadorum* (amphipod)
Hydrobia minuta (gastropod)   *Corophium acutum* (amphipod)
Gemma gemma (pelecypod)   *Paraphoxus oculatus* (amphipod)
Microdeutopus gryllotalpa (amphipod)   *Leptosynapta* sp. (holothurian)
Acanthohaustorius millsi (amphipod)   *Asterias forbesi* (asteroid)
Elasmopus laevis (amphipod)

These 11 species are the ones most commonly taken in this habitat, although some, particularly the amphipods, occur in other habitats in lower concentrations. There are also several species of polychaetes common in the sand flats (but not listed here as this taxon has not been fully identified). Altogether, 126 species of other taxa have been identified from the stations occurring in the unique portions of the sand flat habitat (see Table III). The most abundant species inhabiting the sand flats are suspension feeders, although the majority of all species (common or rare) are deposit feeders. A

TABLE III

Complete list of animals, with average number of individuals per station and percent of occurrences within station groups for the four habitats (Stations used in computer sorting at end of Table)

	Inner Harbor (40 stations)		Sand Flats (30 stations)		Channels (24 stations)		Eel grass (19 stations)	
	No. per station	% of occur.	No. per station	% of occur.	No. per station	% of occur.	No. per station	% of occur.
Hydrozoa	1	3	2	21	2	16	3	11
Anthozoa			1	11				
Haloclava producta	1	3						
Turbellaria								
Plagiostomum sp.	2	9	6	50	3	42	7	26
Austrorhynchus sp.	1	2	2	13	2	12	1	5
new species "A"	1	2			4	17		
Cylindrostomidae sp.	1	4						
Scanorhynchus sp.	1	4						
Phonorhynchus helgolandicus			1	3				
Phonorhynchus n. sp. "A"			1	10				
Utelga heineckei			1	3	1	4		
Clyporhynchus sp.			1	3				
new species "B"			1	3				
new species "C"			1	3				
Gnathorhynchidae sp.			1	3				
Kalyptorhynchia			1	3				
Polycladida						4		
Stylochus ellipticus						4		
Rhyncocoela Anopla	9	14	9	18	9	10	10	16
Kinorhyncha	10	40	12	28	25	42	36	68
Pycnophes frequens	4	35	12	23	6	37	18	58
Trachydemus mainensis	2	10	1	3	10	4	2	26
Nematoda	225	97	28	100	514	100	525	90
Ectoprocta	1	3						

TABLE III (*continued*)

	Inner Harbor (40 stations)		Sand Flats (30 stations)		Channels (24 stations)		Eel grass (19 stations)	
	No. per station	% of occur.	No. per station	% of occur.	No. per station	% of occur.	No. per station	% of occur.
Aplacophora								
Chaetopleura apiculata							3	11
Gastropoda								
Lacuna neritoides -vincta							3	11
Littorina littorea	3	59	40	85	35	94	57	90
Hydrobia minuta	2	5	1	17	1	4		
Caecum pulchellum	1	3	47	27	8	33	6	26
Caecum cooperi	1	3	26	17	1	8		
Bittium alternatum	3	10	44	54	36	54	25	84
Niso sp.			2	3	1	4		
Crepidula fornicata	5	3	5	17	6	12	2	10
Crepidula convexa	1	3	2	20	1	8	1	5
Crepidula plana			2	3	1	8		
Polinices duplicatus	1	3						
Polinices immaculata			6	3	1	4		
Natica pusilla					1	8		
Urosalpinx cinerea					1	4		
Anachis avara	1	3						
Anachis translirata			1	3	2	17	1	16
Mitrella lunata	1	10	3	13	3	13	2	48
Lora cancellata							1	5
Odostomia bisurturalis					1	4	1	5
Odostomia seminuda	1	3	7	3			1	11
Odostomia sp.					1	4		
Pyramidella sp.					1	4		
Turbonilla interrupta	2	20	1	13	4	25	8	31
Acteon punctostriatus							1	5

TABLE III (continued)

	Inner Harbor (40 stations)		Sand Flats (30 stations)		Channels (24 stations)		Eel grass (19 stations)	
	No. per station	% of occur.	No. per station	% of occur.	No. per station	% of occur.	No. per station	% of occur.
Haminoea solitaria	1	5	1	3	1	8	2	11
Cylichna oryza	2	25	1	3	2	4	1	5
Retusa canaliculata	1	17					1	5
Diaphana debilis								
Nudibranchia					4	4		
Pelecypoda	18	95	64	100	11	89	11	68
Solemya velum	2	10	6	27	9	71	10	42
Nucula proxima	1	10			1	4		5
Yoldia limatula	9	85			1	8	3	16
Mytilus edulis	1	3	2	10	1	13	1	11
Aequipecten irradians								
Anadara transversa	1	5					1	5
Laevicardium mortoni			3	3	1	12	1	21
Cerastoderma pinnulatum			2	5	1	12		
Mercenaria mercenaria	1	17	1	7	2	21	2	16
Gemma gemma			67	84	1	12		
Pitar morrhuana	1	3						
Tellina agilis	6	37	5	50	4	42	1	11
Macoma calcarea					1	4		
Macoma tenta	10	37			1	4	2	5
Cumingia tellinoides	1	3			2	13	2	11
Abra aequalis							1	5
Tagelus divisus							1	4
Mulinia lateralis	5	65						
Arctica islandica	1	3			3	4		
Aligena elevata	1	8			1	12	1	11
Mysella planulata	1	3			1	8		

TABLE III (continued)

	Inner Harbor (40 stations)		Sand Flats (30 stations)		Channels (24 stations)		Eel grass (19 stations)	
	No. per station	% of occur.	No. per station	% of occur.	No. per station	% of occur.	No. per station	% of occur.
Pseudopythina sp.	1	3						
Turtonia minuta			3	3			1	5
Petricola pholadiformis	1	3						
Ensis directus					1	8		
Lyonsia hyalina			1	3	1	17	1	11
Sipunculoidea					1	5		
Golfingia gouldi					1	5		
Oligochaeta	77	77	46	71	93	94	241	73
Polychaeta	46	95	48	96	116	100	77	89
Harmothoe extenuata	4	8					1	5
Harmothoe imbricata	1	3			2	12	14	5
Lepidonotus squamatus	1	5						
Sthenelais boa	2	5	2	3	1	8	1	11
Eteone lactea	1	3	1	3	1	4		
Eteone sp.								
Eulalia viridis					1	8		
Eumida sanguinea	1	5			1	8	1	8
Phyllodoce arenae					2	12	3	5
Brania clavata	1	3			1	25		
Exogone dispar								
Exogone verugera			3	3	1	8	1	5
Parapionosyllis longicirrata					1	4		
Sphaerosyllis hystrix			3	3	1	8		
Streptosyllis varians	1	5			2	4		
Nereis arenaceodonta	4	40	5	3	2	25		
Nereis succinea			8	7	5	17	1	5
Nereis virens			4	3	2	4	1	5

TABLE III (continued)

	Inner Harbor (40 stations)		Sand Flats (30 stations)		Channels (24 stations)		Eel grass (19 stations)	
	No. per station	% of occur.	No. per station	% of occur.	No. per station	% of occur.	No. per station	% of occur.
Nereis pelagica			2	3	1	4		
Platynereis dumerilii	2	8					3	16
Nephtys incisa	1	20			3	4	1	5
Nephtys picta	1	1	1	3	4	12		
Nephtys sp.	1	3						
Glycera americana	2	15			2	13	1	11
Glycera capitata			2	3	4	8	3	21
Lumbrineris tenuis	3	15	8	13	12	46	2	5
Scolopus acutus	7	10	1	7	1	8		
Scolopus fragilis	3	7						
Scolopus robustus								
Scolopus sp.	2	15	2	3			1	5
Paraonis fulgens			2	10				
Aricidea jeffreysi	3	3	5	3			1	11
Polydora ligni	1	3						
Polydora ciliata			2	3				
Prionospio heterobranchia	1	5	1	7			3	1
Pygospio elegans			1	3				
Spiophanes bombyx			1	7				
Streblospio benedicti	10	15	1	3				
Cirratulus grandis								
Capitella capitata			2	10			2	5
Heteromastus filiformis	1	3						
Notomastus latericeus	1	3						
Axiothella catenata	1	3						
Clymenella torquata	2	15	7	7			90	11
Clymenella sp.			1	3				

TABLE III (continued)

	Inner Harbor (40 stations)		Sand Flats (30 stations)		Channels (24 stations)		Eel grass (19 stations)	
	No. per station	% of occur.	No. per station	% of occur.	No. per station	% of occur.	No. per station	% of occur.
Clymenella zonalis	2	13					1	11
Maldanopsis elongata	1	3						
Praxiella sp.							1	5
Sabella microphthalma			1	3				
Melinna cristata	1	3						
Pista palmata							2	5
Polycirrus eximius								
Polycirrus medusa	15	3	1	3			1	11
Arthropoda								
Cephalocarida	30	15	5	4			2	16
Hutchinsoniella macracantha	30	13	5	3			29	11
Acarina	2	3	7	32	3	21	3	21
Copidognathus sp.	2	3	7	32	3	21	3	21
Xyphosura								
Limulus polyphemus	1	3	1	7				
Pycnogonida								
Callipallene brevirostris	1	3	1	7				
Copepoda	91	100	234	100	213	100	283	90
Ostracoda	6	87	176	90	186	100	141	90
Propontocypris edwardsi	2	15	11	30	30	76	18	47
Pterygocythereis sp.					1	4		
Cytheretta sahnii			2	13				
Cyprideis floridana	1	8					2	5
Haplocytheridea bradyi	1	2	2	7	1	4		
Cushmanidea ashermani			1	3				
Cushmanidea echolsae	3	4	12	37	7	8	2	21
Cushmanidea magniporosa	3	2	4	40				
Cushmanidea sandersi	3	2	4	33			2	5

TABLE III (continued)

	Inner Harbor (40 stations)		Sand Flats (30 stations)		Channels (24 stations)		Eel grass (19 stations)	
	No. per station	% of occur.	No. per station	% of occur.	No. per station	% of occur.	No. per station	% of occur.
Cytherura sp.					3	4	3	5
Semicytherura elongata	1	2	1	13	2	4	1	5
Aurila amygdala			1	13	3	17	1	5
Acuticythereis gigantea	1	2	1	17				
Acuticythereis multipunctata	1	2	1	17	1	4		
Camylocythere laeva	1	2	5	80				
Callistocythere sp.					2	4		
Leptocythere paracastanea			1	3	1	17	1	5
Cytheromorpha warneri			1	10	2	13	4	5
Hirschmannia viridis					10	4		
Loxoconcha granulata			2	17	3	4	1	5
Loxoconcha impressa	1	2	1	3	1	4		
Cythereis zostericola			2	3	2	8	5	21
Megacythere robusta	2	2	20	7				
Paradoxostoma delicata							1	21
Sclerochilus sp.					1	8		
Puriana sp.			1	3	2	13	7	5
Trachyleberis vineyardensis			1	3	10	8		
Pseudocythereis sp.	1	2			2	4		
Parasterope pollex	4	48	22	73	83	92	58	90
Sarsiella angusta					1	4		
Sarsiella tubipora			1	3	1	13	1	5
Sarsiella zostericola	1	2			3	13	1	21
Ciripedia	11	15			122	8		
Balanus amphitrite niveus	11	15			122	8		
Amphipoda	10	94	135	100	192	100	85	90
Elasmopus laevis	1	5	10	7	16	25	1	11

TABLE III (continued)

	Inner Harbor (40 stations)		Sand Flats (30 stations)		Channels (24 stations)		Eel grass (19 stations)	
	No. per station	% of occur.	No. per station	% of occur.	No. per station	% of occur.	No. per station	% of occur.
Carinogammarus mucranatus			1	3	1	4		
Listriella clymenellae	1	3						
Listriella barnardi	2	5	2	10	4	46	8	51
Listriella sp.							1	5
Leptocheirus pinguis	2	5			1	12		
Microprotopus ranei	1	3	2	10	6	29	1	16
Microprotopus maculatus					1	4		
Eurystheus sp.							4	5
Lembos smithi			10	3				
Microdeutopus damnoniensis	9	40	9	27	52	80	15	82
Microdeutopus gryllotalpa	12	3	306	13	19	54	25	42
Microdeutopus sp.	1	3	7	3				
Jassa falcata	5	30	1	13	3	50	2	47
Parajassa pelagica	29	3	3	3				
Corophium acutum	7	15	10	20	29	50	9	42
Corophium acherusicum	1	3			1	8		
Corophium bonelli					21	8	1	5
Corophium insidiosum	2	10	11	23	5	46	24	42
Corophium tuberculatum					6	12		
Corophium sp.	1	3	1	3	4	12		
Ampithoe longimana	1	8	12	13	12	46	2	32
Cymadusa compta	1	5	2	7	8	37	1	32
Dexamine thea	2	5	3	3	10	12	5	11
Batea catherinensis	1	3	2	3	2	4		
Monoculodes edwardsi			1	3				
Paraphoxus epistoma			8	27	2	4		
Paraphoxus spinosus					10	4		

TABLE III (continued)

	Inner Harbor (40 stations)		Sand Flats (30 stations)		Channels (24 stations)		Eel grass (19 stations)	
	No. per station	% of occur.	No. per station	% of occur.	No. per station	% of occur.	No. per station	% of occur.
Paraphoxus oculatus			6	7	4	25	2	26
Paraphoxus sp.	2	10	7	10				
Phoxocephalus holbolli	2	3	2	13	11	75	32	47
Acanthohaustorius millsi	1	8	58	47	1	4	1	11
Lysianopsis alba	1	3	17	13	28	75	16	47
Tmetonyx nobilis	3	27						
Ampelisca macrocephala	2	10	1	10	2	25	4	11
Ampelisca abdita	1	3	1	3	1	21	8	26
Ampelisca vadorum	2	3	2	3	3	21	1	11
Caprella geometrica	1	3	4	10	11	12	1	5
Paracaprella tenuis	16	86	1	3	15	21		
Cumacea	1	5	1	7	3	42	4	42
Oxyurostylis smithi					6	17	2	11
Cyclaspis varians					1	4		
Leucon americanus	17	85	1	7	1	25		
Mysidacea					14	1	5	31
Tanaidacea and Isopoda	1	20			41	94	2	1
Leptochelia savignyi	1	15	5	39	27	71	7	53
Cyathura (2 sp.)	1	3	5	33	1	4	6	53
Edotea triloba	1	3	1	3				
Erichsonella filiformis					3	8		
Decapoda	1	20			2	42	1	16
Crangon septemspinosus	1	5	1	32	1	4	1	21
Libinia dubia			1	3	1	4	1	5
Neopanope texana sayi					2	33		
Pinnixa sayana			1	7	1	4	1	5
Pagurus longicarpus	1	13	2	17			1	5

TABLE III (continued)

	Inner Harbor (40 stations)		Sand Flats (30 stations)		Channels (24 stations)		Eel grass (19 stations)	
	No. per station	% of occur.	No. per station	% of occur.	No. per station	% of occur.	No. per station	% of occur.
Insecta	2	10	2	25	2	40	1	11
Asteroidea			1	29				
Asterias forbesi			1	27				
Ophiuroidea	2	3			1	1		
Amphioplus abditus					1	4		
Amphipholis squamata	2	3			1	4		
Holothuroidea			1	39	2	5	2	5
Leptosynapta n. sp.			1	36	2	4		
Cephalochordata	3	6	163	4				
Saccoglossus kowalewskyi	3	5	163	3				
Urochordata			27	4				
Osteichtyes							120	5

List of station numbers for the stations used in the above analysis:
Inner Harbor habitat (40 stations): 73, 77, 82, 83, 90, 139, 142, 159, 160, 168, 174, 185, 193, 202, 207, 214, 224, 228, 234, 238, 241, 243, 250, 256, 261, 267, 271, 901, 902, 903, 904, 905, 906, 907, 908, 909, 910, 911, 912, 913.
Sand flats habitat (30 stations): 76, 81, 132, 136, 147, 154, 163, 171, 180, 219, 223, 245, 253, 258, 265, 270, 273, 2401, 2402, 2403, 2404, 2405, 2406, 2407, 2408, 2409, 2410, 2411, 2412, 2413.
Channel habitat (24 stations): 70, 71, 84, 87, 89, 127, 131, 135, 140, 146, 150, 165, 166, 195, 196, 199, 204, 208, 209, 210, 232, 248, 281, 286.
Eel grass habitat (19 stations): 121, 126, 128, 138, 141, 145, 151, 155, 173, 182, 183, 191, 201, 229, 233, 251, 262, 268, 274.

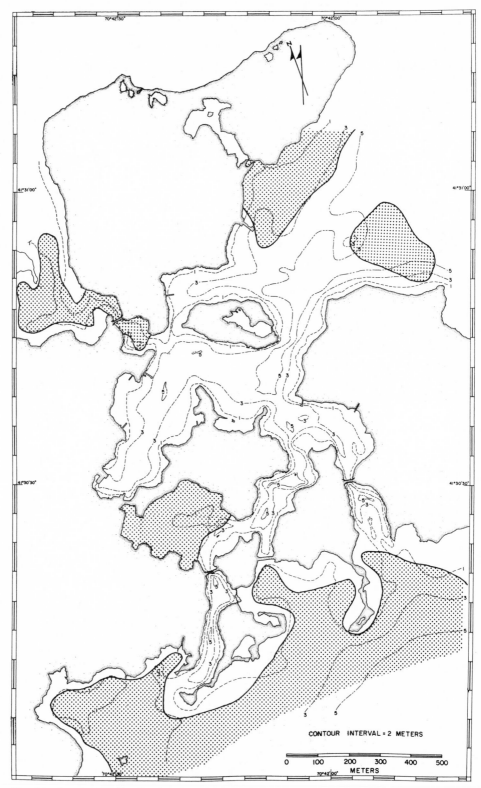

Fig. 64. Composite distributional pattern of 11 species of invertebrates characteristic of the sand flat habitat, based on individual species plots.

list of 47 dominant species of the unique sand flat areas can be found in Table II; equal numbers of mega- and meiofaunal species are present in this habitat.

Deep-channel or current-influenced habitat

A third community pattern was discerned in the area characterized as the major deep channels leading from Buzzards Bay to Vineyard Sound (Fig. 65). As stated earlier, the deep channels were areas of strongest current flow characterized by a heterogenous mixture of mostly poorly sorted sediments. Predominant current flow is from Buzzards Bay into Vineyard Sound, which is reflected in the derivation of many of the typical animals from Buzzards Bay rather than Vineyard Sound. Because the channels have no morphological barriers to exclude immigration from Buzzards Bay, Vineyard Sound, or the Inner Harbor, and because bottom vegetation was characteristically high, the channels produced the largest number of species in unique combination for this habitat. At least 81 species had their centers of abundance, or were found only, in the channels (see Tables II, III). In contrast to the previous two habitats, where only 10 and 11 species respectively characterized the communities, 28 species are considered characteristic in the channels, and were used to construct the chart on Fig. 65. A list of these species follows:

Crepidula fornicata (gastropod)	*Lysianopsis alba* (amphipod)
Caecum pulchellum (gastropod)	*Cymadusa compta* (amphipod)
Turbonilla interrupta (gastropod)	*Paracaprella tenuis* (amphipod)
Solemya velum (pelecypod)	*Lembos smithi* (amphipod)
Lyonsia hyalina (pelecypod)	*Leptocheirus pinguis* (amphipod)
Laevicardium mortoni (pelecypod)	*Propontocypris edwardsi* (ostracod)
Cerastoderma pinnulatum (pelecypod)	*Hydrobaenus* sp. (insect)
Tagelus divisus (pelecypod)	*Oxyurostylis smithi* (cumacean)
Ensis directus (pelecypod)	*Neopanope texana sayi* (decapod)
Corophium bonelli (amphipod)	*Callipallene brevirostris* (pycnogonid)
Corophium acherusicum (amphipod)	*Trachydemus mainensis* (kinorhynch)
Microdeutopus damnoniensis (amphipod)	*Plagiostomum* sp. (turbellarian)
Listriella barnardi (amphipod)	*Edwardsia elegans* (anemone)
Microprotopus ranei (amphipod)	*Arbacia punctulata* (echinoid)

Examination of the list of species from all stations used to provide data for the unique combination of species in the channel habitat revealed that over half of them (55%) were of meiofaunal size. The other three habitats were characterized by a predominance of megafaunal species. With the exception of *Turbonilla* and several of the amphipods, most of the genera are

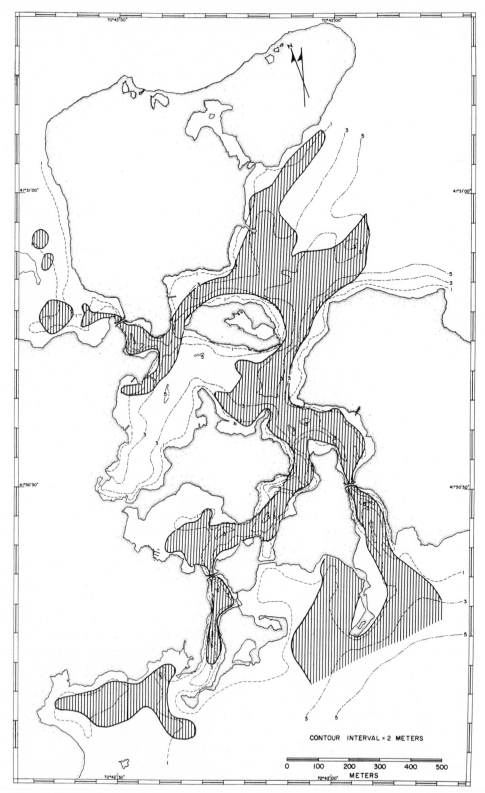

Fig. 65. Composite distributional pattern of 28 species of invertebrates characteristic of the channel habitat, based on individual species plots.

considered to be suspension feeders or algae eaters, a feeding behavior well adapted to swiftly flowing waters. It is also significant that many of the channel species were more characteristic of the deeper waters of Buzzards Bay than of Hadley Harbor, and in this respect the channels are faunistic extensions of the open bay. Because many of the channel species are dependent upon eel grass for protection and perhaps sustenance, it is difficult to separate the channel community from the pure eel grass community found on the banks of the channels.

Eel grass beds

Eel grass thrived not only in the deep channels, but also was found elsewhere throughout the Hadley Harbor Complex with the exception of the fine silty bottoms of the Inner and Outer Harbor. The shallow portions of the complex with heavy stands of eel grass, neither part of the deep channels nor of the shallow sand flats, also supported a distinctive fauna. Concentrations and composition of species indicated that this fauna was dependent upon the eel grass itself, as many of these forms feed directly on the eel grass or its decomposition products. Autecological studies of the dominant species on eel grass showed that many amphipod species were dependent upon the epiphytic algae growing on the eel grass blades. Furthermore, the base and root systems of the eel grass act as collectors for organic debris, which supports a large number of deposit feeders. This is evident when one examines the composition of the community during the summer when eel grass is high and the sediments at the bases of the eel grass are mostly sandy silts, and then re-examines the same community in the winter when the eel grass has died down and sediments have changed to silty sand. In the absence of the thick blades of eel grass in the winter, the finer silts and organic matter are winnowed out and settle into the deeper basins. Correspondingly, many of the deposit feeders, so prevalent in these beds in the summer, disappear in the winter.

As with the other three habitats, it was possible to construct a composite map of the distributions of the predominately eel grass species (Fig. 66). When this map was superimposed upon the other three composite maps, there resulted a series of stations with an unique composition related to areas of eel grass. In these areas there were 17 characteristic species of invertebrates, although most of them were also found in lower concentrations in other portions of the Complex, especially the channels. A list of the characteristic species is given below.

Mitrella lunata (gastropod)   *Parasterope pollex* (ostracod)
Anachis translirata (gastropod)   *Leptochelia savignyi* (tanaid)

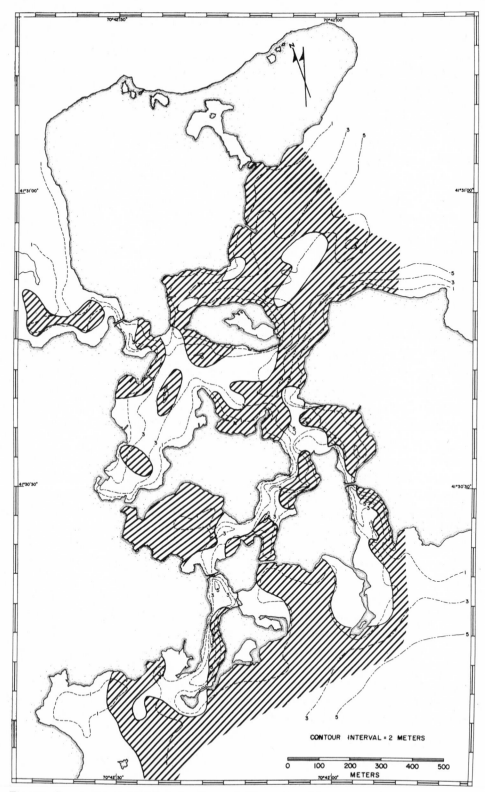

Fig. 66. Composite distributional pattern of 17 species of invertebrates characteristic of the eel grass habitat, based on individual species plots.

Bittium alternatum (gastropod)
Ampelisca abdita (amphipod)
Corophium insidiosum (amphipod)
Caprella geometrica (amphipod)
Ampithoe longimanna (amphipod)
Dexamine thea (amphipod)
Phoxocephalus holbolli (amphipod)

Erichsonella filiformis (isopod)
Edotea triloba (isopod)
Crangon septemspinosum (decapod)
Palaemonetes vulgaris (decapod)
Hippolyte zostericola (decapod)
Austrorhynchus sp. (turbellarian)

In all, 42 species are considered typical of the eel grass beds (Table II); 28 of these were megafaunal and 14 meiofaunal. It seems that the majority of species were either herbivores or deposit feeders. No pelecypods were restricted to or indicators of eel grass beds, although *Solemya velum* was frequently an inhabitant of the sparser beds. It is significant that, by and large, the largest number of organisms per square meter were found in the eel grass beds, with populations in excess of $250,000/m^2$ in the more luxurious stands. Species found in the eel grass stations with unique faunal composition are listed in Table III.

Overlapping community patterns

Examination of the four community patterns (Fig. 63, 64, 65, 66) superimposed upon each other, discloses considerable overlap (Fig. 67). Although the original community patterns plotted individually on Fig. 63 through 66, showed relatively large geographic areas for each community, they are reduced to relatively small patches, each occupying central parts of the original habitats when overlapping areas are eliminated. The largest "pure" area was that of Inner Harbor which filled most of the Harbor, plus one small patch in the Outer Harbor. The sand flat community area was also reduced to two small patches at the wide entrance to the Outer Harbor, two small patches in the entrance of Northwest Gutter and four small patches in Lackey's Bay and East Gutter entrance. The channel community was reduced to a number of patches in the inner portions of the three gutters and two small patches in the Outer Harbor. The eel grass community showed the greatest reduction of all, as, with the exception of the Inner Harbor, it was a major component of the other habitats. The unique portions of the eel grass community were confined almost entirely to the narrow, subtidal margins of the Complex (Fig. 67), even though the most luxurious portions of the eel grass stands were located in slightly deeper waters. Thus, most of the eel grass community formed portions of the overlapping "common" community areas (Fig. 66). It is significant that, if only a few quantitative samples were taken in this region, probably none of the unique areas, with the exception of the Inner Harbor, would be sampled and recognized. It is possible that the Inner Harbor is the only really distinctive community in the Complex.

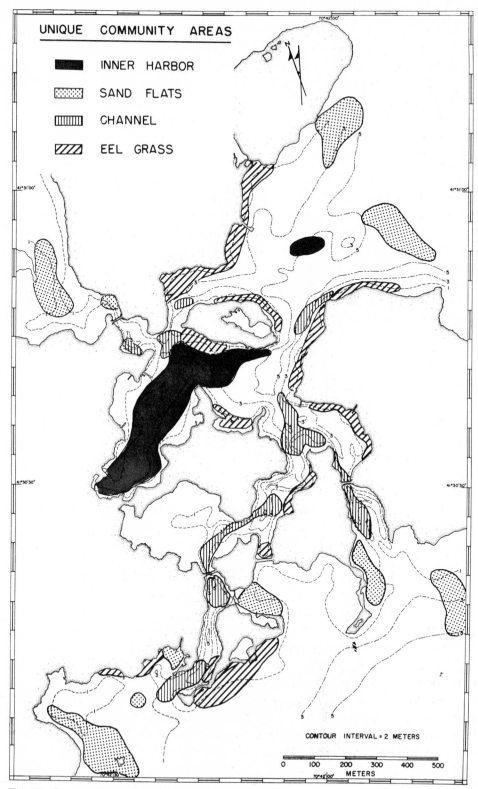

Fig. 67. Community patterns derived from station plots with unique species composition, with no overlap from species of neighboring communities.

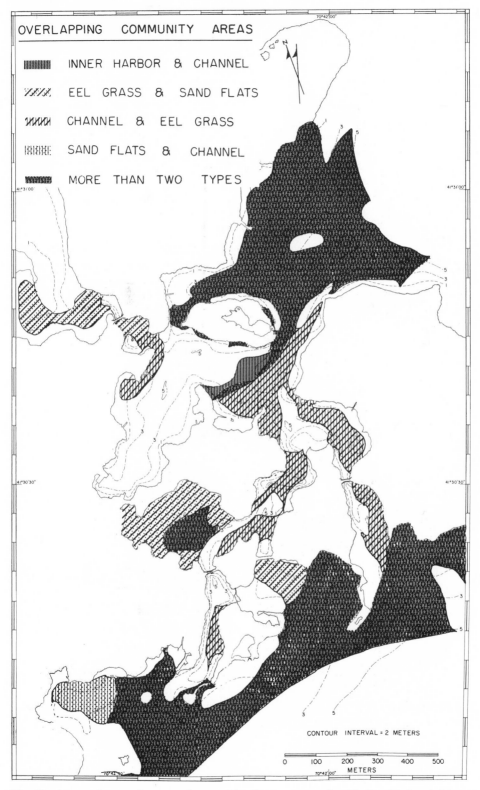

Fig. 68. Areas where unique species combinations representing Hadley Harbor habitats overlap one another.

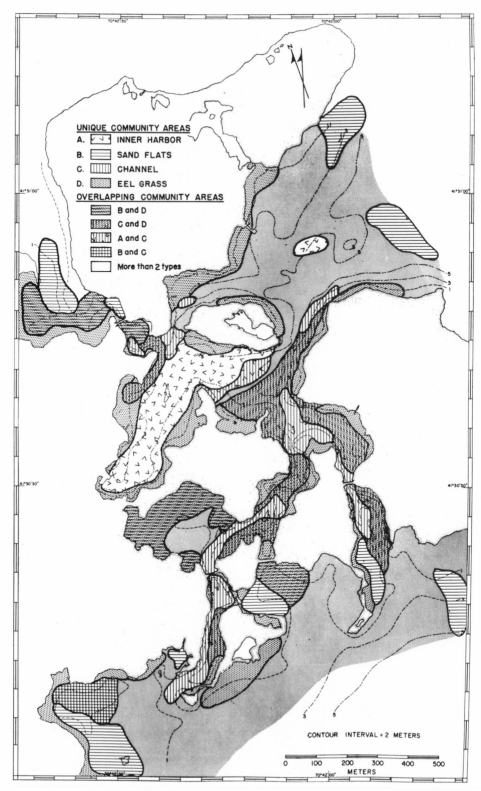

Fig. 69. Total picture of community organization showing both pure and overlapping community patterns.

A second chart was derived by superimposition of individual plots of the community patterns (Fig. 68), but this time including only the overlapping areas of the communities. Figs. 67 and 68, when combined (Fig. 69), illustrate the complete community coverage of the Complex. Overlapping adjacent communities form either pairs or areas in which more than two communities overlap (Fig. 68). The larger portions of paired overlap areas include eel grass in combination with either the sand flat or channel habitats, which is to be expected as eel grass occupies so much of the Complex.

The most striking feature of this community analysis is that large areas of overlap between several communities are all in the entrances of the gutters (with the exception of two small patches in Southwest Gutter), and appear to merge with the broad level-bottom communities of Buzzards Bay and Vineyard Sound. It is the author's interpretation that the fauna of the Hadley Harbor Complex is derived primarily from the large and evenly distributed Buzzards Bay and Vineyard Sound communities described by Sanders (1958, 1960). As the components of this community invade the complex physiography of the Complex, they apparently divide into associations of species seeking optimal biological and environmental conditions. Those organisms preferring clayey sediments "seek" and settle on the muds of Inner Harbor. As they may also tolerate low Eh and high turbidity to the exclusion of other species, they form a restricted and distinct community. Likewise, other organisms from the open embayments with low tolerances for soft-bottom conditions and preferring a hard sandy bottom in relatively shallow depths seek out and settle on the sand flats forming centers of population there. Many of the Buzzards Bay species would be eliminated because of warm summer or cold winter temperatures and the lack of organic-rich deposits between the closely packed sand grains. The majority of the typical open bay and sound species are successfully established within the Complex in the deeper channels, which more closely resemble the deeper habitats of open waters. As eel grass also thrives in the channels throughout the year, a combination of eel grass—channel communities is produced.

AREAL AND TEMPORAL CHANGES AT TOTAL POPULATION AND HIGHER TAXA LEVELS

In the preceding section, discussion was based on an analysis of the distribution of individual species or combinations of species as they related to the communities. Investigations were carried out of seasonal distributions at the higher taxon level and of total sample populations within the Complex. The rather striking changes which took place in total sample populations during the year provide a partial explanation for the difficulties in establishing "normal" species populations relative to each other within each community and the normal areal extent of each community. Large-scale fluctuations of total sample populations suggest that animals migrated from one place to another within the Complex, or else species populations varied significantly in one spot. Evidence suggests that both phenomena were involved in the seasonal changes, although reproduction and predation probably are the strongest contributors to total population fluctuations.

Plots of the distribution of density of total animals per $1/25 \text{ m}^2$ were drawn up for each 3-month season, starting in the spring of 1964 and running through the winter of 1964—65. Changes taking place between spring and summer for populations over 3,000 per $1/25 \text{ m}^2$ and under 1,000 per $1/25 \text{ m}^2$ are illustrated in Fig. 70. Areas not shaded contained populations between 1,000 and 3,000 individuals per $1/25 \text{ m}^2$, the mean population being about 2,700 per $1/25 \text{ m}^2$ or 67,500 per m^2. During the spring, large populations were limited to three small areas; one in Lackey's Bay, one in the entrance of Northwest Gutter, and the third in the wide portion of Southwest Gutter. Areas of low-density populations were located in the Inner Harbor, west side of the Outer Harbor, and in the western portion of Grassy Pond. Although not illustrated in Fig. 70, most of the blank area on the chart in the spring had populations between 1,000 and 2,000 animals per $1/25 \text{ m}^2$.

Summer concentrations provided a completely different picture. More extensive areas of high populations were observed and were correlated primarily with dense eel grass growth in the shallower portions of the Complex, especially in Southwest Gutter, the entrance into the Inner Harbor and in Lackey's Bay. Intermediate populations were also prevalent in eel grass areas and at all gutter entrances except the East Gutter. Low populations were found in both the Inner and Outer Harbor and in Grassy Pond. For some reason, most of the Vineyard Sound entrance to East Gutter was characterized by sparse populations.

Total animal counts per station in fall and winter are depicted on Fig. 71, in the same manner as illustrated on Fig. 70. Radical departures from spring and summer were observed. In the fall, most of the southern portion of the Inner Harbor was characterized by low population counts, as were the Northwest and Southwest Gutters and much of Lackey's Bay. On the other hand, a fairly large part of the Outer Harbor stations had high counts, while only two small patches in the southern part of the Complex had high concentrations. High intermediate densities occupied the rest of the Outer Harbor, grassy parts of the gutters, and the northern part of the Inner Harbor. Low intermediate station counts were found mostly in Grassy Pond and in parts of Southwest Gutter.

The winter of 1964—65, although not a severe one for the Cape Cod

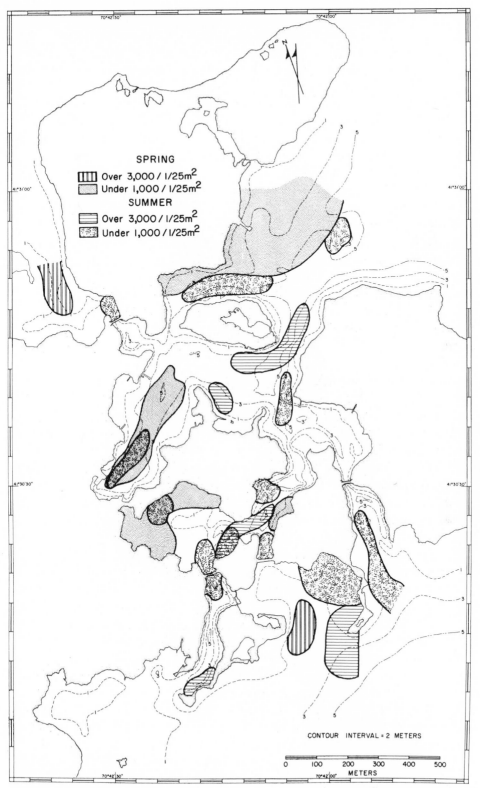

SPRING
|||| Over 3,000 / 1/25m^2
▦ Under 1,000 / 1/25m^2
SUMMER
▤ Over 3,000 / 1/25m^2
▨ Under 1,000 / 1/25m^2

CONTOUR INTERVAL = 2 METERS

0   100   200   300   400   500
METERS

Fig. 70. Distribution of total population density per station (1/25 m^2) in Hadley Harbor Complex during spring and summer (1964).

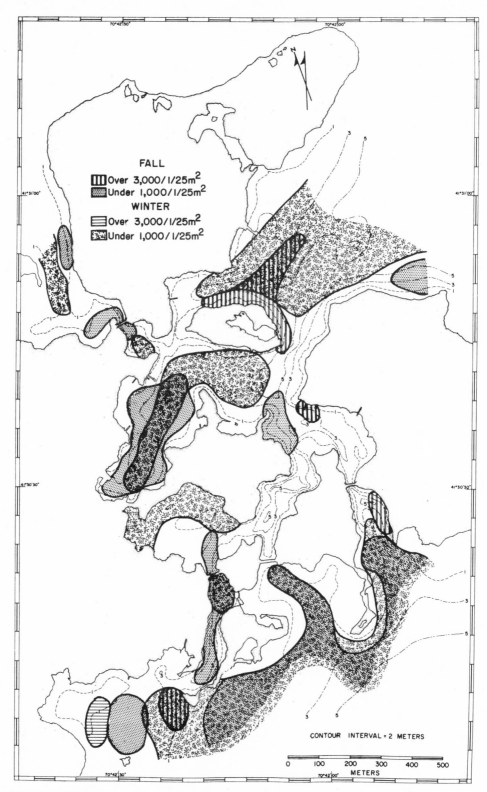

Fig. 71. Distribution of high and low total populations per station (1/25 m^2) in Hadley Harbor complex during fall and winter (1964—65).

region, must have been limiting to high standing crops of benthos. Two-thirds of the Complex was characterized by populations under 1,000 per $1/25$ m^2 (Fig. 71). Only one station, located in the western part of Lackey's Bay, had a count over 3,000, and only 7 stations out of 38 had counts above 2,000 per $1/25$ m^2. Virtually all of Inner Harbor and deeper parts of the Outer Harbor samples had counts below 500 individuals per station, and also most of the stations in eel grass areas had very low counts. This period was characterized by sub-zero temperatures, high Eh's, low pH's, and high light penetration, suggesting that primary production was at a comparatively low level.

Changes in total populations by habitats are depicted graphically on Fig. 72. Stations from four selected habitats were examined for total popula-

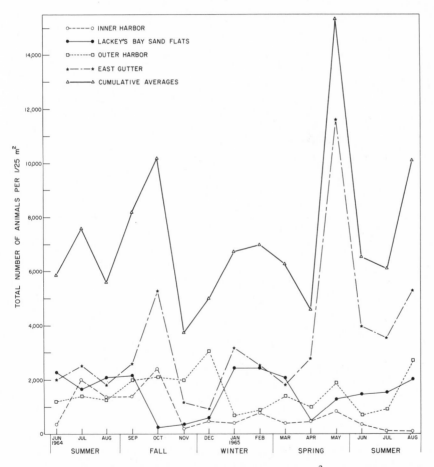

Fig. 72. Averages of total numbers of animals per $1/25$ m^2 per month from June, 1964, to August, 1965, in representative parts of four habitats of Hadley Harbor, Massachusetts.

tions from June, 1964, through August, 1965. Where more than one station was taken during a particular month, averages are given. Four curves, one for each habitat, were constructed. A cumulative curve derived from the four individual curves is given to show overall monthly variation. Each of the habitats was characterized by a particular level of standing crop, regardless of the season of the year. For instance, throughout the year Inner Harbor had the lowest counts, with less than 500 individuals per $1/25$ m^2 during nine months of the year. The next lowest counts are characteristic of the Lackey's Bay sand flats, the average count being around 1,000. However, this habitat showed the greatest variation between seasons, being over 2,000 in the summer and winter and below 500 in the spring and fall. East Gutter, representing the channel habitat, had the highest overall counts, with averages well over 3,000 individuals per $1/25$ m^2. Counts from the Outer Harbor region were intermediate but relatively uniform from one season to the next. The Outer Harbor waters were mostly an extension of the Buzzards Bay environment, which is considerably more stable than any of the Hadley Harbor habitats. The cumulative totals of all stations per month show the seasonal variation of animals as a whole for the Complex. Highest numbers occurred toward the end of September and in May, coincident with breeding periods of many of the amphipod species. Low totals were found in November—December and in April. The extremely high peak in May was almost entirely derived from one station taken in East Gutter, which is somewhat anomalous, considering that all other habitats had very low counts in both May of 1964 and 1965.

All individual station counts of total organisms, regardless of season, were plotted and isoplethed (Fig. 73). Although a meaningful picture of standing crop is derived from this plot, it masks completely the wide variations that took place seasonally. It does show, however, that areas of low standing crop corresponded fairly closely to parts of the Complex characterized by low Eh, fine well-sorted sediments, coarse well-sorted sediments, and areas which had only seasonal cover of eel grass. On the other hand, areas of high standing crop were found either near the margins of the Complex on poorly sorted sands and silty sands, and areas with either very high summer eel grass cover or year-round stands of eel grass. There is considerable correlation between areas of uniform standing crop, high or low, and the community areas derived from superimposition of individual species plots and their abundances.

Areal extent of the communities relative to total populations as they changed through the seasons was not plotted. It can be inferred from the data just discussed, however, that the areal extent of the communities expanded and contracted coincident with physical—chemical and biological changes associated with the seasons. The Inner Harbor community had its greatest areal extent coincident with the large areas of low standing crop as

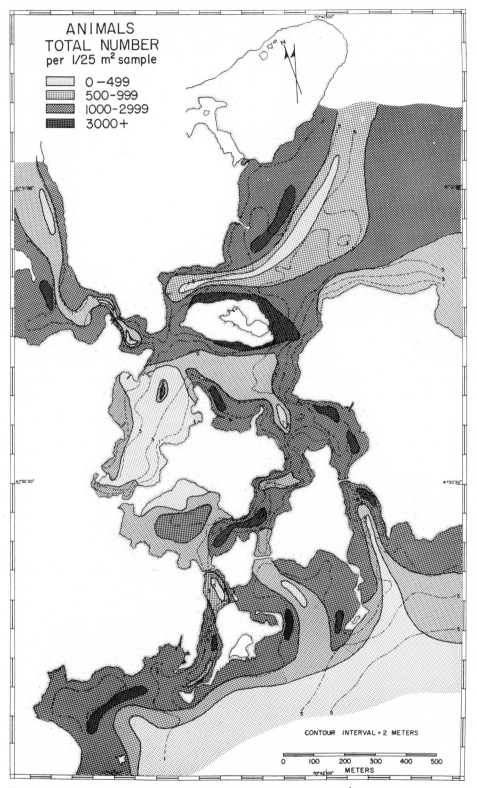

Fig. 73. Areal plot of total number of organisms per 1/25 m² per station in Hadley Harbor, Massachusetts, for all biological stations taken between October, 1963, to September, 1965.

depicted on the chart of winter standing crop (Fig. 71). The area delineating this community shrank in size during spring and fall months. The sand flat community had its greatest areal extent during the summer months and virtually disappeared in the winter when ice cover reached to the bottom. The eel grass community had its greatest areal extent in the early fall, coincident with the largest and tallest stands of eel grass in the gutters and when eel grass covered most of the sand flats. Of the four communities, the channel community showed the least variation from season to season. It was also the most stable in terms of physical—chemical factors. H.L. Sanders (personal communication, 1965) investigated the seasonality of the benthic fauna at Station "R" in Buzzards Bay over several years, and, although there was considerable variation in the number of individuals for various species from season to season, the variation was far less than that found in the shallower portions of the Hadley Harbor Complex.

Another source of evidence on seasonal changes in the composition of benthic communities was the relative abundance of meiofaunal invertebrates at the higher taxa level. Although data were not available on species densities for certain taxa (oligochaetes, nematodes, copepods), the total populations of each higher taxon at each station proved valuable in demonstrating seasonal changes and possible habitat preferences. Depicting these changes, however, was a major task as 7 variables, 4 seasons, and 300 stations were involved.

On the basis of total counts per station of individuals smaller than 1 mm only, percentages of each major meiofaunal taxon were calculated for each station sampled weekly, between the first week of September, 1964, and the end of August, 1965. Individual bar graphs were constructed for each station using a uniform ranking system with the first bar representing percentage of nematodes; second, oligochaetes; third, polychaetes; fourth, copepods; fifth, amphipods; sixth, ostracods; and the seventh representing all other smaller taxa, including kinorhynchs, turbellaria, mites, cumaceans, insects and cephalocarids. Black and white bars on a broad arrow pointing to the station sampled were then plotted for each season (Fig. 74—77). The numbers given on the top of each bar correspond to the individual black and white areas within the bar. For instance, at Station *176* (the top of Fig. 74), the five numbers on top correspond to the five areas within the bar as follows: *1* (nematodes) equals approximately 70% of the total; *2* (oligochaetes) equals 20%; *3* (polychaetes) equals 3%; *4* (copepods) equals 4%; and *7* (all other) equals 3%. Using the scale given on the illustrations, one can determine the approximate percentages of each taxon at each station. In arrow-blocks without numbers, all seven groups were present in the order listed in the legend. Numbered arrow-blocks indicate that one or more taxa were missing at that station.

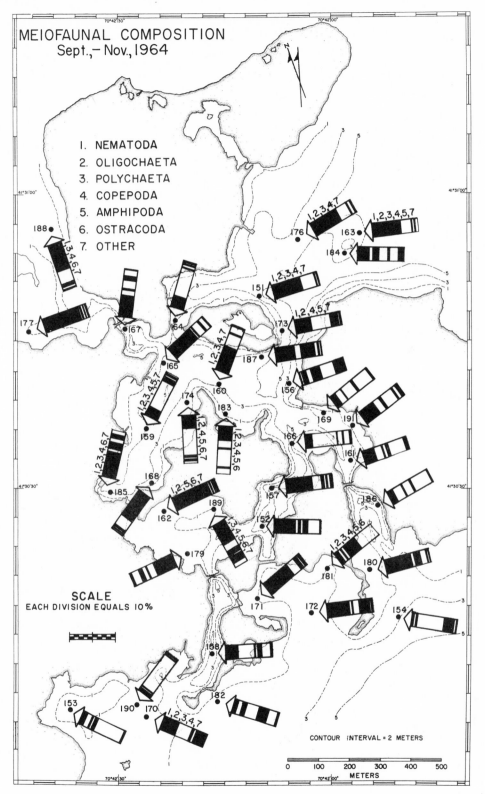

Fig. 74. The percentage composition of the fall, 1964, stations for meiofaunal taxa (less than 1 mm).

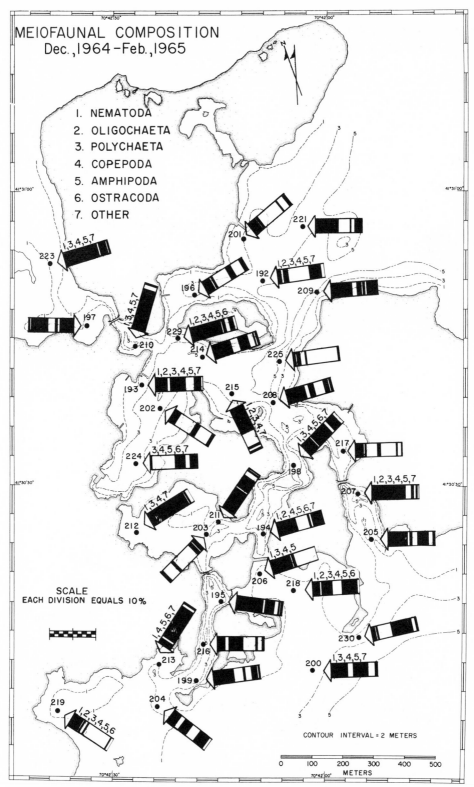

Fig. 75. The percentage composition of the winter, 1964—65, stations for meiofaunal taxa (less than 1 mm).

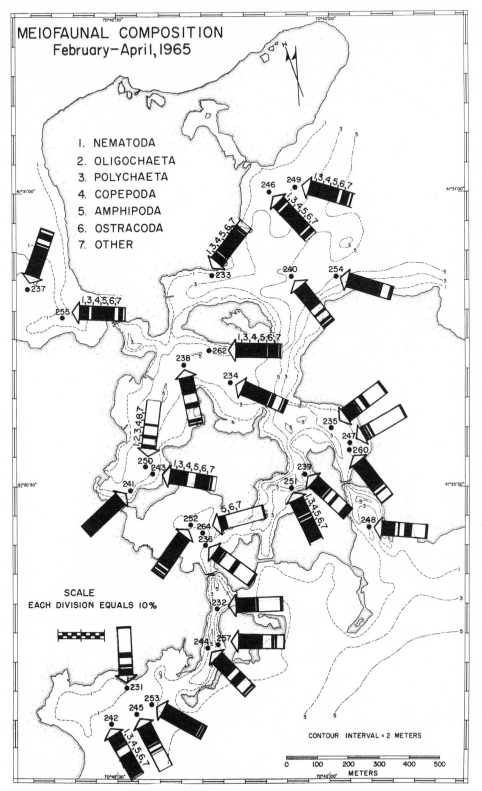

Fig. 76. The percentage composition of the spring, 1965, stations for meiofaunal taxa (less than 1 mm).

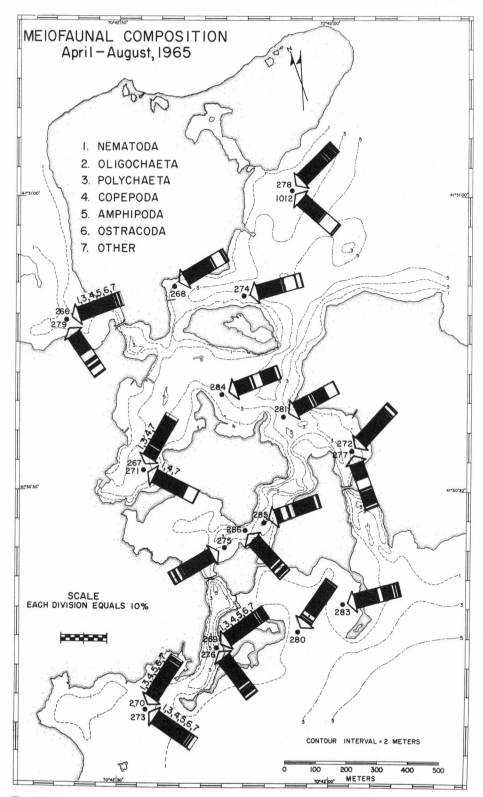

Fig. 77. The percentage composition of the summer, 1965, stations for meiofaunal taxa (less than 1 mm).

TABLE IV

Change in composition of major meiofaunal taxa by season

Habitat	Taxa	Fall (Fig.74)	Winter (Fig.75)	Spring (Fig.76)	Summer (Fig.77)
Outer Harbor					
	1. Nematodes	20—70*	10—45	12—70	56—64
	2. Oligochaetes	10—30	0—12	0—15	2— 4
	3. Polychaetes	10—20	2—10	4— 8	2— 8
Inner Harbor					
	1. Nematodes	25—70	10—85	8—70	25—75
	2. Oligochaetes	10—60	0—20	0—20	0— 4
	3. Polychaetes	5—20	2—15	2—12	0— 4
Northwest Gutter sand flats					
	1. Nematodes	70—90	20—65	20—60	44—86
	2. Oligochaetes	0— 5	0— 2	0— 4	0—15
	3. Polychaetes	5—30	2— 5	4— 8	5— 8
Lackey's Bay sand flats					
	1. Nematodes	20—40	15—30	25—80	80—85
	2. Oligochaetes	5—30	0—10	0— 2	0
	3. Polychaetes	5—15	4—25	2— 4	2— 4
Southwest and East Gutters (channels)					
	1. Nematodes	20—60	10—70	10—50	35—85
	2. Oligochaetes	10—40	0—20	0—20	2—20
	3. Polychaetes	5—10	0—30	4—15	4—10

* Percentage total extremes.

The changes of any one taxon may be followed from season to season in the same habitat with these diagrams. An example of changes for the first three taxa in five habitats for the four seasons is given in Table IV.

Within the Outer Harbor the percentage of nematodes dropped considerably in the winter and was highest at all stations in the summer; the oligochaetes were highest in the fall and apparently lowest in the summer; while the polychaetes were highest in fall and winter and lowest in spring and summer. Inside Inner Harbor the percentage of nematodes was high in fall and summer and low in winter and spring; oligochaetes were high in the fall and low during the rest of the months; and polychaetes were highest in fall, lowest in summer, and maintained about the same levels through winter and spring. The two sand flat habitats, one in Buzzards Bay and the other in Vineyard Sound extensions, were quite different. In the Northwest Gutter area, nematodes were highest in the fall and lowest in the spring, while in Lackey's Bay they were highest in the summer and lowest in the winter. Oligochaetes were missing or very low at all seasons in Northwest Gutter, but were relatively abundant in Lackey's Bay during the fall and were completely missing in the summer. Polychaetes were also uniformly low in the sand flat areas, but were relatively high in Northwest Gutter in the fall and in the fall and winter in Lackey's Bay. All three taxa constituted the major percentages of the fauna in the channel habitat throughout the year. In fact, there was little change from season to season in most of the taxa, substantiating the premise that the channels were the most stable of the habitats in Hadley Harbor. It should be emphasized that fluctuations of individual species within these taxa were so great that these figures may not be entirely representative. The original plots of these data also gave the total populations upon which the percentages were based, but there was insufficient space to include them in the figures.

FACTOR ANALYSIS OF AGGREGATIONS OF BENTHIC ANIMALS

In the early stages of analysis of the density and distribution data from Hadley Harbor we devised several computer programs for reducing the data, but these proved impracticable because of programming limitations. One of these, a modified cluster analysis (general cluster), based in part on the program used to deduce invertebrate assemblages in the Gulf of California (Parker, 1964a), and similar to one devised by Valentine and Peddicord (1967), was only partially successful.

Factor analysis was the principal component of these initial programs, and was continued as the sole means of reducing the data in subsequent programs. Several factor analysis programs in both Q- and R-modes (35 variables × 35 variables × 35 stations and 35 variables × 35 variables × 72 stations matrices) were run, at the Woods Hole Oceanographic Institution, using the program for a GE 225 Computer compiled by Dr. D.W. Spencer (unpublished manuscript, Woods Hole Oceanographic Institution). Only a limited number of species and a small number of stations could be included in these matrices, because of limitations of the core storage of the 225 computer, and so the results are not discussed here. However, the factor score plot for the sediment factor on the largest matrix is shown on Fig. 22. In order to compute a factor matrix large enough to be significant, we had to utilize a larger computer. The modified factor analysis program ultimately used[1] was written by Dr. W. Sconyers formerly of the Texas Christian University Computation Center[2]. The program was run twice on an IBM 360-50 at the South-

---

[1] Derived from the Program "Factor Analysis" in the *IBM Systems/360, Scientific Subroutine Package (360A—LM—03X) Version II, Programmer's Manual* (1967).

[2] This program and complete documentation can be obtained upon request from the Texas Christian University Computation Center, *Facto Version 3*, T.C.U. Library Number 0360-06-06.001.

west Center for Advanced Studies, now University of Texas, Dallas.

Both factor analyses were run in the "R"-Mode, which examines the relationship between variables on the basis of samples or stations at which the variables were measured. As the variables measured in this study consisted of species of animals and their size classes (related to number found in each sieve fraction) and physical—chemical and sediment data, it was advisable to use the "R"-Mode to correlate communities and their environmental variables. A description of the basis for factor analysis as used in the physical sciences rather than the behavioral sciences can be found in Imbrie and Van Andel (1964). In the factor analysis employed in Hadley Harbor, eigenvalues were calculated from the correlation matrix, the initial factor matrix was computed, and a Varimax orthogonal factor rotation was performed. Factor scores (the influence that the various factors derived from the rotated factor matrix have upon the individual stations) were calculated. The factor loadings (Table V) were used to determine the species composition of the communities and the environmental variables which appeared to influence them, while the factor scores were used to plot the areal extent and intensity from center to fringe of the communities within the Complex. In a sense, the factor scores gave us much the same information as if we had computed these same data through a factor analysis in the "Q"-Mode. Should we have tried the "Q"-Mode analysis first, a considerable plotting of loadings on Varimax factor axes would have been involved in order to determine the composition of the communities. Using both scores and loadings from the rotated factor matrix in the "R"-Mode gave all the required information in one computer run.

Examination of the factor loadings on the unrotated factor matrix from the 100 variables × 100 variables × 137 stations matrix indicates that many species had loadings above 0.40 on most of the 31 factors derived from the correlation matrix. Scores from the unrotated matrix were also plotted on a chart with the 137 stations chosen for the analysis (Fig. 78, p. 171). Several of the unrotated factors contained highly correlated species variables which showed close correspondence to the community aggregations derived from the subjective analysis presented in the first two-thirds of this study. As these unrotated factors changed their values considerably upon rotation, only the rotated factor data are discussed.

The loadings on the Varimax matrix were much lower than on the unrotated matrix on all factors for most of the variables, although there were always a few very high loadings for one or two variables on each factor. It should be pointed out that, even with the full capacity of an IBM 360-50, there were severe limitations on the number of variables which could be used. With 100 variables and 137 stations, this program utilized the total capacity of the computer. Of these 100 variables, 86 were biological — consisting of size

TABLE V

Factor loadings above 0.4 for significant factors derived from the Varimax matrix factor analysis of 100 variables × 100 variables × 137 stations

Variable	Size fraction (mm)	Loading[1]	Variable	Loading[1]
Factor 1 (Channels, high-currents community; 8 species)				
Elasmopus laevis	0.5	+ 0.93	Light penetration	+ 0.16
Cymadusa compta	1.0	+ 0.86	Bottom Eh	+ 0.11
Microprotopus ranei	1.0	+ 0.80	Depth	+ 0.10
Ampithoe longimana	0.25	+ 0.80	Sediment sand	+ 0.09
Elasmopus laevis	1.0	+ 0.64		
Copidognathus sp.	1.5	+ 0.61		
Ampithoe longimana	1.0	+ 0.57		
Cymadusa compta	0.25	+ 0.52		
Solemya velum	0.5	+ 0.48		
Caprella geometrica	1.0	+ 0.48		
Corophium acutum	1.0	+ 0.35		
Factor 2 (Amphipod—crustacean community; 6 species)				
Corophium acutum	0.25	- 0.99	Surface Eh	+ 0.13
Corophium insidiosum	0.25	- 0.99	Bottom Eh	+ 0.12
Corophium insidiosum	0.5	- 0.98	Time	- 0.16
Corophium insidiosum	1.0	- 0.97		
Dexamine thea	0.5	- 0.97		
Copidognathus sp.	0.25	- 0.66		
Microdeutopus gryllotalpa	0.25	- 0.63		
Sarsiella americana	0.5	- 0.37		
Factor 3 (Eel grass, eddy portions community; 8 species)				
Loxoconcha impressa	0.25	- 0.80	Bottom Eh	+ 0.16
Paraphoxus oculatus	1.0	- 0.78	Depth	+ 0.16
Cythereis vineyardensis	0.25	- 0.74	Surface Eh	- 0.13
Paraphoxus oculatus	0.5	- 0.72	Total animals	- 0.11
Parasterope pollex	0.5	- 0.70		
Solemya velum	0.25	- 0.56		
Lysianopsis alba	1.0	- 0.45		
Microdeutopus damnoniensis	2.0	- 0.41		
Phoxocephalus holbolli	1.0	- 0.40		
Factor 4 (Amphipod—crustacean community; 4 species)				
Microdeutopus gryllotalpa	1.0	- 0.94	Bottom temperature	+ 0.17
Microdeutopus gryllotalpa	0.5	- 0.87	Surface temperature	+ 0.16
Nereis succinea	1.0	- 0.79	Sediment sorting	+ 0.13
Elasmopus laevis	2.0	- 0.51		
Microdeutopus damnoniensis	2.0	- 0.45		
Microdeutopus gryllotalpa	0.25	- 0.44		
Factor 5 (Channels and eel grass community; 4 species)				
Bittium alternatum	1.0	+ 0.90	Sediment sorting	+ 0.23
Bittium alternatum	4.0	+ 0.80	Surface Eh	+ 0.22

TABLE V *(continued)*

Variable	Size fraction (mm)	Loading[1]	Variable	Loading[1]
Mitrella lunata	2.0	+ 0.68	Sediment diameter	+ 0.11
Mitrella lunata	0.5	+ 0.67		
Bittium alternatum	2.0	+ 0.54		
Caecum pulchellum	0.5	+ 0.46		
Copidognathus sp.	0.25	+ 0.35		

Factor 6   (Channels and eel grass community; 8 species)

Anachis translirata	4.0	+ 0.83	No physical variables over	0.05
Parasterope pollex	1.0	+ 0.83		
Propontocypris edwardsi	0.25	+ 0.74		
Anachis avara	4.0	+ 0.65		
Cymadusa compta	0.5	+ 0.60		
Lysianopsis alba	0.5	+ 0.51		
Solemya velum	4.0	+ 0.43		
Hutchinsoniella macracantha	0.25	+ 0.35		

Factor 8   (Channels, high-currents community; 3 species)

Propontocypris edwardsi	0.5	+ 0.88	Depth	+ 0.12
Hutchinsoniella macracantha	0.5	+ 0.84		
Hutchinsoniella macracantha	0.25	+ 0.76		
Parasterope pollex	0.25	+ 0.69		

Factor 9   (Channels, high-currents community; 4 species)

Ampelisca macrocephala	0.5	+ 0.90	Sediment sorting	+ 0.11
Lumbrineris tenuis	2.0	+ 0.85		
Phoxocephalus holbolli	0.5	+ 0.64		
Sarsiella americana	0.5	+ 0.54		

Factor 10   (Eel grass, eddy portions community; 4 species)

Corophium acutum	1.0	− 0.84	Bottom salinity	+ 0.18
Microdeutopus damnoniensis	1.0	− 0.81	Bottom temperature	+ 0.14
Corophium acutum	0.5	− 0.72	Time	− 0.17
Lysianopsis alba	1.0	− 0.63	Sediment sorting	− 0.12
Microdeutopus damnoniensis	0.5	− 0.50	Total animals	− 0.11
Ampithoe longimana	1.0	− 0.43		

Factor 11   (Sand flats community; 2 species)

Gemma gemma	0.5	+ 0.95	Time	+ 0.15
Tellina agilis	1.0	+ 0.93	Surface Eh	− 0.12
Gemma gemma	1.0	+ 0.47	Bottom Eh	− 0.12
Tellina agilis	0.5	+ 0.26		

Factor 12   (Channels and eel grass community; 2 species)

Listriella barnardi	0.25	+ 0.84	Sediment sorting	+ 0.17
Propontocypris edwardsi	1.0	+ 0.77		
Listriella barnardi	0.5	+ 0.56		

Factor 13   (Sediment factor; 1 species)

Caecum pulchellum	0.5	− 0.35	Sediment silt	+ 0.91

TABLE V *(continued)*

Variable	Size fraction (mm)	Loading[1]	Variable	Loading[1]
(Bittium alternatum	2.0	+ 0.22)	Bottom Eh	+ 0.13
(Leucon americanus	0.5	+ 0.20)	Sediment sand	− 0.93
Only species with			Sediment diameter	− 0.84
+ loadings over 0.10			Surface salinity	− 0.12
			Light penetration	− 0.12
			Bottom salinity	− 0.10

Factor 17 (Eel grass, eddy portions community; 2 species)

Variable	Size fraction (mm)	Loading	Variable	Loading
Pycnophes frequens	0.5	− 0.84	Surface Eh	+ 0.22
Solemya velum	1.0	− 0.69	Depth	+ 0.10
Solemya velum	0.5	− 0.56	Time	− 0.30
			Total animals	− 0.26

Factor 18 (Inner Harbor silts community; 3 species)

Variable	Size fraction (mm)	Loading	Variable	Loading
Yoldia limatula	1.0	+ 0.81	Time	+ 0.17
Yoldia limatula	4.0	+ 0.80	Depth	+ 0.12
Lumbrineris tenuis	4.0	+ 0.58	Total animals	+ 0.12
Retusa canaliculata	1.0	+ 0.21	Sediment silt	+ 0.12
			Surface Eh	− 0.20
			Sediment sorting	− 0.19
			Sediment sand	− 0.12

Factor 19 (Inner Harbor silts community; 5 species)

Variable	Size fraction (mm)	Loading	Variable	Loading
Turbonilla interrupta	0.5	+ 0.82	Depth	+ 0.13
Retusa canaliculata	1.0	+ 0.78	Sediment sorting	− 0.18
Cylichna oryza	1.0	+ 0.71		
Sarsiella americana	0.5	+ 0.49		
Copidognathus sp.	0.5	+ 0.41		
Turbonilla interrupta	1.0	+ 0.34		

Factor 29 (Sand flats community; 2 species)

Variable	Size fraction (mm)	Loading	Variable	Loading
Parasterope pollex	2.0	+ 0.75	Bottom Eh	− 0.12
Hydrobia minuta	0.5	+ 0.71	Time	− 0.11
			Total animals	− 0.11

[1] Rounded off to two places from five decimal places.

classes of abundant species with the total number of individuals for each species for each size class at each station as raw data. All data used in this analysis had to be transformed and linearized first. The remaining 14 variables are physical—chemical—sediment variables such as depth, bottom salinity, surface salinity, sorting coefficients, etc. Unfortunately, with only 84 biological variables permitted, three-quarters of the biological data was not used. Most of the species selected were abundant in 2—3 size fraction classes (each size class considered as a separate variable), thus, the actual number of

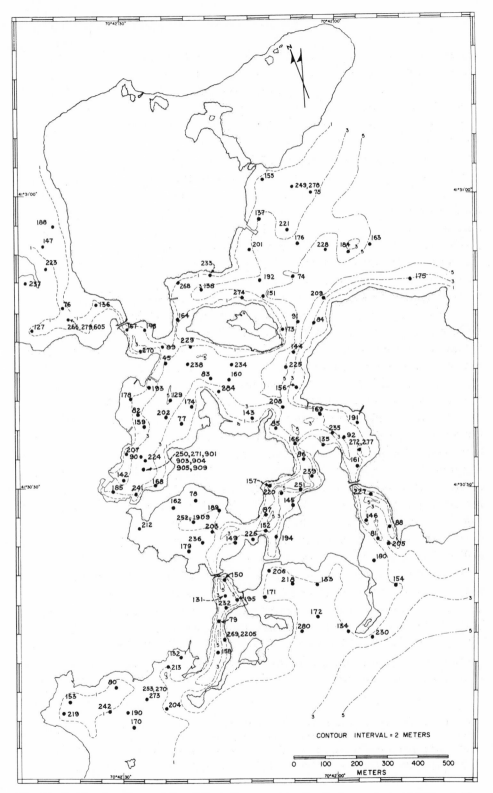

Fig. 78. Station locations of the 137 stations used in the factor analysis of 100 variables × 100 variables × 137 stations.

species used was only 43, of which 15 were mollusks, 2 polychaetes, 1 mite, 1 cephalocarid, 2 cumaceans, 5 ostracodes, and 17 were amphipods.

Many of the more diagnostic mollusks used to define the communities by plots of species were inadvertently omitted when the data was prepared for the factor program; as well as all kinorhynchs, most of the polychaetes, and all decapods and echinoderms. Selection of the species to be inserted in the analysis was determined primarily by the number of occurrences and the number of individuals taken at each station. Naturally, the larger the populations and the more station occurrences per species the more valid the statistics. The omission of such molluscan species as *Macoma tenta*, *Mulinia lateralis*, and *Nucula proxima* meant that a rather weak correlation would be produced for the Inner Harbor group of species, as these three species were the most restricted of all species of that habitat. Of the known sand flat species, such invertebrates as *Acanthohaustorius*, *Lacuna*, and *Leptosynapta* were excluded. Most of the common channel and eel grass species of mollusks and amphipods were included, and therefore, the strongest factors involve channel or eel grass inhabitants. All physical—chemical and sediment variables were included except dissolved oxygen, current strength and current direction. Only 137 stations were selected for the run, as these were the only stations which had measurements for all of the physical—chemical—sediment variables[1]. From these data it was possible to determine the species composition of the communities (based only on those species chosen), determine the communities in which stations scored high, and then look at the total composition of these stations, much in the same manner that the communities were analyzed for total composition on the basis of plots of the most abundant species. Considering that only 30% of the total data was used for the larger factor analysis, it is quite surprising that communities and areas were not only so clear cut, but were similar to those defined by the more subjective method. It is hoped that eventually some means can be found to utilize the entire 200,000 pieces of data in the form of multivariate analysis.

In order to demonstrate similarities between habitat or community location and composition as established through the time-consuming subjective analysis just discussed and the more efficient and objective factor analysis, both methods will be compared. An Inner Harbor community will be discussed first. It will be recalled that the Inner Harbor clayey silt habitat contained four dominant pelecypods, two gastropods, one kinorhynch, two amphipods, and one cumacean. Of the ten species, whose distribution maps

---

[1] All the rest of the biological stations had at least one variable missing. Since the value "zero" is a valid one, especially for water and air temperature, and occasionally for total number of animals per station, we could not use blanks or zeros for missing data in the other stations for fear of causing the computer program to stop.

delineated the habitat, only six were used for the factor analysis matrix. Three of these six species had very high loadings for the group of factors which comprised the factor score plot shown on Fig. 79. The combined plots of scores over +0.4600 for factors 18 and 19 (both having as high loadings, species which were known to be Inner Harbor species) compare very favorably with the plot of the composite distributional map of Inner Harbor species on Fig. 63. Table VI includes the loadings and communalities for the highly loaded species (above 0.4) for the two factors, 18 and 19, making up what this author considers a common factor. Actually, by superimposing and comparing species loadings and factor scores visually, the author has performed a rather primitive oblique or full rotation of the factor matrix. Some justification for lumping the two factors together can be found (Table VI) in that most of the variables which occurred on one of the factors also occurred on the other factors with both high loadings and the same sign. In fact, one-fifth of the variables had high loadings on both factors. Both depth and sorting coefficients loaded high on both of the factors; and sediment, as silt-sized material, was positive, while sand-sized sediment was negative, indicating that depth, poor sorting, and fine sediments were the controlling physical—chemical and sediment variables. These also correlated well with individual species plots for the Inner Harbor habitat. Species correspondence for this habitat was determined by comparing the factor analysis with species plots and includes one pelecypod (the other three did not enter into the analysis); three gastropods, two of which were unique to the Inner Harbor habitat and the third a common associate; one polychaete, known to be common in the Inner Harbor; one ostracod which was not limited to the Inner Harbor, and the mite *Copidognathus*, which was considered more of a deep-channel species than an Inner Harbor species. Both the subjective and the statistical methods gave results which are in good agreement for this particular habitat.

The next habitat to be discussed is the shallow sand flat habitat. Like the Inner Harbor habitat, this had relatively few species and most of these were unique to this particular environment. The major difference in the composition of the community as determined by both the superimposition of species plots and factor analysis is that only four species had high loadings for factors 11 and 29 which identify the community (Table VI) versus 11 species suggested by the subjective method. Two of the species, *Gemma gemma* and *Hydrobia minuta*, were common to both methods of analysis of communities. However, *Parasterope pollex* and *Tellina agilis*, which loaded heavily on these two factors, are not designated as obligate residents in the subjective appraisal. Both species did occur on the sand flats but also were taken elsewhere in the Complex. It is possible that abundance makes them sand flat species, which could not be deduced from the subjective appraisal. Five

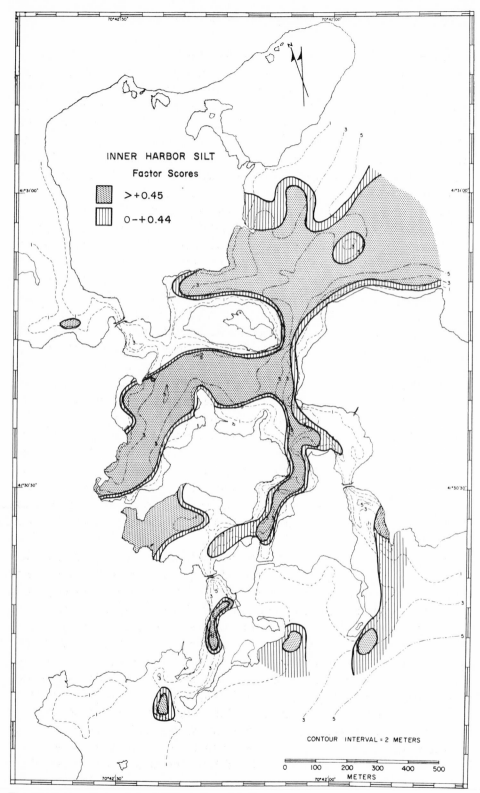

Fig. 79. Factor score plot of 137 stations for Factors 18 and 19, representing the Inner Harbor community of the Hadley Harbor Complex.

TABLE VI

Factor loadings and communalities for grouped factors, comparing all species and physical variables within each habitat or community group

Species	Size fractions (mm)	Loadings Factor numbers		Communalities
Inner Harbor group		18	19	
Turbonilla interrupta G[1]	0.5	− 0.07843	+ 0.81907	0.87419
Yoldia limatula P	1.0	+ 0.80926	+ 0.00149	0.70233
Yoldia limatula P	4.0	+ 0.80400	+ 0.00622	0.83666
Retusa canaliculata G	1.0	+ 0.20577	+ 0.78751	0.83282
Cylichna oryza G	1.0	− 0.00285	+ 0.70935	0.66134
Lumbrineris tenuis PO	4.0	+ 0.57561	+ 0.09337	0.57161
Sarsiella sp. OS	0.5	− 0.03764	+ 0.49335	0.75352
Copidognathus sp. AC	0.5	− 0.05389	+ 0.40531	0.84325
Time		+ 0.16565	− 0.00041	0.75871
Depth		+ 0.12283	+ 0.13433	0.83223
Total animals per station		+ 0.12325	− 0.02921	0.68347
Percent silt		+ 0.12782	− 0.02016	0.92819
Surface water Eh		− 0.19954	+ 0.06604	0.73095
Sediment sorting		− 0.18912	− 0.17722	0.71023
Percent sand		− 0.11708	+ 0.03419	0.93746

Retusa canaliculata high on both. Depth and sediment sorting same on both factors.

Sand flat group		11	29	
Gemma gemma P	0.5	+ 0.95029	+ 0.02926	0.94626
Tellina agilis P	1.0	+ 0.92955	+ 0.05747	0.89793
Parasterope pollex OS	2.0	+ 0.03181	+ 0.74828	0.70704
Hydrobia minuta G	0.5	− 0.05893	+ 0.70924	0.68820
Gemma gemma P	1.0	+ 0.47442	+ 0.02811	0.69671
Tellina agilis P	0.5	+ 0.25925	+ 0.05747	0.54390
Time		+ 0.15318	− 0.11073	0.75871
Surface water Eh		− 0.12251	− 0.07078	0.73095
Bottom sediment Eh		− 0.12053	− 0.11879	0.75857
Total animals per station		+ 0.02948	− 0.10715	0.68347

Both time and bottom Eh have relatively high loadings, although signs differ. Signs on most of biological variables agree.

Eel grass and channels group A		5	6	12	
Bittium alternatum G	1.0	+ 0.90127	+ 0.03708	+ 0.02366	0.75753
Listriella barnardi AM	0.25	+ 0.01385	+ 0.01971	+ 0.84497	0.78753
Anachis translirata G	4.0	+ 0.08067	+ 0.83342	− 0.06028	0.78074
Parasterope pollex OS	1.0	− 0.05666	+ 0.82664	− 0.07536	0.85667
Bittium alternatum G	4.0	+ 0.79973	+ 0.03921	− 0.02146	0.83666
Propontocypris edwardsi OS	1.0	− 0.06056	− 0.02582	+ 0.76761	0.73198
Propontocypris edwardsi OS	0.25	+ 0.02114	+ 0.74338	+ 0.11184	0.85378
Mitrella lunata G	2.0	+ 0.67887	+ 0.15633	+ 0.01434	0.80579
Mitrella lunata G	0.5	+ 0.67081	+ 0.01098	− 0.08543	0.82540

TABLE VI *(continued)*

Species	Size fractions (mm)	Loadings Factor numbers			Communalities
Anachis avara G	4.0	+ 0.22580	+ 0.65375	+ 0.07689	0.76072
Cymadusa compta AM	0.5	+ 0.09360	+ 0.59764	+ 0.12287	0.86628
Listriella barnardi AM	0.5	+ 0.26320	+ 0.27794	+ 0.55858	0.81486
Bittium alternatum G	2.0	+ 0.53651	+ 0.12126	+ 0.03843	0.75753
Lysianopsis alba AM	0.5	- 0.03199	+ 0.50869	+ 0.22145	0.79382
Caecum pulchellum G	0.5	+ 0.45718	+ 0.03604	+ 0.18247	0.67114
Solemya velum P	4.0	+ 0.16570	+ 0.42533	+ 0.11512	0.78886
Sediment sorting		+ 0.22734	- 0.02845	+ 0.17166	0.71023
Surface water Eh		+ 0.21843	+ 0.05979	- 0.02147	0.73095
Sediment median diameter		+ 0.11051	- 0.04058	- 0.04474	0.80253

Anachis avara, Lysianopsis alba, Caecum pulchellum, and Solemya velum and the physical variable sediment sorting have high and similar loadings on at least two factors.

Eel grass and channels group B		3	10	17	
Corophium acutum AM	1.0	- 0.26318	- 0.84102	+ 0.01911	0.90396
Pycnophes frequens K	0.5	+ 0.01947	+ 0.03515	- 0.84801	0.77493
Microdeutopus damnoniensis AM	1.0	- 0.11955	- 0.80822	- 0.00364	0.84354
Loxoconcha granulata OS	0.25	- 0.79929	- 0.15187	- 0.08603	0.83701
Paraphoxus oculatus AM	1.0	- 0.78101	- 0.04236	- 0.03984	0.83549
Cythereis vineyardensis OS	0.25	- 0.74091	- 0.15187	- 0.08603	0.70921
Paraphoxus oculatus AM	0.5	- 0.71720	+ 0.69349	+ 0.12422	0.80520
Corophium acutum AM	0.5	- 0.05037	- 0.71783	+ 0.01449	0.88947
Parasterope pollex OS	0.5	- 0.70010	- 0.14220	- 0.09671	0.83675
Solemya velum P	1.0	- 0.31126	- 0.00334	- 0.67037	0.81638
Lysianopsis alba AM	1.0	- 0.45174	- 0.63402	- 0.02909	0.90699
Solemya velum P	0.5	- 0.22165	- 0.07532	- 0.55990	0.77167
Solemya velum P	0.25	- 0.55922	- 0.03108	- 0.19090	0.67757
Microdeutopus damnoniensis AM	0.5	+ 0.06631	- 0.49831	- 0.02640	0.73951
Ampithoe longimana AM	1.0	- 0.08534	- 0.42801	- 0.04132	0.91021
Microdeutopus damnoniensis AM	2.0	- 0.40968	- 0.29672	+ 0.03937	0.84352
Phoxocephalus holbolli AM	1.0	- 0.39905	- 0.26319	- 0.08790	0.67270
Surface water Eh		- 0.13000	- 0.07007	+ 0.22180	0.73095
Bottom salinity		- 0.00135	+ 0.18114	- 0.02698	0.91937
Bottom sediment Eh		+ 0.15102	- 0.05724	- 0.05250	0.75857
Depth		+ 0.15709	+ 0.07941	+ 0.10264	0.83223
Bottom water temperature		+ 0.06315	+ 0.13707	- 0.30206	0.75871
Total animals per station		- 0.10903	- 0.11453	- 0.25576	0.68347
Sediment sorting		+ 0.07410	- 0.11711	- 0.05550	0.71023

The following species have high and similar loadings on each of two of these factors: *Corophium acutum*, *Microdeutopus damnoniensis*, *Loxoconcha granulata*, *Paraphoxus oculatus*, *Parasterope pollex*, *Solemya velum*, *Lysianopsis alba*, and *Ampithoe longimana*. The physical variables bottom salinity, bottom temperature, and depth, are also similar on at least two factors.

TABLE VI *(continued)*

Species	Size fractions (mm)	Loadings Factor numbers			Communalities
Eel grass and channels group C		1	8	9	
Elasmopus laevis AM	0.5	+ 0.92492	+ 0.00141	− 0.01266	0.93608
Ampelisca macrocephala AM	0.5	+ 0.04379	+ 0.01408	+ 0.90167	0.86033
Propontocypris edwardsi OS	0.5	− 0.03138	+ 0.88114	− 0.02347	0.83861
Cymadusa compta AM	1.0	+ 0.85457	+ 0.03760	+ 0.00777	0.93134
Lumbrineris tenuis PO	1.0	− 0.02791	− 0.01490	+ 0.85743	0.80874
Hutchinsoniella macrocantha CE	0.5	− 0.01787	+ 0.84262	+ 0.01009	0.88638
Microprotopus ranei AM	1.0	+ 0.79669	− 0.02377	+ 0.01315	0.86733
Ampithoe longimana AM	0.5	+ 0.79840	− 0.00344	− 0.00394	0.88681
Hutchinsoniella macracantha CE	0.25	+ 0.01760	+ 0.75529	− 0.01724	0.81051
Parasterope pollex OS	0.25	+ 0.04119	+ 0.68565	− 0.00140	0.76230
Elasmopus laevis AM	1.0	+ 0.63817	+ 0.04591	+ 0.00563	0.86396
Phoxocephalus holbolli AM	0.5	− 0.02839	− 0.02338	+ 0.64459	0.79276
Copidognathus sp. AC	0.5	+ 0.61285	− 0.00972	+ 0.05275	0.84325
Ampithoe longimana AM	1.0	+ 0.56592	− 0.00383	+ 0.00701	0.91021
Sarsiella sp. OS	0.5	− 0.01004	− 0.05318	+ 0.54040	0.75352
Cymadusa compta AM	0.25	+ 0.51588	+ 0.09167	+ 0.03704	0.86628
Solemya velum P	0.5	+ 0.47747	+ 0.00725	− 0.02000	0.77167
Caprella geometrica AM	1.0	+ 0.47712	− 0.05115	− 0.03068	0.52379
Corophium acutum AM	0.5	+ 0.35386	− 0.04705	− 0.03605	0.90396
Light		+ 0.15766	− 0.03773	− 0.06124	0.81526
Depth		− 0.09661	+ 0.11868	+ 0.07533	0.83223
Bottom sediment Eh		− 0.10863	− 0.03438	+ 0.00999	0.75857
Sediment sorting		+ 0.04354	− 0.01190	+ 0.11455	0.71023
Percent sand		+ 0.08694	+ 0.00381	+ 0.02790	0.93746

None of the variables on these three factors have high loadings on more than one factor.

[1] AC = Acarina; AM = Amphipoda; CE = Cephalocarida; G = Gastropoda; K = Kinorhyncha; OS = Ostracoda; P = Pelecypoda; PO = Polychaeta.

of the most abundant sand flat species did not enter into the factor analysis, so it is not surprising that of the eleven key species, only two appeared on the factors. The plot of the factor scores for a combination of factors 11 and 29 is shown on Fig. 80. Again, the resemblance between the plot of the factor scores and the plot from superimposition of individual species distributions is remarkable. The only real discrepancy observed is that a sand flat type community appeared in the Inner Harbor near the entrance to the Outer Harbor and in two portions of the gutters. As observed in the previous group of factors, one-fifth of the variables had high loadings which are common to both factors 11 and 29, although in this case they are not species variables but time and surface Eh. Species plots through time have shown

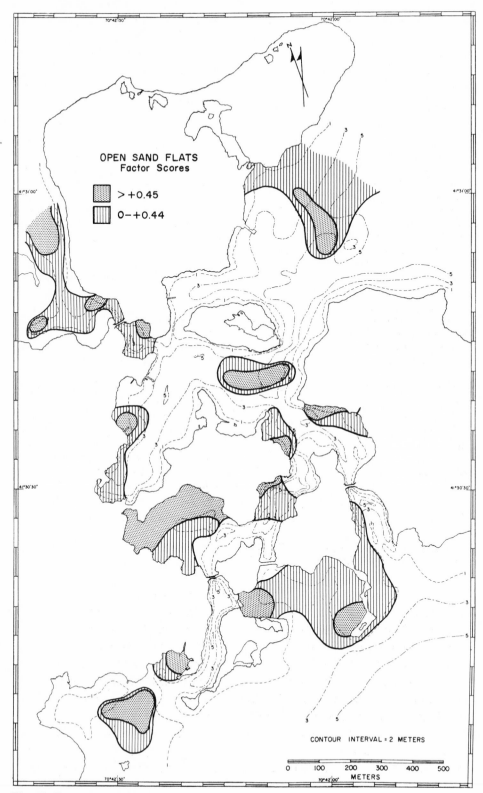

Fig. 80. Factor score plot of 137 stations for factors 11 and 29, representing the sand flat community of the Hadley Harbor Complex. All scores above +0.4600.

that most of the sand flat species are time-dependent, being present in large numbers in the summer and absent or at very low densities during the winter when ice reaches or nearly touches the bottom. The factor loadings for Eh or redox-potential were negative in both factors, which also makes sense, as virtually all Eh values in the sand flats habitat were high positive values of about 300—400 mV. The total number of animals occurred as a negative loading, which again corresponds to the subjective analysis, since it was deduced that, as a habitat, except for one or two species, it was not a very productive one. It is somewhat puzzling that the percent of sand did not load heavily as a positive loading for these two factors, as it is true that most of the stations in this habitat were characterized by well-sorted fine sand. Possibly not enough species or stations were included to bring out all the properties peculiar to this habitat in the factor analysis.

The other factors obviously related to community composition were involved with both the eel grass and channel related habitats. Although it was possible to designate an eel grass group of factors and a channel group of factors, it was also possible to ascertain a combined eel grass—channel set of factors; in fact, nine interrelated factors can be discerned (Table VII). There are three relatively distinct groups of factors designated as A, B and C. The first group, A, is a composite of factors 5, 6 and 12, which the author believes is the eel grass portion of the channel habitat. There are nine species with high communalities (Table VI), and eight species which are unique to this grouping of stations and variables (Table VII). A comparison of the list for group A of the channel groups with the subjective list for the same habitat shows that only five species are common to both lists. (It should be emphasized, however, that sixteen of the species considered dominant in the subjective list were not used in the factor analysis; this is over half of the subjective list). A plot of the factor scores for factors 5, 6, and 12 is shown on Fig. 81. Again there is close resemblance between the plot as shown on Fig. 65 for the subjective channel community and Fig. 81, the factor score plot for channels. The primary difference between the two is the much larger area occupied by the channel community on Fig. 65 than on Fig. 81. The physical factors loading, high on this factor group, were sorting coefficients, surface Eh, and large median diameter of sediments, three physical variables predicted as relating to channel habitats.

A second group of channel-influenced factors is one designated eel grass, which is based on correlations between negative loadings and negative factor scores, the opposite of the previously discussed factors but having the same effect. Perhaps this list is closer to the channel list based on subjective reasoning, but factor score plots more nearly fit the plots of species thought to represent an eel grass assemblage. Comparison of the list of species (Table VII) with the list of eel grass species given earlier for the subjective

TABLE VII

Comparisons of species and physical variables with high factor loadings for three groups of factors related to the eel grass—channel habitats

	Size fractions (mm)	Factor Group on which loadings are high		
		A[1]	B[1]	C[1]
Species				
Bittium alternatum G[2]	1.0 , 4.0, 2.0	X		
Listriella barnardi AM	0.25, 0.5	X		
Anachis translirata G	4.0	X		
Parasterope pollex OS	(all size fractions)	X	X	X
Propontocypris edwardsi OS	1.0 , 0.5, 0.25	X		X
Mitrella lunata G	2.0	X		
Anachis avara G	4.0	X		
Cymadusa compta AM	1.0 , 0.5, 0.25	X		X
Lysianopsis alba AM	1.0 , 0.5	X	X	
Caecum pulchellum G	0.5	X		
Solemya velum P	(all size fractions)	X	X	X
Corophium acutum AM	1.0 , 0.5		X	
Pycnophes frequens K	0.5		X	
Microdeutopus damnoniensis AM	2.0 , 1.0, 0.5		X	
Loxoconcha guttata OS	0.25		X	
Paraphoxus oculatus AM	1.0		X	
Cythereis vineyardensis OS	0.25		X	
Ampithoe longimana AM	1.0 , 0.5		X	X
Phoxocephalus holbolli AM	1.0 , 0.5		X	X
Elasmopus laevis AM	1.0 , 0.5			X
Ampelisca macrocephala AM	0.5			X
Lumbrineris tenuis PO	1.0			X
Hutchinsoniella macracantha CE	0.25			X
Microprotopus ranei AM	1.0			X
Copidognathus sp. AC	0.5			X
Sarsiella sp. (2) OS	0.5			X
Caprella geometrica AM	1.0			X
Physical variables				
Sediment sorting		X	X	X
Surface water Eh		X	X	
Sediment median diameter		X		
Bottom salinity			X	
Bottom sediment Eh			X	X
Depth			X	X
Bottom water temperature			X	
Time			X	
Total animals per station			X	
Light				X
Percent sand				X

TABLE VII *(continued)*

Group A (Résumé)

8 species unique to Group A	1 physical variable was unique
2 species common to Groups B, C too	2 physical variables common to Group B too
3 species common to Group B too	1 physical variable common to Groups B, C too
4 species common to Group C too	

Group B (Résumé)

6 species unique to Group B	4 physical variables unique to Group B
3 species common to Group A too	1 physical variable common to Group A too
3 species common to Group C too	2 physical variables common to Group C, too
2 species common to Groups A, C too	1 physical variable common to Groups A, C too

Group C (Résumé)

8 species unique to Group C	2 physical variables unique to Group C
2 species common to Groups A, C too	1 physical variable common to Groups A, B too
2 species common to Group A too	2 physical variables common to Group B too
3 species common to Group C too	

---

[1] Group A composed of factors 5, 6, 12; Group B composed of factors 3, 10, 17; Group C composed of factors 1, 8, 9. (Loadings given in Table VI.)

[2] AC = Acarina; AM = Amphipoda; CE = Cephalocarida; G = Gastropoda; K = Kinorhyncha; OS = Ostracoda; P = Pelecypoda; PO = Polychaeta.

discussion, shows that all of the gastropods considered as part of the eel grass community load very heavily on factors 5, 6, and 12 and not at all on factors 3, 10, and 17, of the channel—eel grass factors. It is possible that gastropods known to live on the eel grass blades (J.S. Nagle, personal communication, 1968), do so only on grass found in the channels. Although the plot of the scores of these three factors shows a closer fit to a true eel grass community, the species making up the high loadings for these factors indicate more of a channel than a pure eel grass community. Many water and sediment variables were loaded high against these factors, but the most important were depth, bottom temperature, and bottom salinity, once again indicating more of a channel community per se than an eel grass community. Bottom waters are generally different from surface waters in the deeper channels of the Complex, whereas little difference exists between surface and bottom in shallow eel grass beds. A factor score plot of factors 3, 10, and 17, the eel grass community group (based on negative correlations), is shown on Fig. 82. A comparison of the areas covered in this plot with that designated for eel grass shown on Fig. 66 substantiates the hypothesis that this group of factors is more closely allied with eel grass alone than with channels alone. Comparisons of factor loadings and communalities for all the variables entering into groups A and B among the eel grass—channel factors are shown in Table VI.

The third and final group of factors related to the eel grass—channel habitat is designated as the deep-channels group C, factors 1, 8, and 9 (Table VI). Three of the species listed in Tables VI and VII were common to the

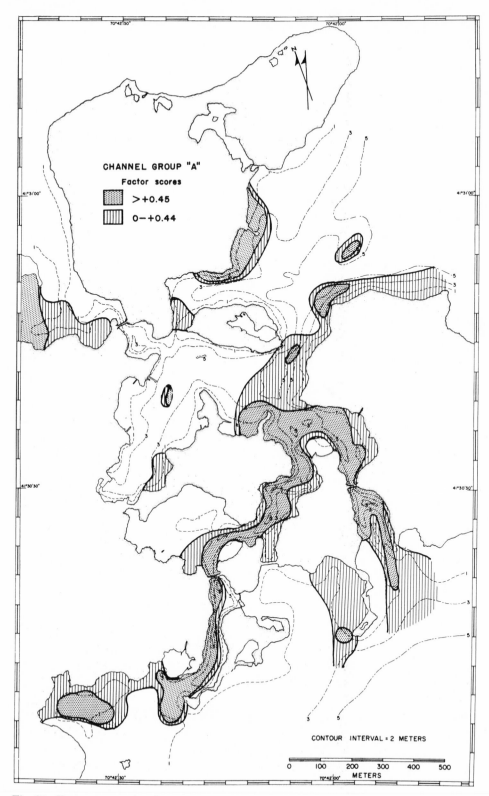

Fig. 81. Factor score plot for 137 stations for factors 5, 6, and 12, representing group "A", the deeper eel grass portion of the channels of the Hadley Harbor Complex.

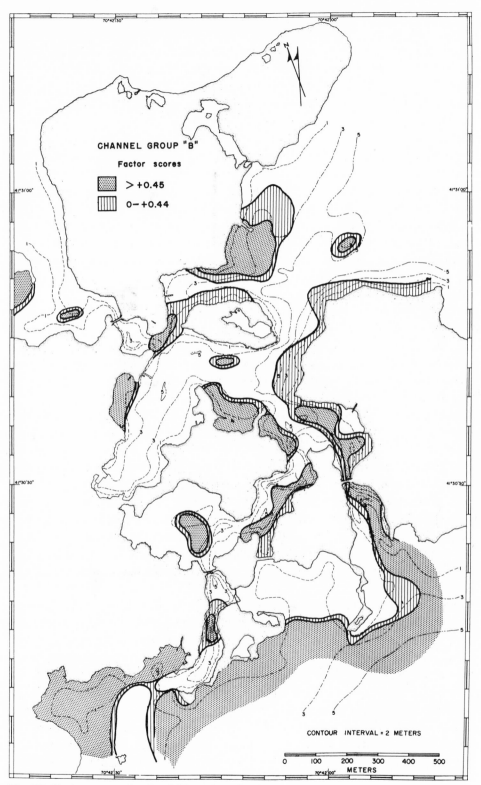

Fig. 82. Factor score plot for 137 stations for factors 3, 10, and 17, representing group "B", the shallow eel grass community of the Hadley Harbor Complex. All scores over +0.0100.

list of species for the channel habitat discussed previously, while the other unique species are also common to the Inner Harbor habitat. Seven species in this group are common to groups A and B (Table VII), and more physical— sediment variables are highly correlated with groups B and C than with A. The special physical—chemical variables for group C were percent light trans- mission and sand, both positive loadings, indicating a high correlation be- tween light transmission, coarse sediments, and this combination of species. In general, this is typical for the channel communities on the subjective basis, since for the most part the floors of the channels were sand or gravel- sized sediments, and waters were relatively transparent compared to other habitats. Although there is some question as to whether the three channel— eel grass communities grouped through factor analysis should be dealt with as one, we will consider them separately for the moment. The factor score plot for group C is shown on Fig. 83, and can be compared with the channel plot described subjectively on Fig. 65.

The same process of overlaying unique compositional areas of factor- delineated communities was used in treating factor analysis results, produc- ing small or more unique and overlapping areas for the subjective analysis discussed earlier. Again, the correspondence of the unique and overlapping areas between the two types of analyses was very close. Each of the areas on Fig. 79 through 83 were superimposed upon each other, using only the highly positive loadings above +0.50. Fig. 84 is the plot of the high factor scores for the sand flat, Inner Harbor, eel grass, and channel "factor groups" in which no overlap of high scores is evident. There is considerable corre- spondence between Fig. 84 and Fig. 67, the unique areas plot for the subjec- tive appraisal. Virtually the only difference is that the Inner Harbor and eel grass groups are much larger on the factor score plot than on the subjective plot. Although these two charts are similar, it should be kept in mind that the subjective plots were based on at least 300 biological stations and as many species, while the factor plots were based on only 137 stations and 43 species. Broad areas on the factor plot result from interpolation between the widely spaced factor analysis stations.

The areas of overlap between communities resulting from the plot of factor scores (Fig. 85) are also somewhat similar to the overlap areas shown on Fig. 68 for the subjective discussion. Although the same overlapping com- munity areas occur in the same places for both analyses, it is apparent that the factor score plot of overlapping community areas (Fig. 85) is made up mostly of small patches, while the overlapping areas from the subjective plots are much larger. More significantly, the area of overlapping of three or more communities which occupied most of the entrances to the Complex in the subjective analysis is limited to a few very small patches in the entrances and four patches in the channels. The discrepancy between the two plots

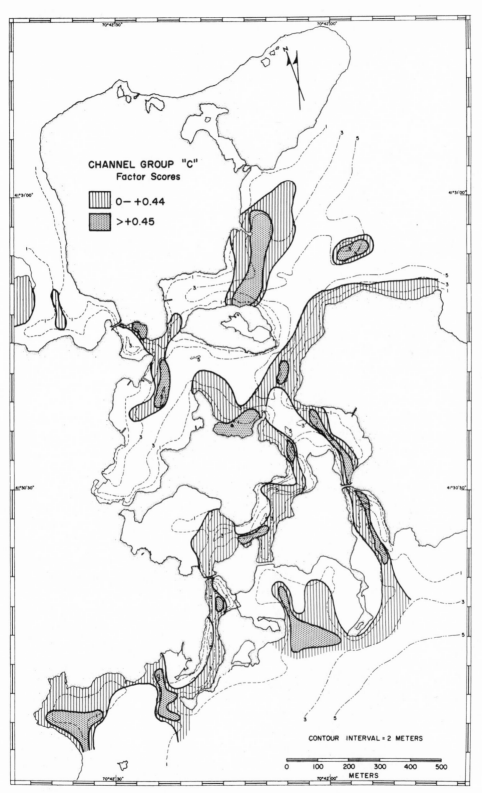

Fig. 83. Factor score plot for 137 stations for factors 1, 8, and 9, representing group "C", the basic channel community of the Hadley Harbor Complex. All scores positive.

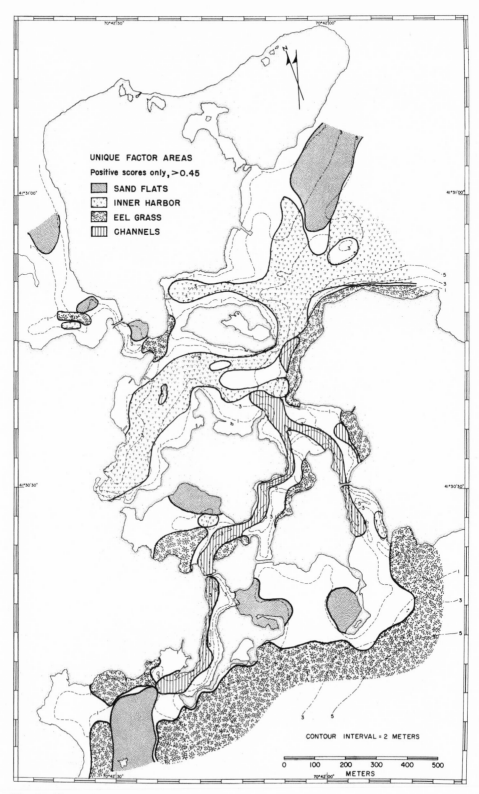

Fig. 84. Plots of unique factor score areas for the Inner Harbor, sand flats, eel grass, and channel communities of the Hadley Harbor Complex.

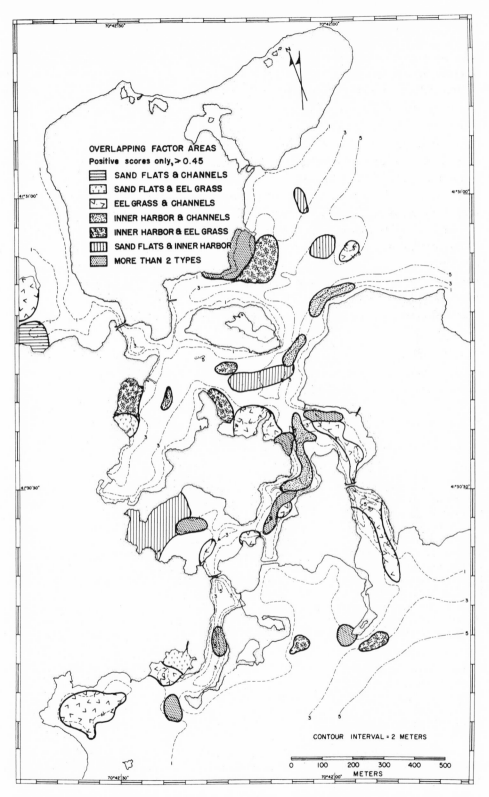

OVERLAPPING FACTOR AREAS
Positive scores only, > 0.45

SAND FLATS & CHANNELS
SAND FLATS & EEL GRASS
EEL GRASS & CHANNELS
INNER HARBOR & CHANNELS
INNER HARBOR & EEL GRASS
SAND FLATS & INNER HARBOR
MORE THAN 2 TYPES

CONTOUR INTERVAL = 2 METERS

0   100   200   300   400   500
METERS

Fig. 85. Plots of overlapping areas resulting from the superimposition of factor score plots of the four basic community factors in the Hadley Harbor Complex.

may be explained by the differences in the number of stations and species used in the two methods.

In addition, the large matrix factor analysis produced one other distinctive factor group which the author interprets as an amphipod—small arthropod community, found in close association because of food requirements. The factor loadings for the two similar factors 2 and 4 were almost exclusively small size-fractions of amphipods and small arthropods such as mites and ostracodes. The factor loadings for these two factors can be found in Tables V and VIII. The areas plotted are for the highly negative scores, as all species loadings in Table VIII were also highly negative. Water temperatures had high positive loadings as did surface and bottom Eh, suggesting that this was a community of agitated shallow waters. The plots of the factor scores substantiate this (Fig. 86). Although this grouping included species which were part of the eel grass and channel communities, the combination does not resemble any of the other factor plots and may actually be a discrete entity related to a certain trophic level. It is quite possible that other factors,

TABLE VIII

Factor loadings and communalities for the amphipod—small arthropod factor group

	Size fractions (mm)	Loadings Factor numbers		Commu- nalities
Species		2	4	
Corophium acutum AM[1]	0.25	− 0.98607	+ 0.01581	0.98258
Corophium insidiosum AM	0.25	− 0.99220	+ 0.00872	0.99017
Corophium insidiosum AM	0.50	− 0.98243	− 0.05443	0.93368
Corophium insidiosum AM	1.00	− 0.96704	− 0.15243	0.97445
Dexamine thea AM	0.50	− 0.96551	+ 0.04291	0.97711
Microdeutopus gryllotalpa AM	1.00	− 0.02147	− 0.94047	0.95137
Microdeutopus gryllotalpa AM	0.50	− 0.19832	− 0.86874	0.93349
Nereis succinea PO	1.00	+ 0.01507	− 0.79461	0.81259
Copidognathus sp. AC	0.25	− 0.65596	+ 0.01378	0.71814
Microdeutopus damnoniensis AM	2.00	+ 0.00423	− 0.45415	0.84352
Microdeutopus gryllotalpa AM	0.25	− 0.63124	− 0.43746	0.92131
Sarsiella americana[2] OS	0.50	− 0.37032	+ 0.00937	0.75352
Physical variables				
Bottom temperature		− 0.07295	+ 0.16683	0.92773
Surface temperature		− 0.06847	+ 0.16293	0.92663
Sediment sorting		+ 0.03833	+ 0.12977	0.80243
Surface water Eh		+ 0.13130	− 0.02734	0.73095
Bottom sediment Eh		+ 0.11445	+ 0.05432	0.75857

[1] AC = Acarina; AM = Amphipoda; OS = Ostracoda; PO = Polychaeta.
[2] Later analysis of ostracodes produced different name and split genus into three species.

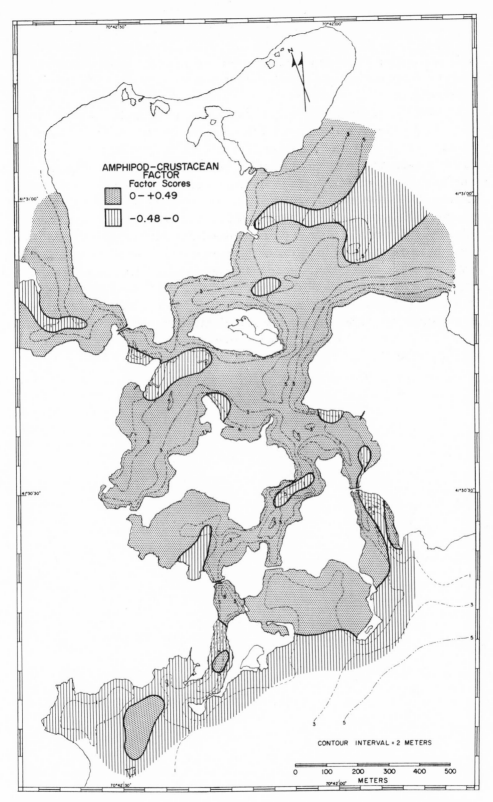

Fig. 86. Factor score plot for 137 stations for factors 2 and 4, representing an amphipod—small arthropod (crustacean) community in Hadley Harbor Complex.

both on the unrotated and rotated matrices, would reveal other small or separate communities controlled by variables not evident or measured during this study.

Although considerable time and energy were expended in compiling the data and preparing the computer programs to perform the factor analysis, the author feels that the results justified the effort. The number of calculations necessary to perform the large matrix factor analysis using a desk calculator or figuring by hand would have taken at least ten years at eight hours a day, while the computer calculations on the IBM 360-50 took 43 minutes. The most striking outcome of this essentially mathematical and objective treatment of data was that the results did not differ essentially from those obtained by the subjective methods, also used by the author in treating benthic invertebrate data in the past for the Gulf of California, the Mississippi Delta region, and the coast of Texas. This suggests that previous groupings of species in earlier papers (Parker, 1956, 1959, 1960) are valid even though not based on sophisticated statistical analyses. This present treatment suggests further that factor analysis is a new and perhaps more reliable method for analyzing marine faunal communities.

CHAPTER 5

COMPARISONS BETWEEN BENTHIC STUDIES

There are only a few papers which deal with the invertebrates of the Hadley Harbor Complex in sufficient detail so that direct comparisons can be made. Results obtained by earlier investigators (between the years of 1873 and 1936), as they relate to results obtained in this study, are discussed first. Numerous other studies were carried out in other portions of the Cape Cod region and northern Massachusetts during the past thirty years. As the general environments of these later studies do not differ radically from the present study, these too can be compared directly with our results. There is a small set of papers concerned with benthic communities just outside of the southeast Massachusetts region or dealing with plant associations which can be discussed in context with the Hadley Harbor investigation.

As the classical approach to benthic community studies originated primarily with Danish biologists, a section is devoted to comparisons of Danish bottom communities with those obtained in Hadley Harbor. Comparisons are a bit more difficult, but similar climatic zones in the two regions produced similar community types which can be recognized. Finally, Hadley Harbor communities and habitats are compared with the results obtained in warm temperate and tropical regions of the Americas, which substantiate the premise that principles obtained in the study of communities in colder regions can be applied to almost any climatic zone.

BENTHIC COMMUNITIES OF WOODS HOLE, MASSACHUSETTS

Period of 1873—1874 (Verrill and Smith, 1874)

The earliest reports which contain information relating to the fauna of the Woods Hole region and presumably the Hadley Harbor area are those of Verrill (1873), Verrill et al. (1873) and Verrill and Smith (1874). All data relating to species distributions were extracted from the reprinted 1874 version of this work and compared with the distributions of the same species taken 100 years later in this study. Verrill and Smith (1874) recognized ten major habitats for the near-normal salinities of the Woods Hole region and a number of similar habitats for the "brackish waters", including the eel grass beds of brackish waters. For each of these habitats, a list of typical species was given. All species which occurred in both Verrill's habitats and those we studied in Hadley Harbor are listed separately, and the habitats assigned by Verrill were tabulated after each species (Table IX). There were 118 species of invertebrates collected in both Verrill's and in the present study, those which occurred in Verrill's eight habitats closely resembling those in Hadley Harbor. Such habitats as wharfs, pilings, swimming communities, and the communities of the outer beaches and shelf depths were not considered here. The eight habitats for which species group comparisons were made are: rocky intertidal shores; sand and gravel shores; muddy shores and flats; rocky subtidal areas; stony, gravel, and shelly subtidal bottoms; subtidal sand bottom; subtidal mud bottom; and the brackish-water eel grass habitat. It is interesting to note that of the 118 species, which can be recognized as collected during both investigations, 40 species or 34% were listed in four or more of the habitats assigned by Verrill, 51 species or 43% were confined to two or three habitats, and 27 species or 23% were specific to one habitat. Those species which occurred in two or three habitats usually did so on similar types of bottom, i.e., the same species was listed by Verrill and Smith (1874) as typical of both muddy shores and flats and subtidal muds, or the same species on both rocky intertidal shores and rocky subtidal bottoms of sounds and bays. The majority of species cited could be divided into two major groups, those found on hard bottom and those found on soft bottom (Table IX). The motile epifaunal species were typical of virtually all habitats described by Verrill, except some of the very low salinity facies. There are no quantitative data on the various species found by Verrill in the period 1870–1872, and even very little data on relative abundance. However, much of Verrill's results were summarized in Sumner et al. (1913), which includes distributions of species during Verrill's time and also of species taken by them during 1907 and 1908.

Period of 1907–1908 (Sumner et al., 1913)

Of immense value in Sumner et al. (1913) is a discussion of the environmental conditions of the region some sixty years before the present study. One particular feature of the hydrography during Sumner's time, which has not changed significantly to the present day, is the apparent difference between the physical characteristics of the Buzzards Bay and Vineyard Sound waters. We found that the temperatures and salinities differed significantly between two stations measured throughout the year in the two separate bodies of water (Fig. 33, 35, 37). Sumner also reported differences between these two embayments in the vicinity of Hadley Harbor. Both salinity and temperatures were higher in Vineyard Sound than in Buzzards Bay in the summer, which is identical to our own findings. Sumner explained that average salinities throughout the year would be lower in Buzzards Bay than Vineyard Sound because of the greater number of estuaries off Buzzards Bay.

During colder months of the year, salinities and temperatures were often lower in Vineyard Sound than in Buzzards Bay, which the author attributes to the greater influx of ground water into Vineyard Sound, the string of estuaries running into Vineyard Sound along lower Cape, and the movement of this fresher water along the Elizabeth Islands side of the Sound out into the Atlantic. Sumner also graphs the water temperatures, taken weekly for one year, in the Woods Hole area. His observations indicate that waters were a little colder in 1906—1907 than during 1963—1965 in the summer, rising to 21.6°C only on August 15. Winter temperatures were not quite as low as those measured during the present study, being only −1.11°C on February 19.

Substantiating the different water characteristics between the two bodies of water bounding the Hadley Harbor Complex is the fact that Sumner also found significant differences between the invertebrate fauna of Buzzards Bay and Vineyard Sound. These differences were expressed by Sumner et al. (1913, pp.64—70 and 78), as the number of species for each major taxon for the Bay and the Sound based on percentage occurrences of species in dredge hauls. For instance, fifteen species of amphipods were restricted to Vineyard Sound, two were restricted to Buzzards Bay, and two were found in both areas. Apparently Vineyard Sound supports a greater variety of amphipods. On the other hand, only seven species of pelecypods were restricted to Vineyard Sound, while nine were restricted to Buzzards Bay. The same was true for the gastropods, where three species were confined to the Sound and seven to the Bay. It would seem from these data that the Sound is a better environment for crustaceans, while the Bay is better for mollusks. Sumner also stated that, in terms of the overall number of invertebrate species, Buzzards Bay supported a greater variety than did Vineyard Sound. As mentioned previously, it is surprising that so many of the species found during the present study were restricted to different sides of the Complex. Even though water flows freely between the two bodies of water through the Complex, the real difference between temperature and salinity of the Bay and Sound seems to be sufficient to restrict certain species to the side of the habitat contiguous to each of the water masses.

Sumner et al. (1913) made no attempt to create benthic faunal communities in the sense described in the present study, but did show, although in a very gross manner, that there were specific associations between certain species and sediment types. They found that species could be divided into three associations, one living on sand bottom, one on gravel and stones, and

TABLE IX (A—D)

Compilation of distributional data for previous collections of invertebrates in Hadley Harbor, 1871 to 1936[1]

A. 1871—1873 (Verrill and Smith, 1874)

Verrill's habitats

1 = Rocky intertidal shores
2 = Sand and gravel shores
3 = Muddy shores and flats
4 = Rocky subtidal

5 = Stony, gravel and shell, subtidal
6 = Subtidal sand
7 = Subtidal mud
8 = Eel grass (estuarine)

Numbers following species agree with numbered habitats as assigned by Verrill et al. (1874).

Parker's habitats

IH = Inner Harbor
SF = Sand flats

CH = Channels
EG = Eel grass

Letters following species agree with habitats as assigned within the present study.

	Verrill's habitats	Parker's habitats
Polychaeta		
Lepidonotus squamatus	1, 4, 5, 8	IH
Harmothoe imbricata	1, 4, 5	CH
Phyllodoce arenae	1, 4, 5	CH
Podarke obscura	1, 6, 8	SF
Nereis virens	1, 2, 3	SF, CH
Nereis pelagica	1, 4, 5, 6, 7	SF
Lumbrineris tenuis	1, 2, 3, 5	SF, CH
Glycera americana	1, 2, 3, 6, 7	IH, CH
Glycera dibranchiata	1, 2, 3, 6, 7	SF, CH
Cirratulus grandis	1, 2, 3, 5	EG
Pectinaria gouldi	1, 2, 3, 5, 6, 7	IH, CH
Nicolea (venustula?)	1, 4, 5, 8	IH
Amphitrite ornata	1, 2, 3, 5, 6	CH, EG
Polycirrus eximius	1, 3, 4, 5, 7, 8	SF
Sthenelais (boa?)	2, 5, 7	CH, EG
Nephtys picta	2, 5, 6	CH
Eteone sp.	2, 5	IH
Diopatra cuprea	2, 3, 5, 7	SF
Spio setosa	2, 7	SF
Maldanopsis elongata	2, 3	IH, EG
Clymenella torquata	2, 5, 7	IH, EG
Notomastus (latericeus?)	2, 3	IH
Marphysa sanguinea	4	CH
Nephtys bucera	5	CH
Eumida (sanguinea?)	5	CH, EG
Sabella macropthalma	5	SF
Melinna cristata	7	IH

---

[1] Where possible present-day nomenclature is used for species designations. Habitat designations are of previous investigators unless otherwise indicated. Parentheses indicate either doubtful species designations or difficulty in establishing proper name.

TABLE IXA *(continued)*

	Verrill's habitats	Parker's habitats
Sipunculida		
Phascolosoma gouldi	2, 5	CH, EG
Gastropoda		
Urosalpinx cinerea	1, 3, 4, 5, 6	CH, EG
Eupleura caudata	1, 3, 5, 6, 7	CH
Nassarius trivittatus	1, 2, 4, 5, 6, 7	IH, CH
Mitrella lunata	1, 2, 3, 4, 5, 6, 8	EG
Anachis avara	1, 4, 5, 6, 8	SF, CH
Pyramidella fusca	1, 6, 7	CH
Odostomia bisurturalis	1, 5	EG
Lacuna vincta	1, 2, 3, 5	SF
Bittium alternatum	1, 2, 3, 4, 5, 8	SF, CH, EG
Crepidula fornicata	1, 2, 4, 5, 6, 7	SF, CH
Crepidula convexa	1, 2, 3, 5, 6, 7, 8	SF, EG
Nassarius obsoletus	2, 3, 6, 7, 8	SF
Lunatia triseriata	2	CH
Polinices duplicatus	2, 6	IH
Littorina irrorata	3	SF
Haminoea solitaria	3, 7	IH
Chaetopleura apiculata (chiton)	4, 5	CH, EG
Odostomia trifida	5	CH
Odostomia seminuda	5, 6, 7	SF, EG
Turbonilla interrupta	5, 6, 7	CH, EG
Caecum pulchellum	5, 6	CH
Natica pusilla	5, 6	CH
Cylichna oryza	6, 7	IH
Retusa canaliculata	6, 7	IH
Mangelia cerina	7	CH
Hydrobia minuta	8	SF
Pelecypoda		
Mya arenaria	1, 2, 3, 4, 5, 6, 7	SF
Mysella planulata	1, 3, 5, 7	CH
Anadara transversa	1, 4, 5	IH
Mytilus edulis	1, 2, 3, 4, 5, 6, 7, 8	SF, CH
Anomia simplex	1, 4, 5, 6, 7	CH
Lyonsia hyalina	2, 5, 6, 7	CH, EG
Tellina agilis	2, 3, 5, 6, 7	IH, SF, CH
Mercenaria mercenaria	2, 3, 6, 7	IH, CH
Gemma gemma	2, 6	SF
Laevicardium mortoni	2, 6	CH, EG
Solemya velum	2, 6, 7	CH, EG
Aequipecten irradians	2, 3, 6, 8	SF, EG
Mulinia lateralis	3, 5, 6, 7	IH
Cumingia tellinoides	3, 5, 7	CH, EG
Petricola pholadiformis	3, 7	IH
Pandora gouldi	5, 6, 7	IH, CH
Cerastoderma pinnulatum	5, 7	CH
Aligena elevata	5, 7	CH, EG

TABLE IXA *(continued)*

	Verrill's habitats	Parker's habitats
Crassinella mactracea	5	CH
Nucula proxima	5, 7	IH
Macoma tenta	6, 7	IH
Tagelus divisus	7	CH
Yoldia limatula	7	IH
Crustacea		
Neopanope texana sayi	1, 3, 4, 5, 6, 8	CH
Pagurus longicarpus	1, 2, 3, 4, 6, 7, 8	IH, SF
Homarus americanus	1, 4, 5, 6	CH
Melita nitida	1, 7, 8	CH
Caprella geometrica	1, 4, 5, 8	CH, EG
Erichsonella filiformis	1, 4, 5	CH, EG
Libinia dubia	2, 3, 7, 8	SF
Libinia emarginata	2, 7, 8	CH, EG
Crangon septemspinosus	2, 3, 8	SF, EG
Palaemonetes vulgaris	2, 3, 8	CH, EG
Pinnixa (cylindrica?) sayana?	3	CH, EG
Pinnixa chaetopterana	3, 6	IH, CH
Hippolyte zostericola	3, 8	SF, EG
Cymadusa compta	3, 7, 8	CH, EG
Ampithoe longimana	3, 4, 8	CH, EG
Corophium (insidiosum?)	3, 5, 7, 8	CH, EG
Erichsonella attenuata	3, 8	EG
Heteromysis formosa	4, 5	CH
Edotea triloba	6, 7, 8	IH, EG
Limulus polyphemus	6, 7, 8	CH
Paraphoxus (kroyeri?)	7	CH
Ampelisca sp. *(abditas?)*	7	SF
Ampelisca sp. *(vadorum?)*	7	IH
Leptocheirus pinguis	7	CH, EG
Microdeutopus sp. *(damnoniensis?)*	8	CH, EG
Microdeutopus sp. *(gryllotalpa?)*	8	EG
Idotea baltica	8	EG
Echinodermata		
Arbacia punctulata	1, 4, 5	CH
Asterias forbesi	1, 2, 3, 4, 5, 6, 7	SF, CH
Thyone briareus	2, 3, 5, 6, 7	SF, EG
Leptosynapta sp.	2	SF
Amphipholis squamata	5	SF
Amphioplus abditus	7	IH

TABLE IX (*continued*)

B. 1907—1908 (Sumner et al., 1913)

Sumner's habitats

1 = Deep mud bottom   3 = Channel, gravel, deep sand bottom
2 = Sandy shores, flats, mud flats and sand bottom   4 = Eel grass, roots of eel grass
    Numbers following species agree with numbered habitats as assigned by Sumner et al.
(1913).

Parker's habitats

IH = Inner Harbor   CH = Channels
SF = Sand flats   EG = Eel grass
    Letters following species agree with habitats as assigned within the present study.

	Sumner's habitats	Parker's habitats
Coelenterata		
Edwardsia elegans	4	SF, EG
Gastropoda		
Retusa canaliculata	1	IH
Cylichna oryza	1	IH
Turbonilla interrupta	1	CH, EG
Natica pusilla	1	CH
Lunatia triseriata	1	CH
Lacuna vincta	2, 4	SF
Lacuna (neritoides?)	2	SF, EG
Caecum pulchellum	2, 3	CH
Anachis avara	3	CH, SF
Anacha (translirata)	3	CH, EG
Crepidula fornicata	3	CH
Mitrella lunata	4	EG
Bittium alternatum	4	SF, CH, EG
Crepidula convexa	4	SF, EG
Pelecypoda		
Anadara transversa	1	IH
Nucula proxima	1	IH
Yoldia limatula	1	IH
Cerastoderma pinnulatum	1	CH
Pitar morrhuana	1	IH
Tellina agilis	1	IH, SF, CH
Macoma tenta	1	IH
Mulinia lateralis	1	IH
Laevicardium mortoni	2, 4	CH, EG
Gemma gemma	2	SF, EG
Mercenaria mercenaria	2	IH, CH
Ensis directus	2	CH
Cumingia tellinoides	2	SF, CH
Lyonsia hyalina	2	CH, EG
Solemya velum	3	CH, EG
Crassinella mactracea	3	CH

TABLE IXB *(continued)*

	Sumner's habitats	Parker's habitats
Aligena elevata	3	CH, EG
Pandora gouldi	3	CH
Aequipecten irradians	4	SF, EG
Crustacea		
Phoxocephalus holbolli	1	CH, EG
Jassa falcata	1	IH, CH
Cyclaspis varians	1	IH
Oxyurostylis smithi	1	CH
Acanthohaustorius millsi	2	SF
Corophium acutum	2	CH, EG
Edotea triloba	2	IH
Heterocrypta granulata	2	CH
Libinia emarginata	2	SF
Ovalipes ocellatus	2	SF
Lysianopsis alba	3	CH, EG
Elasmopus laevis	3	CH
Microdeutopus damnoniensis	3	CH, EG
Neopanope texana sayi	3	CH
Sarsiella zostericola	4	EG
Dexamine thea	4	CH, EG
Microdeutopus gryllotalpa	4	SF, EG
Ampithoe longimana	4	CH, EG
Cymadusa compta	4	CH, EG
Caprella geometrica	4	EG
Leptochelia savignyi	4	EG
Idotea baltica	4	EG
Erichsonella attenuata	4	EG
Erichsonella filiformis	4	EG
Palaemonetes vulgaris	4	EG
Crangon septemspinosus	4	EG
Echinodermata		
Amphioplus abditus	1	IH
Amphipholis squamata	2	SF
Leptosynapta inhaerans	2	SF

C. 1916—1923 (Allee, 1923a)

Allee's habitats

1 = Mud   3 = Gravel
2 = Sand   4 = Eel grass

Numbers following species agree with numbered habitats as assigned by Allee (1923a).
Numbers in parentheses indicate number of observers finding the particular species in these four habitats over the period of investigation (Allee, 1923a). Parentheses around specific names indicate guesses were made regarding specific identifications given by Allee's students.

TABLE IXC *(continued)*

The designation "epifaunal habitat" indicates that species was cited by Allee, but did not occur in the four main level-bottom habitats used in this compilation, or else its habitat was difficult to determine from Allee's remarks.

Parker's habitats

IH = Inner Harbor   CH = Channels
SF = Sand flats   EG = Eel grass
  Letters following species agree with habitats as assigned within the present study.

	Allee's habitats	Parker's habitats
Coelenterata		
Edwardsia elegans	2(5)	CH, EG
Polycladida		
Stylochus ellipticus	1(3), 2(2), 3(1), 4(1)	CH
Polychaeta		
Amphitrite ornata	1(19), 2(8), 4(3)	CH, EG
Arabella (opalina?)	1(8), 2(17), 3(2), 4(5)	CH, EG
Cirratulus grandis	1(11), 2(16), 3(1)	EG
Capitella (capitata)	(epifaunal habitat)	SF
Diopatra cuprea	1(6), 2(14), 4(2)	SF
Drilonereis (magna)	1(4), 2(7), 3(1)	CH, EG
Glycera (2 sp.)	1(20), 2(53), 3(1), 4(12)	IH, SF, CH
Harmothoe imbricata	1(2), 2(5), 3(1), 4(3)	CH
Lepidonotus squamatus	1(3), 2(5), 3(2), 4(2)	IH
Lumbrineris tenuis	1(7), 2(19), 3(2), 4(1)	SF, CH
Nereis pelagica	1(4), 2(6)	SF
Nereis virens	1(17), 2(20)	SF, CH
Nicolea simplex (venustula)	1(1), 2(3)	IH
Pectinaria gouldi	1(9), 2(18), 3(1), 4(5)	IH, CH
Phyllodoce (arenae)	1(3), 2(6)	CH
Pista palmata	1(3), 2(1), 4(1)	EG
Platynereis dumerilii	4(1)	EG
Podarke obscura	1(2), 4(4)	SF
Polycirrus eximius	1(10), 2(14), 4(4)	SF
Sabella micropthalma	1(1), 2(1), 3(2)	SF
Scolopus fragilis	1(8), 2(19), 4(9)	IH
Spio setosa	2(1)	SF
Sthenelais (boa)	1(6), 2(5), 4(4)	CH, EG
Sipunculida		
Phascolosoma gouldi	1(13), 2(22), 4(3)	CH, EG
Crustacea		
Lembos smithi	2(1)	SF
Ampithoe longimana	(epifaunal habitat)	CH, EG
Caprella geometrica	2(1), 4(6)	CH, EG
Corophium insidiosum	(epifaunal habitat)	CH, EG
Edotea triloba	1(3), 4(2)	IH, EG

TABLE IXC *(continued)*

	Allee's habitats	Parker's habitats
Erichsonella filiformis	2(1), 4(2)	CH, EG
Acanthohaustorius millsi	2(2)	SF
Idotea baltica	1(5), 2(4), 4(20)	EG
Unciola irrorata	(epifaunal habitat)	CH
Crangon septemspinosum	1(3), 2(4), 3(4), 4(16)	SF, EG
Heteromysis formosa	1(3), 2(3), 4(1)	CH
Libinia dubia	1(14), 2(8), 3(1), 4(10)	SF
Ovallipes ocellatus	1(1), 2(3), 4(3)	SF
Pagurus longicarpus	1(19), 2(16), 3(5), 4(10)	IH, SF
Palaemonetes vulgaris	1(9), 2(7), 4(16)	SF, EG
Neopanope texana sayi	1(17), 2(12), 3(3), 4(12)	CH
Pinnixa chaetopterana	1(2), 4(2)	IH, CH
Pinnixa sayana	(epifaunal habitat)	CH, EG
Hippolyte zostericola	1(4), 2(2), 4(25)	SF, EG

Pycnogonida

Anoplodactylus lentus	(epifaunal habitat)	CH

Chitonida

Chaetopleura apiculata	(epifaunal habitat)	CH, EG

Gastropoda

Bittium alternatum	1(6), 2(6), 3(2), 4(20)	SF, CH, EG
Caecum pulchellum	(epifaunal habitat)	CH
Anachis avara	1(3), 2(5), 3(1), 4(9)	SF, CH
Mitrella lunata	1(3), 2(7), 4(12)	EG
Crepidula convexa	1(12), 2(10), 3(1), 4(6)	SF, EG
Crepidula fornicata	1(6), 2(15), 3(1), 4(2)	SF, CH
Crepidula plana	1(7), 2(16), 3(2), 4(2)	CH
Eupleura caudata	1(1), 2(3), 3(1)	CH
Lacuna vincta	1(4), 2(4), 4(14)	SF
Littorina littorea	1(15), 2(8), 3(6), 4(18)	SF
Nassarius trivittatus	1(13), 2(16), 3(1), 4(3)	IH, CH
Polinices duplicatus	1(2), 2(6), 3(1), 4(3)	IH
Natica pusilla	1(1), 4(1)	CH

Pelecypoda

Anomia simplex	1(2), 4(1)	CH
Anadara transversa	1(1), 2(1)	IH
Cerastoderma pinnulatum	(epifaunal habitat)	CH
Pandora gouldi	(epifaunal habitat)	IH, CH
Cumingia tellinoides	1(10), 2(11), 4(6)	CH, EG
Ensis directus	1(9), 2(9), 4(2)	CH
Gemma gemma	2(3)	SF
Laevicardium mortoni	1(11), 2(5), 3(2), 4(4)	CH, EG
Macoma tenta	1(2), 2(2), 4(1)	IH
Mulinia lateralis	2(1)	IH
Mya arenaria	1(23), 2(21), 3(3), 4(6)	SF
Mytilus edulis	1(11), 2(11), 3(5), 4(4)	SF, CH
Nucula proxima	1(3), 2(3), 3(1)	IH

TABLE IXC *(continued)*

	Allee's habitats	Parker's habitats
Crassostrea virginica	1(10), 2(5)	CH
Aequipecten irradians	1(9), 2(9), 4(11)	SF, EG
Petricola pholadiformis	1(3), 2(2), 3(3)	IH
Solemya velum	1(10), 2(20), 4(4)	CH, EG
Tellina agilis	1(5), 2(16), 3(3), 4(4)	IH, SF, CH
Mercenaria mercenaria	1(19), 2(14), 3(2), 4(1)	CH
Yoldia limatula	(epifaunal habitat)	IH
Protochordata		
Saccoglossus kowalewskyi	1(12), 2(14), 3(6), 4(2)	SF

D. 1936—1937 (Stauffer, 1937)

Stauffer's (1937) list of invertebrates, compared with Allee's (1923a) and the present study, for lagoon portion of Northwest Gutter only

Legend: AM = Amphipoda; AR = Arthropoda; BR = Bryozoa; D = Decapoda; G = Gastropoda; H = Hydroidea; HO = Holothuroidea; I = Isopoda, P = Pelecypoda; PO = Polychaeta; PR = Protochordata; R = Rhynchocoela; SI = Sipunculida. X = Rare; XX = common; XXX = abundant.

Where possible present-day nomenclature is used for species designations. Habitat designations are of previous investigators unless otherwise indicated. Parentheses indicate either doubtful species designations or difficulty in establishing proper name.

Species		Allee	Stauffer	Parker
Living on eel grass				
Sagartia luciae	(H)	X		Not collected
Bugula turrita	(BR)	XXX		XXX
Idotea baltica	(I)	X		X
Bittium alternatum	(G)	XX		XXX
Lacuna vincta	(G)	XX		XX
Littorina sp.	(G)	X	X	X
Mitrella lunata	(G)	X		XX
Swimming around plants				
Podarke obscura	PO	X		X
Crangon septemspinosus	D	X	X	XX
Gammarus sp.	AM	XX	XX	XXX
Palaemonetes vulgaris	D	XX	XX	XX
Hippolyte zostericola	D	XX		XX
Aquipecten irradians	P	XX		X
Living on mud surface (epifaunal)				
Hydractinia echinata	H	XX	XX	Present, not identified
Carcinaedes maenas	D	XX		Not collected
Libinia emarginata	D	X	X	Not collected

TABLE IXD *(continued)*

		Allee	Stauffer	Parker
Libinia dubia	D	X		X
Pagurus longicarpus	D	XXX	XXX	XXX
Pagurus pollicaris	D	X	X	Not collected
Neopanope texana sayi	D	XX	XX	XX
Limulus polyphemus	AR	XX	X	Not collected
Crepidula convexa	G	XX	XX	XX
Crepidula fornicata	G	X	X	XXX
Crepidula plana	G	XX	X	X
Nassarius obsoletus	G	XXX	XX	Not collected
Nassarius trivittatus	G	XX	XX	Not collected
Modiolus demissus	P	XXX		Not collected
Crassostrea virginica	P	X	X	Not collected
Burrowing forms (infaunal)				
Cerebratulus lacteus	R	X	X	Not collected
Micrura leidyi	R	XXX		Not collected
Leptosynapta inhaerens	HO	XXX	X	X
Thyone briareus	HO	XXX	XX	Not collected
Amphitrite ornata	PO	XX	X	X
Arabella (opalina) iricolor	PO	XX	XX	X
Pectinaria gouldi	PO	XX	XX	XX
Clymenella torquata	PO	XX	XX	XX
Diopatra cuprea	PO	X		X
Glycera (2 sp.)	PO	XXX	X	XX
Lumbrineris tenuis	PO	X	XXX	XXX
Maldane (urceolata)	PO	X	X	(XX)?
Nereis virens	PO	XXX		XX
Scolopus fragilis	PO	XXX	XXX	XXX
Spio setosa	PO	X	XXX	XXX
Phascolosoma gouldi	SI	X	X	X
Pinnixa chaetopterana	D	X	X	X
Cumingia tellinoides	P	XX		XX
Ensis directus	P	X	X	Not collected
Mulinia lateralis	P	X	X	Not collected here
Mya arenaria	P	XXX	X	Juveniles only X
Solemya velum	P	XX		XX
Tellina agilis	P	XX	XX	XX
Mercenaria mercenaria	P	XX	XX	Juveniles only XX
Saccoglossus kowalewskyi	PR	X	X	X
Total on eel grass		7	1	6
Total swimming		6	3	6
Total on mud surface		15	12	7
Total burrowing forms		25	20	20
Total number of species		53	36	39

a third on mud or mud sand bottom. The greatest average number of species (38) per station was found on stones and gravel, presumably because of the large number of epifaunal and encrusting species in this type of habitat. The smallest average number of species (36) was taken on a sand bottom, while mud bottom supported an intermediate number (37). No figures were given on the number of specimens per species in each of the three associations. This is to be expected as non-quantitative dredges were used as collecting devices. Some idea of relative abundances of the various invertebrates taken in that study was given in Sumner's discussion of individual species.

Fortunately, habitats were listed for most of the abundant species taken by Sumner. Such descriptions as "within the sand of eel grass roots, clean sand entrances to Hadley Harbor, deep mud bottom, or sheltered eel grass" made it possible to organize many of the species common to both studies into community groups. These are listed in Table IXB.

An examination of the environments of the species as deduced from Sumner's survey and reorganized in Table IXB reveals that: (1) of the 18 species given by Sumner as deep mud bottom types, 14 were characteristic of the Inner Harbor group of animals in the present study; (2) of the 17 species reported by Sumner as found on sandy shores, flats, mud flats, and sand bottom, 11 were characteristic of the sand flat habitat in the present study; (3) of the 12 species in Sumner's list for channels, gravel, and deep sandy bottom, 10 species were characteristic of this study's channel, high-current group; and (4) of the 22 species that Sumner gave as living on or within the eel grass, 19 were characteristic eel grass species in the present study. Some of the species noted in the present study were also taken in other habitats than those stated by Sumner. A total of 69 species (collected and identified in both surveys) was used to compile this portion of Table IXB. Of the 69 species listed in the table, 60 were recognized as occurring in the same habitat; of these 60, 9 were also taken in other habitats as well during the present study, while 15 species were not in agreement as to habitat in the two studies. Considering that different methods were used to assay the benthos in the two studies and that 60 years separate them, it is assuring to find that 87% of the species were placed in the same habitats by the two investigations and that presumably so little change has occurred in the ecology of the region. Major differences can be attributed to collecting methods (dredges in Sumner's study and grabs in the present one) and to differences in the state of the taxonomy of the major taxa in the last 60 years.

Period of 1916—1923 (Allee, 1923a)

The next concentrated effort to study the invertebrate fauna of the Woods Hole region, and Hadley Harbor in particular, was made during the period of 1916—1923 through the efforts of Allee and his co-workers with the help of students in Allee's classes at the Marine Biological Laboratory (Allee, 1922a,b,c, and 1923a,b,c). Collecting localities utilized by the Invertebrate Course at the Laboratory were selected for a long-term study of the effects of environmental conditions on changes in populations at these localities. Fortunately, the majority of the localities were located in the Hadley Harbor Complex. Incidentally, it was Allee (1923a, p.172) who first applied the name "Complex" to this area. A great deal of qualitative data on the distribution of invertebrate animals and considerable chemical—physical data were collected over the seven years. The environmental data, for the most part, was taken at Woods Hole rather than in Hadley Harbor. It is interesting to note that Allee (1923b) made a number of pH measurements in which there was considerable variation, although not as great as that manifested in the present study. Allee (1923b) felt that there was considerable effect of pH on animal aggregations, a radical viewpoint for marine communities at that time. A discussion of the relation of pH and animal communities and its importance relative to oxygen concentration, temperature, and salinity can be found in Allee (1923b, pp.244—246). Our own studies also resulted in conclusions regarding the importance of pH as an ecological controlling factor and these parallel those of Allee. It should be mentioned that Allee (1922b), a year earlier than his major study of physical factors, stated that pH varied more regularly with animal associations than any other variable.

A major difficulty encountered in Allee's (1922c and 1923a) discussion of the individual distributions of the animals and their associations as communities is that apparently many of the identifications were subject to error, having been supplied by students in the Marine Biological Laboratory Invertebrate Course who did not have the systematic background necessary to separate many of the species in such difficult groups as polychaetes and minute crustaceans. Furthermore, many of the specific names given in these publications are no longer valid, and genera have been separated or synonymized; thus, it is almost impossible to tell whether a species mentioned as a member of a particular association according to Allee is the same species discussed in the present study. An attempt was made to list the species which Allee's groups found only in the Hadley Harbor region in Table IXC. The habitats are those listed by Allee (1923a, pp.175—183), but, in order to separate records of Hadley Harbor from observations in other parts of the Woods Hole region, it was necessary to check the unpublished list of invertebrates found in the Marine Biological Laboratory Library (Allee, 1922c). The specific portions of the Complex sampled by Allee were given as: Southwest and Southeast Gutters, the narrow rock-walled portions about 6 ft. deep; Northwest Gutter, primarily the 250 X 400-m embayment at the

Buzzards Bay terminus; and in Lackey's Bay near the entrance of what was formerly Middle Gutter, but now called Blind Gutter, resulting from an artificial closing of the Gutter. With these descriptions it was possible to assign distributions to most of the species in specific habitats, similar to those designated in the present study.

Most of the species selected from Allee's study in Table IXC were level-bottom species (both epi- and infaunal), since the species he found on rocky and intertidal surfaces were not investigated by the present author. Only four of Allee's habitats are given in Table IXC: mud bottom, sand bottom, gravel bottom, and eel grass. Of these, only the eel grass community is completely analogous to any of our habitats, although one might infer that mud bottom refers to the Inner Harbor area, sand bottom to the sand flats and margins of the channels without eel grass, and gravel bottom to the high-current portions of the channels. A total number of 91 species was reported as common to Allee's and the present investigation. Allee listed a large number of encrusting species not taken by us, whereas we have identified a large number of small or meiofaunal species which would have escaped Allee's students because of their collecting methods. Of the 91 jointly reported species, 68 were designated as mud species, 71 as sand species, 33 as gravel species, and 63 as eel grass species by Allee (see Table IXC). According to Allee, the largest number of species is found on sand bottom, the next largest on mud bottom, and the lowest on gravel bottom. This differs somewhat from Sumner et al. (1913), who found the largest number of species on gravel and the least on sand. The greatest number of discrepancies, 24, between Allee's habitat preferences and our own were for the mud bottom. The lowest number of discrepancies, only 5, occurred in reference to the eel grass habitat. There seems to be little doubt that both Allee and we are in agreement as to what constitutes an eel grass assemblage, but what Allee called a mud bottom form is not the same as an Inner Harbor species in this study. This difference can probably be attributed to the individual student's concept of what constituted a mud or sand bottom. Almost half of the species considered as channel species here are not listed as on gravel by Allee, but are listed as wharf, piling, or rock species. Because of collecting methods used in Allee's time, it is probable that the gravel bottom in the high-current portions of the gutters was not thoroughly collected. Unfortunately, it is not possible to make quantitative comparisons between Allee's early (1922) investigations and our own. His published data referred only to the number of collections made of a particular species over the seven years of study. One individual or a thousand could have been taken at each of these sightings. Figures on comparative abundance were given in Allee (1922c), but the habitats to which they were assigned are no different than those given in

Table IX. A more useful comparison between the work of Allee and the present study is given in Table IXD which compares Stauffer's (1937) study of the eel grass community with the results of our and Allee's investigations.

Period of 1936 (Stauffer, 1937)

By 1936, most of the eel grass in the Woods Hole region had been completely destroyed by the wasting disease of *Zostera* caused by *Labyrinthula* (Milne and Milne, 1951). Stauffer noted that one of the favorite collecting localities for Allee's students was the lagoon entrance of Northwest Gutter at the Buzzards Bay terminus. When Allee had investigated this area, eel grass formed dense mats and supported a rich fauna adapted to the eel grass habitat. However, in 1936 the former eel grass-covered lagoon was a black muddy morass, and eel grass was limited to two or three small patches not more than a meter across (Stauffer, 1937). Stauffer took 10 stations in this lagoon by digging out $1/10$ m^2 to a depth of 30—40 cm, and washing all sediment through a 3.5-mm mesh screen. All organisms larger than 3.5 mm were identified, counted, and tabulated as shown in column two of Table IXD. These counts were contrasted with Allee's (1923a) data to demonstrate the change in invertebrate fauna coincident with the disappearance of the eel grass. Allee's and Stauffer's data are compared in Table IX with the relative abundances of species from Northwest Gutter resulting from the present investigations. As can be expected, there are some discrepancies in species names among the three studies, but, by and large, the same sets of species are discussed in all three studies. As Stauffer pointed out, there was a notable decrease in the species known to live on eel grass. Where Allee found seven species supposedly living on eel grass, Stauffer found only one. All but one species had returned to Northwest Gutter by 1964, and that one species (*Sagartia luciae*) may possibly be living there, but was not collected by us. In two cases, we have considered the species as abundant, whereas Allee reported them as only common (a relative thing to the observer). Although the eel grass is luxuriant in Northwest Gutter now, it certainly was not ten years ago (Fig. 16), and may not yet have regained the growth it had during Allee's time.

Allee designated six species of invertebrates thought to swim around in the eel grass. Stauffer found only three. All six had returned by 1964, the only difference being that we had extremely large populations of amphipods, which were listed only as common by Allee. It is suspected that amphipods would have escaped collection by the methods used by Allee and Stauffer, whereas it appears that the fast-closing Van Veen captured the majority of small crustaceans living on the $1/25$ m^2 sampled. Within the habitat where organisms are thought to live epifaunally on the mud or sand surface between the eel grass plants, Allee found twice as many species (in the Northwest Gutter Lagoon) as we had taken, and a quarter more than Stauffer. Although Stauffer found the same species as Allee occurring as epifaunal dwellers on the mud, in several cases they were less common. Most of those species not collected as part of the present study were the larger motile species not apt to be taken by a small bottom grab sampler. However, these species are reported to be present in the same region by the Supply Department of the Marine Biological Laboratory (Fig. 62). As expected, burrowing forms (infaunal species) showed the least decrease between Allee's and Stauffer's time. In fact, the populations were larger in 1936 than in 1922 for a number of species. The list for 1964, however, is smaller than either of the others. The discrepancy here is apparently not the fault of the sampling methods, but simply that many of the infaunal species taken by the two previous investigators are not now living in that particular part of the Complex. Such species as *Thyone briareus, Ensis directus, Mulinia lateralis, Mercenaria mercenaria* and *Mya arenaria* were taken in other habitats, mostly in the Inner Harbor muds or in the deeper channels. It is possible that the lagoon portion of Northwest Gutter has changed significantly in some other environmental factor than eel grass cover in the last forty years. The comparison of total species for the three periods of collection shows better correspondence between the present study and that of Stauffer than between either this one or Stauffer's and Allee's investigations.

Direct comparison of numbers of individuals per species per unit area was possible between Stauffer's study and the present one. These comparisons are given in Table X. Although it would have been possible to list the numbers of individuals for each of Stauffer's species taken in our own study, it was simpler to list the total numbers of individuals from each major taxon and convert Stauffer's data to the same format. Ten stations from the present set were selected from the Northwest Gutter Lagoon, all taken in the late spring or summer of 1964–1965. Stauffer's ten stations were all taken at one time in the summer of 1936, and thus do not show the monthly variation evident in our own data. The tabulation in Table X for data obtained in the present study is based upon the fractions of animals retained by screens with 4 mm pore size. Total numbers of specimens for each taxon in all fractions are given also in order to show how many specimens were washed through the 4-mm mesh screen into smaller mesh screens. Some of these specimens might constitute the intermediate size of 3.5 mm used by Stauffer. Data on individual species, the only form given by Stauffer, were lumped into major taxa for comparison with our major taxa counts and totaled by station and by taxa for ten stations (Table X), although not done in the original table as given by Stauffer.

There were twice as many animals taken in ten stations during 1964 and

TABLE X

Comparison between composition at the major taxa level of 10 samples each for 0.1 m² of level bottom in the eel grass portion of Northwest Gutter in the summer of 1936 (Stauffer, 1937) and summer of 1964 and 1965

A. Summer, 1936 (1 day)

Station no.:	1	2	3	4+5	6	7	8	9	10	Total
Taxa										
Pelecypoda	4	1	3	2	10	2	2	6	5	35
Gastropoda	6	1	1	0	1	0	0	2	0	11
Polychaeta	5	42	38	63	12	17	21	15	15	228
Amphipoda	0	0	0	1	0	0	0	0	0	1
Protochordata	2	0	0	0	0	0	0	0	0	2
Decapoda	0	0	0	3	0	0	0	2	0	5
Sipunculida	1	0	0	0	0	0	0	0	0	1
Totals	18	44	42	69	23	19	23	25	20	283

Average number of animals over 3.5 mm per station: 28.3

B. Summer, 1964 and 1965

Station no.:	June 1964 76		August 1964 136		October 1964 177		April 1965 255		May 1965 266		June 1965 279		June 1965 0605		July 1965 0608		August 1965 0610		August 1965 0612		Total (4 mm size)
	All sizes	4 mm size	All sizes	4 mm size	All sizes	4 mm size	All sizes	4 mm size	All sizes	4 mm size	All sizes	4 mm size	All sizes	4 mm size	All sizes	4 mm size	All sizes	4 mm size	All sizes	4 mm size	
Taxa																					
Pelecypoda	108	3	25	5	33	20	25	10	5	0	8	0	5	3	5	0	30	3	3	0	44
Gastropoda	193	5	23	8	203	90	60	18	10	0	33	13	53	18	5	5	105	8	20	5	170
Polychaeta	575	20	185	15	110	44	205	25	38	3	268	65	90	0	128	5	200	10	73	5	205
Amphipoda	5	0	25	0	198	13	430	35	85	0	313	35	78	0	263	5	2170	18	1117	5	111
Protochordata	0	0	0	0	0	0	0	0	0	0	0	0	0	0	0	0	0	0	0	0	0
Decapoda	0	0	0	0	3	3	0	0	0	0	3	3	0	0	3	3	6	3	3	3	15
Sipunculida (?)	0	0	0	0	0	0	0	0	0	0	50	8	8	3	3	3	15	0	68	0	11
Totals		28		28		170		88		3		124		32		23		42		18	556
Total animals per 0.1 m²	8,857		3,522		5,577		2,585		2,100		1,895		1,612		5,105		5,660		6,165		

Average number of animals over 4 mm per station: 55.6

1965 as in 1936. Whether this can be attributed to collecting techniques or the return of eel grass cannot be stated. The number of pelecypods for the two sets of stations is almost the same — 44 for our study and 35 in 1936. These are infaunal species and should not be greatly affected by loss or growth of eel grass. There were an order of magnitude more gastropods in the present study, most of which were *Bittium alternatum* which seems to be dependent upon eel grass as a habitat. For some reason this species was not abundant in Allee's time. Polychaetes were nearly twice as abundant in 1936 as they were in 1964—65. This is not surprising as polychaetes are primarily infaunal, and the lagoon as described by Stauffer at that time was a black organic "morass", a good habitat for worms. Amphipods were the third most abundant taxon taken in the present study, while only one individual was taken by Stauffer in 10 stations. This discrepancy can be attributed to the manner of collection and also the absence of eel grass, which is the primary habitat for most of the amphipods in Hadley Harbor. Protochordates, decapods, and sipunculids were rare according to Stauffer and relatively uncommon from our own stations. We found no protochordates, and our identification of sipunculids is questionable. Decapods were more common than during Stauffer's time, attributable to the eel grass cover necessary to their existence. The average total population of invertebrates per station was greater for the 1964—65 stations than for the 1936 stations. Although it has been possible to make some valid comparisons among the three studies of the same area over a 40-year period, how much better the comparisons would have been if identical methods had been used in each study, and if there had been no revisions of some of the animal groups! It is obvious that there should be some unanimity in methods of study for benthic communities (Longhurst, 1964).

There have been no concentrated studies on the Hadley Harbor fauna per se since that of Stauffer's, although the Complex has been the favorite collecting spot for the Marine Biological Laboratory and Woods Hole Oceanographic Institution personnel for the last thirty years. It appears that not even student predation and weekly Supply Department forays into the Complex for live material have seriously reduced the populations of most of the animals. Sea urchins are now found in only two small patches, although they were once abundant on hard bottom throughout the Complex. Large tube worms and certain large mollusks also were formerly more abundant. Human predation can be suggested for this, but certainly it has not been proved. Even during the brief interval of this study, a number of species which had been common in 1964 disappeared completely in 1965. It has been jokingly suggested that the massive sampling attack made on this one-third square kilometer of sea bottom by our recent efforts were responsible for substantially reducing the Hadley Harbor invertebrate population. However, when these samples are considered for what they were, $1/25$ m^2 of bottom 20 cm deep, it can be seen that 350 or so would account for only about 16 m^2 of bottom. Although no recent studies have been published on Hadley Harbor, several investigations have been made of similar habitats in the Cape Cod region. The results of these can be compared with those of the present study, and these investigations will now be discussed in chronological order.

OTHER MASSACHUSETTS' COMMUNITIES

Benthic communities of Cape Ann tidal inlet (Dexter, 1947)

An area some 100 miles to the north of Woods Hole, the Annisquam River, is similar to the Hadley Harbor Complex in physiography, although it is larger and is in a Boreal climate rather than in a cold-temperate climate. A study by Dexter (1947) was carried out in this tidal inlet during the years 1935—1937. A discussion of Dexter's investigations logically follows that of Stauffer, both having been carried out at roughly the same time during the almost complete disappearance of the eel grass. Although there are many habitats in Annisquam River (the "tidal inlet") which parallel those in the Hadley Harbor Complex, they were not sampled by Dexter in the same manner as were those in this work.

Dexter (1947) took 432 samples with a $1/4$ m^2 metal quadrat in the intertidal zone, and a large number of naturalist dredge hauls subtidally. The latter were recorded "quantitatively" by computing the area the dredge covered as about 60 m^2. Some physical—chemical data are given. No mention was made of the mesh size in which the samples were washed, or whether samples were washed through screens. The size of organisms dealt with in Dexter's study indicates that either a very large mesh size was used, or that the study was based only on organisms larger than a centimeter in size. The organisms taken by Dexter will not be listed here, although certain comparisons will be made. Temperatures in Dexter's study ranged from below freezing (the tidal inlet froze over completely in the winter of 1933—34) to as high as 24°C, which was higher than we recorded at Hadley Harbor. Salinity ranged from 29.69‰ to 34.61‰, somewhat greater than the Hadley Harbor values; pH from 7.6 to 8.3; and dissolved oxygen from 3.54 to 7.94 ml/liter. For the most part, the physical factors were not too different in total range from those measured in Hadley Harbor, although the means would be considerably different because of longer winters and shorter summers. Bottom sediments were described subjectively. The subtidal bottom was described as "smooth and firm, except in a few regions of fine mud deposits". The central channel of the river was described as narrow, winding, and steep-sided, very similar to Southwest Gutter in the Hadley Harbor Complex. It had been dredged to a uniform depth of 8 ft., and the maximum depth was given as 34 ft. at mean-low-water.

Dexter (1947) organized faunal and floral distributions into communities, associations, and associes, and listed the species as predominants, dominants, subdominants, influents, subinfluents, and permeant influents as set forth by Shelford (1932). Only two of Dexter's communities are relevant to the Hadley Harbor study, the "Subtidal Bottom Community, *Laminaria—Cancer* faciation" and the "Tidal Communities, *Mya—Nereis pelagica* Biome". The rest of his communities were described from rock surfaces or upper intertidal regions, not collected in the Hadley Harbor Complex. The eel grass had disappeared before the inception of Dexter's investigations. The subtidal *Laminaria—Cancer* facies was based on 110 dredge hauls, each covering about 60 m^2. Of the 38 species listed by Dexter (1947, p.270), only 17 species were also collected in Hadley Harbor in 1963 to 1965. Unfortunately, specific habitats could not be recognized from Dexter's data. The two predominant species of this facies were *Asterias vulgaris* and *Polinices heros*, both considered more as Boreal species than cold-temperate species, and rare south of Cape Cod. At least 10 of the 13 subdominant species listed were also taken in Hadley Harbor and could be assigned to the four separate habitats previously described for the Complex, rather than the single aggregation considered by Dexter. All of the wide-ranging motile species (permeant influents) found by Dexter also occurred in Hadley Harbor, but were too large to be taken by the Van Veen in the present study. Of the 16 "secondary" or rare species listed for the subtidal bottom community at Cape Ann, only six were taken in Hadley Harbor, the remaining species being representative of Boreal waters.

The second community given by Dexter which is relevant to the Hadley Harbor study is the *Mya—Nereis pelagica* biome of intertidal communities. Although 16 of the 29 species reported by Dexter from this "biome" occurred in large numbers as subtidal inhabitants in Hadley Harbor, the habitat for these same species was described as exposed sand bars and flats from mean-low-water to 4 ft. elevation above sea level. Only a small portion of the Hadley Harbor Complex above mean-low-sea level was sampled, therefore, direct comparisons are difficult to make. All of Dexter's dominants for this community were also taken in the subtidal sand and mud flats of Hadley Harbor, but in smaller numbers as most were too large to be collected by the Van Veen. Two of the subinfluents, *Solemya velum* and *Gemma gemma*, were considered members of the same community by Dexter, but did not occur simultaneously in the same habitats in Hadley Harbor. As in Dexter's species list of secondary forms for the subtidal bottom community, most of the secondary tidal community species can be considered as ranging from the

Boreal region to the Arctic, and would not have been taken during the present study. Differences in sampling techniques between the two studies preclude valid comparisons between benthic communities, although many of the same organisms were taken in both studies.

Benthic communities of Menemsha Bight, Vineyard Sound (Lee, 1944)

One of the first genuinely quantitative surveys of the benthos on the Atlantic coast of the United States was carried out by Lee (1944), presumably in the summer of 1943, although no date for collection of the data was given. The area investigated was a small indentation of the shore, Menemsha Bight, 10 × 6 km in total area, located on the western shore of Martha's Vineyard about 20—25 km southeast of Hadley Harbor on Vineyard Sound. Approximately 80 stations were sampled in the Bight using a "clam shell bucket" with a surface area of 0.8 m^2, cutting into a depth of 23 cm; this is about 14 times the surface area of our grab but having about the same penetration. The samples were sieved through 18 mm, 10 mm, and 1.8 mm screens, thus retrieving most of the megafauna but missing all meiofauna and probably the majority of the size fractions of animals dealt with in the Hadley Harbor study. The standard deviation in faunal counts by species from 13 stations from one "uniform" habitat was 18—24%, thus he considered one sample per station sufficient for characterizing the animals quantitatively.

Lee divided the Bight into five zones on the basis of species distributions and numbers of each species per station. These zones were: Zone 1, an *Emerita, Tellina, Ampelisca* group in 2—5 m of water, in a bottom with medium-coarse yellow sand and pebbles predominating; Zone 2, a *Clymenella—Ampelisca* group, in 5—20 m, in fine mixed sands; Zone 3, an *Ampelisca—Cyprina (Arctica)* group, in greater than 20 m depths, in loose coarse sand and pebble bottom; Zone 4, with the same animals as the previous one, but in medium-grained white sand; and Zone 5, a *Crepidula* association, 10—14 m deep, on walnut-sized stones with a soft, fine clay matrix. The only other environmental parameter mentioned by Lee was that the Bight is characterized by strong tidal currents. Complete lists of the animals taken and their abundances were not given, but the numerical breakdown by species for two stations in each zone was given in his Table II (Lee, 1944, p. 89). No data were given for Zone 4, which was considered the same as Zone 3 in faunal composition.

It is significant that most of the species given by Lee as numerically predominant were ubiquitous within Hadley Harbor and also occurred in all five of his zones. This would suggest that Lee was dealing with one major community composed of several sub-communities associated with separate bottom types. For instance, the species of invertebrates collected on the stony bottom with clay matrix (Zone 5) comprised the only assemblage which differed from the other four. *Crepidula fornicata*, an attaching epifaunal gastropod, occurred within this zone in high numbers. Portions of Northwest Gutter with a similar substrate were also characterized by large populations of *Crepidula* and a numb ˙ of the other species cited by Lee for the same zone. Two stations from Zone 1 in Menemsha Bight were inhabited by 10 species, of which 8 were taken also in Hadley Harbor. Two typical stations from the next deepest Zone (2) produced 13 species of invertebrates, of which only 7 were also taken in our study. Within his deepest Zone (3), three times deeper than any part of the Hadley Harbor Complex, Lee found 15 species, of which only 8 were common to both areas. Zone 4 was not tabulated, and samples from Zone 5 contained 21 species, 14 of which were taken in Hadley Harbor. Most species taken only in Menemsha Bight were considered open Vineyard Sound or Atlantic shelf species which seldom invade the shallow waters of the Hadley Harbor Complex. In fact, the Atlantic shelf character of the Menemsha Bight fauna further supports the premise that Atlantic Ocean water flows into Vineyard Sound on the Martha's Vineyard side rather than along the shores of the Elizabeth Islands.

The faunal list for Lee's Zone 1 slightly resembles the list for the silty-sand portions of the sand flat habitat in Hadley Harbor, while the other zones appear to be characteristic of the large level-bottom community which occurred over much of the broad expanse of sandy bottom in Vineyard Sound. There are some similarities to the faunal composition of Sander's (1958) *Ampelisca*, sand bottom community of Buzzards Bay, but significant differences exist, attributable to the different seiving methods employed by the two investigators. The one major level-bottom community sampled by Lee occurs in Vineyard Sound just outside of the Vineyard Sound entrances to Hadley Harbor and breaks up into smaller units within the Harbor. The deeper-dwelling organisms of this large open sound community appear to be excluded from most of the Complex.

Bottom fauna of Rand's Harbor (Burbanck et al., 1956)

These investigations on Cape Cod proper were in progress during the summers of 1946, 1948, 1949, 1950, and with less intensity during the summers of 1951 and 1952 (Burbanck et al., 1956). Two areas were investigated: (1) a small man-made estuary constructed thirty years prior to the study, called Rand's Harbor; and (2) Squeteague Harbor, a larger estuary slightly to the north of Rand's Harbor. Both branch off Megansett Harbor, which in turn is an estuary draining into Buzzards Bay, some 15 km north of Woods Hole. Samples of bottom fauna were collected quantitatively with an

Ekman Grab and an Orange Peel Grab, both of which took approximately $1/20 \, m^2$ of bottom sediment. Samples were sieved through a 1.5 mm mesh screen; and it appears that both the sieved material and finer material passing through the screen were examined for organisms. However, the list of invertebrates was confined to species which for the most part were larger than 1 mm. Bottom water temperatures, pH, and salinity were recorded for several summers, and a few winter bottom water temperatures were taken also. The lowest bottom temperature recorded (late January) was $+3°C$, and the highest recorded was $+26°C$, three degrees higher than the highest temperature recorded in Hadley Harbor during the period of investigation. Salinities ranged from nearly zero over fresh water springs to 30.2‰, or never quite approaching the lowest recorded salinities of 31‰ in Hadley Harbor. The pH values were considerably lower than those obtained in Hadley Harbor. Low values of 6.1—6.5 were recorded in the upper arms of Rand's Harbor, and from 7.1 to 7.6 throughout most of the Harbor. Considerable runoff from the bogs in the vicinity probably contributed to the much lower pH's observed in Rand's Harbor than those observed in Hadley Harbor. The greatest depth in Rand's Harbor was about 8 or 9 m, and the tidal range was 1.3 m. The margins of the Harbor were sand and gravel, while the basins were characterized as filled with "a black tenacious mud reeking of hydrogen sulphide". Rand's Harbor is about 400 m long and 30 m wide, or about the size of the Vineyard Sound section of Southwest Gutter. The actual number of stations occupied in the estuary was not given by Burbanck et al. (1956), but it can be assumed that it was sampled far more heavily than an equivalent area in Hadley Harbor. Some eel grass was living in Rand's Harbor, but few typical eel grass invertebrates are given in Burbanck's list.

At least 67 species of invertebrates in Rand's Harbor were identified and a fairly large number of forms were identified to genus. Only 15 of these species were not collected by us in Hadley Harbor and most of these were intertidal, terrestrial, or rock bottom forms, habitats not investigated in Hadley Harbor. The species tabulation for Rand's Harbor is given in Burbanck's Table I (Burbanck et al., 1956, pp.221—230), but unfortunately distributional data on individual species were given only as distances from the mouth of the Harbor. It cannot thus be determined whether animals were collected intertidally, in the centers of the basin, or on channel slopes. It is possible, however, to determine the depth of invasion of many of the species into the confines of the Harbor. As salinities may have been lower at the upper end of the Harbor, some correlation can be made between salinity and infaunal distribution. More exact information as to habitat specificity for some of the invertebrates is presented in the text discussion on the ecology of representative species (Burbanck et al., 1956, pp.231—237). Of the 18 species of benthic invertebrates discussed individually in detail by

TABLE XI

Habitats of ten species in Rand's Harbor and Hadley Harbor

Species	Rand's Harbor	Hadley Harbor
Clymenella torquata	high salinity, channels	slopes of channels
Scolopus fragilis	high salinity, slopes	sand flats
Heteromastus filiformis	low salinity, slopes	slopes of basins
Pectinaria gouldi	mud, slope and channel[*]	mud, slope and channel
Spio setosa	high salinity, channels	shallow, sandy channel
Macoma baltica	all salinities, intertidal	intertidal sand, mud flats
Mya arenaria	intertidal	eel grass sand flats
Mulinia lateralis	deep mud basins, low to high salinities	deep basins, mud
Mercenaria mercenaria	slopes and basins	slopes and basins
Nassarius obsoletus	intertidal, sand and mud	intertidal, sand and mud

Burbanck, only 10 were also taken in the four main habitats of Hadley Harbor. These 10 are given in Table XI with Burbanck's habitats and their Hadley Harbor equivalents. This list points out the close correspondence between habitats as assigned by Burbanck and by the present author; although data on only a few organisms can be compared from both areas.

Benthic studies in Buzzards Bay (Sanders, 1958, 1960; Wieser, 1960)

Soon after Sanders (1956) completed his survey of Long Island Sound, he transferred his attention to the benthic communities of Buzzards Bay. Three major papers have been published on this research which furnish a valuable background in the structure of the benthic community at the entrances of Hadley Harbor on the Buzzards Bay side (Sanders, 1958, 1960; and Wieser, 1960). Samples of the bottom were taken in the same manner in both of Sanders' studies by utilizing the anchor dredge and converting the volume of sediment taken to a square meter, although the lower mesh size was 0.50 mm in the 1956 research and 0.20 mm in the 1960 work. Because of the small size of the organisms dealt with in Wieser's (1960) study, samples of an area of 9.07 cm^2, 7 cm thick, were taken with a Phleger core sampler. Each sample was separated into a sand fraction, a medium fraction (retained by a 0.160 mm sieve) and a fine fraction consisting of the material which passed through the screen. All three fractions were examined for the animals retained. Analyses for grain size and sorting were made on all sediment samples taken. Although considerable environmental data were collected, only temperature range (2—22°C) and salinity range (29.5—32.5‰) were reported, as Sanders was primarily interested in the biotic interactions of a single widespread community through time rather than areal fluctuations which might be attributable to changes in the external environment.

The first investigation (Sanders, 1958) was carried out between October, 1955, and February, 1957, and involved a reconnaissance of 19 stations, and a detailed study of 4 representative stations over a year's duration. From this reconnaissance, Sanders recognized two communities: (1) the soft-bottom community, essentially the same as the *Nephtys incisa—Yoldia limatula* community of Long Island Sound (Sanders, 1956), but lacking appreciable numbers of *Yoldia*; and (2) the sand bottom community considered as *Ampelisca* ssp. community. The numerically predominant organisms in the Buzzards Bay soft-bottom community consisted of *Nephtys incisa, Nucula proxima, Turbonilla* sp. (may be *T. interrupta), Nerinides* sp., *Retusa canaliculata, Cylichna oryza, Ampelisca* sp., *Cerastoderma pinnulatum, Ninoë nigripes,* and *Pitar morrhuana.* The invertebrate species comprising the greatest percentage composition of the sand bottom community were: *Ampelisca* sp. (a different one), *Byblis serrata, Cerastoderma pinnulatum, Ampelisca macrocephala, Glycera americana, Nephtys bucera, Tellina (agilis), Ninoë nigripes, Lumbrineris tenuis,* and *Nephtys incisa.* The list given by Sanders for the soft-bottom community contained 26 species, each of which comprised more than one percent of the population. Twenty-two of these 26 species were also found in Hadley Harbor. Most of these species (17) were characteristic and abundant in the Inner Harbor habitat, while only 4 were considered channel species and 3 considered sand flat species. None of the soft-bottom community species listed by Sanders was common to the eel grass habitat in Hadley Harbor. An analysis of the species list that Sanders (1958) gives for the more abundant sand bottom fauna (50 species) revealed that of the 41 species, which were also common to the Hadley Harbor Complex, 5 were more frequently taken in Inner Harbor, 3 on the sand flats, 4 in the eel grass, and the remaining 29 species are characteristic of the Outer Harbor and deep channels.

Once again, it is clear that the Buzzards Bay communities described by Sanders were an integral part of the Hadley Harbor Complex. The soft-bottom community encroached upon the Inner Harbor are almost intact, except that the typically shallow-water pelecypods *Mulinia lateralis* and *Macoma tenta* were added to the community. The sand bottom community of Buzzards Bay contained fewer species common to the Harbor, but most of them appeared to form the channel community or were confined to the Outer Harbor. In both of Sanders' communities, few of the components appeared to form appreciable portions of the sand flat and eel grass communities in the Complex. It would appear that within the sand flat habitat, depth was the limiting factor in excluding the Buzzards Bay communities, while eel grass was the controlling factor in maintaining a separate assemblage in the Complex. No eel grass occurred at the depth sampled by Sanders.

Once the identity of the soft-bottom community was established by Sanders, he then carried out a thorough study of its structure and of the feeding relationships among the dominant organisms (Sanders, 1960). The same procedure for collecting and treating bottom samples was employed, covering the period from February, 1956, to January, 1958. Sanders' Station "R", located in the south center of Buzzards Bay in a depth of 19 m, was selected for detailed study, and sampling was done once a month. The composition of the soft-bottom community given by Sanders in 1958 differed somewhat from that of the community for the later work (Sanders, 1960, pp.140—142). Rather than 22 species, 79 species were listed for the total community, presumably because more samples were used to establish its identity. Of these 79 species, we collected 56 in Hadley Harbor. Only 22 (the same 22 which also identified the Inner Harbor from Sanders' previous work) were typical of the soft muds of the Inner Harbor, while 25 species (most of which were not listed previously) were more characteristic of the channel habitat. The sand flats habitat in Hadley Harbor contained the same three species which occurred at Station "R" type sediments in the first study. The major difference was the presence of 11 species from Station "R" which were more typical of the eel grass regions in Hadley Harbor. Most of the eel grass and sand flat species were uncommon at Station "R", forming the group of species in Sanders' (1960) Table 4, which was represented by less than three specimens from all 20 stations. The same was true for the three sand flat species found at Station "R", none of which occurred in more than one or two instances and then as only one or two individuals. It is probable that these "out of place" species at Station "R" were transients from shallower waters.

The other paper in this series on the benthos of Buzzards Bay was written by Wieser (1960) who dealt only with the meiofauna, which he considered metazoans of medium size. Taxa included in this category by Wieser were: nematodes, kinorhynchs, ostracodes, copepods, turbellarians, oligochaetes, halacarids, gastrotrichs, and cephalocarids. This group of taxa also was counted in the Hadley Harbor study, and as was the case with Wieser, only certain groups were completely identified, some were partially identified, and others were only counted at the taxon level. Wieser discussed only the nematodes and kinorhynchs in detail as they constituted 88—99% of the total meiofauna. Counts at the meiofaunal level ranged from 169,000 to over one million individuals per square meter, considerably larger than the counts obtained in Hadley Harbor. Differences can be explained by the larger mesh size (0.25 mm) used in the Hadley Harbor study. Wieser placed no lower limit (except the magnification of the microscope) on the organisms counted. If the material which passed through our screens had been examined for organisms, it is probable that our counts would have been as high or higher than Wieser's as we obtained much larger counts per square meter for the larger organisms than found by Sanders in Buzzards Bay at the same stations.

The only comparisons between Wieser's study and ours can be made at the taxon level, as nematodes are still being identified by Dr. D. Hope. Kinorhynchs were identified by Wieser, but, if comparisons are made at the same size-fraction level, our two common species were more abundant in Hadley Harbor than at Wieser's stations. A third kinorhynch, *Echinoderella remanei*, taken by Wieser apparently was too small to be retained by our sorting methods, although this species was taken in the Complex in large numbers using different methods. Wieser's data on kinorhynchs indicated that Station "R" type mud is a better environment for them than the other two stations, "P" and "J", which had a sand or sand—silt—clay bottom. The same was true to some extent in Hadley Harbor, as both *Trachydemus mainensis* and *Pycnophes frequens* occurred at the same stations, Inner or Outer Harbor localities on clayey-silt bottom. *Pycnophes frequens* had a somewhat wider distribution (Fig. 58 and 59). To some extent, the same correspondence between numbers of meiofaunal taxa and bottom type (P, J, R) that Wieser indicated in his Table 4 (1960, p.125) was demonstrated in the Hadley Harbor investigations. Comparisons are difficult to make, however, except by comparing Fig. 74 through 77 and the maps for various sediment parameters, Fig. 20 through 24, but until individual identifications are established for all taxa of meiofaunal size in both studies, comparisons between the two cannot be made.

Benthic studies in Barnstable Harbor (Sanders et al., 1962)

Another investigation along the same lines was carried out in the Cape Cod region about the same time by Sanders et al. (1962). As the previous studies by Sanders had been carried out at subtidal depths, he decided to test their hypotheses regarding community organization on intertidal habitats. Barnstable Harbor, on the north side of Cape Cod, is a shallow intertidal embayment about 5.5 km long and 1.2 km wide, bordered by extensive salt marshes. Tidal ranges are 3—4 m on the north side of Cape Cod, so that intertidal flats are much more common around the borders of Cape Cod Bay than in Buzzards Bay and Vineyard Sound. Few intertidal flats exist in the Hadley Harbor Complex, and we confined most sampling to subtidal depths. Sampling methods by Sanders et al. (1962) differed substantially from those in his previous investigations in that several different size samples were used (depending upon the size of the organism under study), and screen size depended upon the size sample taken. For instance, 9 m^2 samples were examined unscreened, while smaller-sized samples were washed through screens of 0.75 mm mesh size, and the smallest-size samples (250 cm^2) were examined without washing.

As Sanders et al. (1962) dealt with essentially one habitat, the intertidal sand flats, comparisons can be made only with that community in Hadley Harbor. Sixty-nine species of invertebrates were identified from the six stations sampled in Barnstable Harbor. Of these, 38 species were also collected in the Hadley Harbor Complex. Nineteen species are considered characteristic of the sand flats, four species secondarily related to sand flats, eight species primarily Inner Harbor species, and seven species occurring in more than two habitats. On this basis, it is evident that there was considerable resemblance between the intertidal community of Barnstable Harbor and the sand flat community of Hadley Harbor, even though they are in different climatic zones. Further evidence of their similarity was found by comparing their abundances. Twelve of the Barnstable species were considered common and large enough to constitute most of the biomass of the community. Five of these were more important than the other seven, and these five were also the most abundant in the Hadley Harbor sand flats. Three species were not taken in Hadley Harbor (Boreal species?), three were more common to the Inner Harbor community than the sand flats, and one is considered an eel grass species in Hadley Harbor. Exact comparisons of numbers per square meter cannot be made between these two studies because of different sampling methods employed. However, counts from Barnstable Harbor ranged from 7,000 to 355,000/m^2, while counts from the same habitat in Hadley Harbor ranged from about 10,000 to 198,000/m^2, roughly equivalent in magnitude.

Benthic studies in Pocasset Estuary (Sanders et al., 1965)

A paper on community structure of the Cape Cod benthos resulted from an interest by Sanders et al. (1965) in the role of salinity as a factor limiting diversity. Sanders selected an estuary with a pronounced salinity gradient from head waters to the entrance. This estuary, Pocasset Estuary, empties into the northeastern portion of Buzzards Bay. Biological samples were taken at seven stations, mostly close to the shore of the estuary, relatively close together at the upper end and widely spaced at the lower end. Samples with a surface area of 39.6 cm^2 were collected (in triplicate) by means of a wide diameter corer. Sediment was washed through a screen with minimum pore openings of 0.21 mm, close to the minimum mesh size used in the Hadley Harbor region. Salinities were measured in overlying and in interstitial waters by means of the electrical membrane potential developed across a concentration cell, a new and accurate means of measuring interstitial salinities.

Overlying water salinities fluctuated widely with the tidal cycle, ranging from nearly zero to almost 30‰ at the head waters and between 20 and

30‰ near the entrance. On the other hand, interstitial salinities ranged from 5 to 12‰ at the upper end, and only 0.5‰ at the lower end, indicating that interstitial salinities were remarkably stable throughout the tidal cycles. Distribution of different kinds of organisms paralleled the salinity variations, a brackish-water fauna dominating the upper part of the estuary, a transitional fauna in salinities of 19–22‰, and a marine fauna where normal salinities from Buzzards Bay predominated throughout the tidal cycle.

The Pocasset Estuary study produced 47 different species of invertebrates; a large proportion were identified to species and the remainder to the order level. Of the 29 identified species, 20 were also collected in Hadley Harbor; of these 20 species, 19 were taken in the mouth of the estuary, and the other species from the middle portion of the estuary. None of the forms collected in the upper end of Pocasset River was found in Hadley Harbor. The 19 invertebrate species taken in both Pocasset Estuary and in Hadley Harbor can also be assigned Hadley Harbor habitats. Eight of these jointly occurring species were confined to the Inner Harbor habitat, eight species to the sand flats, one species to the channels, and two species were taken in both the Inner Harbor and channel habitats. Probably Sanders (1965) was dealing with a mixture of communities resembling those of Inner Harbor and the channels. It is evident that the majority of species in Pocasset were probably part of the Buzzards Bay soft-bottom community which divided into smaller associations upon entering Pocasset River, in much the same way that the community separates into the four subcommunities upon entering Hadley Harbor.

OTHER RELATED REGIONAL STUDIES

Bottom communities of Long Island Sound (Sanders, 1956)

During the period of August, 1953, to September, 1954, the second major quantitative study of a marine level-bottom community for the Atlantic coast of America was carried out by Sanders (1956) in Long Island Sound, some 100 km east and slightly south of Hadley Harbor. Sampling techniques differed considerably from previous American investigations in that sampling areas were computed from volumes of sediment taken at each station and counts were made of much smaller animals than in previous investigations. Sanders' smallest screen had a mesh size of 0.297 mm, just slightly larger than the 0.250 mm mesh size used in the present study. An anchor dredge (Hessler and Sanders, 1967) was used to collect relatively large volumes of sediment to a depth of 7.6 cm. In order to obtain the area covered by the dredge, the volume of sediment was divided by 7.6, the limiting cutting

TABLE XII

Environmental data for six stations in Long Island Sound

Station no.	Depth (m)	Temperature (°C)	Salinity (‰)	Bottom sediment (converted)
Charles Island	6.0— 8			silty sand
1	10.0—12	1.55—22.10	24.8—28.7	gravelly sand
3	11.0—14	2.15—21.65	25.5—28.7	sand—silt—clay to silty clay
4	18.0—22	1.25—21.95	25.4—28.7	gravelly coarse sand
5	28.5—31	1.25—21.60	24.8—28.8	silty sand and clayey sand
8	27.0—29	1.35—22.05	25.0—29.2	silty sand

depth of the dredge. All organisms were identified, counted, and their dry weights measured or computed to obtain biomass figures for each station. Productivity of the numerically predominant species was also calculated on the basis of counts, weights, and size classes in monthly increments through an annual cycle. These data provided a thorough analysis of the structure and composition of several level-bottom communities.

Values for all species at all stations taken during the investigation were not given, although Sanders (1956, pp.413—414) recorded the analyses for all species from six representative stations. These data provide the basis for comparison between the Hadley Harbor communities and the Long Island Sound communities. Environmental data for the six stations are given in Table XII. All of the typical stations were considerably deeper than those studied in Hadley Harbor, and the salinities were 6—3‰ lower than in the Hadley Harbor region. Minimum temperatures were higher than the Woods Hole region, while maximum temperatures were lower, attributable to the greater depths of water in which the investigation was carried out.

A complete list of all species taken in Sanders' investigation, including 133 species of invertebrates and one fish, are recorded in Sanders (1956, p.412). Of these 133 invertebrate species, 77 were common also to the Hadley Harbor Complex. A comparison was made of the species composition of the six typical stations and the occurrences of the same species in Hadley Harbor (Table XIII). Inspection of the number of species and the numbers of individuals/m^2 at each station in this list indicates that the Charles Island Station and Station 3 were different in composition and did not represent the same community as stated by Sanders. The Charles Island locality was characterized by a silty-sand substrate and was the shallowest of the six stations, while Station 3, although not much deeper, had a fine sand—silt—clay to silty-clay bottom. In this author's experience silty coarse sand generally supports almost an order of magnitude more animals per unit area than a silty-clay bottom. Likewise, the densest populations are generally closer to shore. The

TABLE XIII

Comparison between number of species and population density in Sanders (1956) and number of species in present study[1]

Station	No. of species	Total population/m^2	Number of same species also found in Hadley Harbor at all Stations
Charles Island	42	13,203	32 (76%)
1	29	6,742	19 (65%)
4	28	28,472	16 (57%)
5	27	5,398	18 (66%)
8	23	13,889	18 (78%)
3	11	2,669	10 (91%)

[1] Populations not comparable on a station basis.

other four stations (Table XIII) were similar in composition, and total populations constituted one community, typically found on glacial relict sand and gravel bottom usually some distance from shore and in reduced salinities. It can be seen that 32 species (76%) of invertebrates are common to both Hadley Harbor and the Charles Island Station and an even larger percentage (91%) are common to both Hadley Harbor and Station 3. This results from the fact that the Charles Island Station was close to shore in depths approaching those of Hadley Harbor, and Station 3 had the same substrate and almost identical composition as Inner Harbor. The other stations were much deeper than those encountered in Hadley Harbor, and the representative sediment types for these stations were rare in Hadley Harbor. Except for Station 8, there was little similarity between the two faunas in these deeper stations.

Sanders (1956) stated that one of the major communities present in Long Island Sound was a soft-bottom community which he designated the *Nephtys incisa—Yoldia limatula* community for the two largest abundant species. These two species, although not as abundant as some other species, contributed most to the total biomass. Subdominant species from this community were: *Cerianthus americanus, Cerebratulus luridus, Mellinna cristata, Ninoë nigripes, Lumbrineris tenuis, Praxillella praetermissa, Leptocheirus pinguis, Siphonaecetes smithianus, Lyonsia hyalina, Macoma tenta, Mulinia lateralis, Pitar morrhuana, (Nucula proxima), Lunatia triseriata, Retusa canaliculata, Cylichna alba*, and two species of *Ampelisca*. Most of these species were taken in Hadley Harbor also, and virtually all of the jointly occurring species were part of the soft-bottom habitat of Inner—Outer Harbor. In fact, the *Nephtys incisa—Yoldia limatula* community was nearly identical to the one large community at the Woods Hole—Buzzards Bay entrance to outer Hadley

Harbor which apparently divides into facies accommodating to the various small habitats within the Complex. Because all of the species data from all stations collected by Sanders (1956) was not listed, it was not possible to recognize any of the other Hadley Harbor species combinations in the Long Island Sound region. It is unlikely that resemblances to other Hadley Harbor communities would be revealed in that most of Sanders' stations are in much deeper water than encountered in Hadley Harbor.

Offshore Cape Cod meiofaunal studies (Wigley and McIntyre, 1964)

A series of 10 stations sampled in June, 1962, by Wigley and McIntyre (1964) is pertinent to this investigation, although they were taken from 30 to 100 miles distance offshore from the Elizabeth Islands across the continental shelf and onto the upper continental slope. Two Smith—McIntyre 0.1 m^2 grab samples were collected at each station, and the sediment was washed through a 1 mm screen for megafaunal examination; a portion of the grab sample was cored by a plastic tube taking a 9.50 cm^2 surface area, 4 cm deep and processed for meiofauna. The material from the core was processed through sieves with a minimum mesh diameter of 0.074 mm (considered the lower limit for the meiofauna). Depths ranged from 40 to 567 m, more than an order of magnitude deeper than the Hadley Harbor region. Bottom temperatures ranged from $3°$ to $14°C$ at shallow stations, and $4°$ to $7°C$ at slope stations, equivalent to Hadley Harbor spring and fall values. Sediments were of two types, silt and clay as the major fraction, and the other a medium sand. Stations 49 through 50 were characterized by well-sorted sediments, while stations 51 through 55 were mostly medium well sorted, with the poorest sorted having a sorting coefficient of 2.56. Total counts of the individual higher taxa are reported in the paper, but no species are listed. Thus, it is possible to make comparisons only of abundance at the level of higher taxa.

It is difficult to make comparisons of numbers of individuals, as Wigley and McIntyre's minimum mesh size was 0.074 mm, while we used 0.250 mm; furthermore our samples covered $1/25 \text{ m}^2$, while their sample was based on 10 cm^2. In all ten of Wigley and McIntyre's samples, nematodes were the most abundant; whereas within the Hadley Harbor Complex nematodes were numerically dominant at about 50% of the stations. Copepods, oligochaetes, amphipods, and sometimes ostracodes predominated at the other stations in Hadley Harbor. Some idea of percentage composition of the meiofauna can be seen in Fig. 74 through 77. The composition of Wigley and McIntyre's Stations 46 through 49 was most similar to that of Outer Harbor stations in December to February (Fig. 75), while their Stations 50 through 54 more closely resembled the composition of most of the Hadley Harbor stations during the summer months (late April through August, Fig. 77). Foraminifera and gastrotrichs were not identified in the Hadley Harbor samples, as our minimum mesh size was too large to retain these small organisms. It is rather surprising that Wigley and McIntyre collected such a small number of ostracodes and found virtually no amphipods, two groups that were often predominant in Hadley Harbor. The total populations per station of meiofauna were also much smaller on the continental shelf and slope than those in the Complex, although Wigley and McIntyre note that their numbers were comparable to other studies made of meiofaunal composition in other shallower regions. Even though some resemblance in the composition of the meiofauna at the taxon level in the two regions may be evident, meaningful comparisons are difficult. For instance, in one area sampled a taxon may consist of only one species, whereas in another area the same taxon may be composed of half a dozen to hundred species. Our studies indicated that there is a seasonal shift of numbers within higher taxa, but we do not know whether these changes were a result of the sudden reproduction of one species or the influx of many new species.

Benthic marine plants (Conover, 1958)

One other paper published in recent years on work conducted in 1952–1954 is relevant to the Hadley Harbor Complex study. Conover (1958) investigated the seasonal growth of benthic marine plants in Great Pond, one of the long estuaries or embayments off the northeastern end of Vineyard Sound near the town of Falmouth. The change in standing crop as grams of wet weight of eel grass per square meter was examined through an annual cycle. Conover's results are of interest because the eel grass in Hadley Harbor is probably one of the major controlling biotic aspects of the benthic fauna. Eel grass in Great Pond was virtually absent in November, quite low in December, January, and February, and attained its greatest growth in middle July. These concentrations agreed closely with the weekly average of solar radiation measured at Newport, Rhode Island (Conover, 1958, p.120), although peak radiation preceded peaks of eel grass concentration by about two to three weeks. Eel grass growth also correlated somewhat with temperatures except that the eel grass had two plateaus of abundance in the spring and fall which did not correspond to temperature variations. Maximum water temperatures fell about a week or two before eel grass weights started to decline. Conover also measured the pH of overlying waters which varied seasonally in about the same direction and magnitude as our own, even though the water is extremely confined in Great Pond.

The following discussion will be confined to research on benthic communities carried out in other parts of the world to see if habitats similar to those in the Cape Cod region and the communities associated with them have been recognized elsewhere, even though species and even genera are quite different from those in the Cape Cod region.

DANISH BOTTOM COMMUNITIES

No synthesis of marine benthic invertebrate communities would be complete without comparisons of our communities with those described by Thorson (1957) and based on the work of Petersen and others in Danish waters. Most of the communities described by Thorson and Petersen cover large uniform areas of level bottom but in waters which are colder and of lower salinity and not optimum for most marine animals. None of these conditions existed in the environments of Hadley Harbor, and thus there seems to be little correlation with the "parallel level-bottom communities" typical of Danish waters. However, a typical eel grass community does exist in Danish waters, particularly in Isefjord, a narrow embayment which partially dissects the main Danish island of Zealand. This fjord has been investigated for over thirty years (since the disappearance of the eel grass and its return) by Dr. Eric Rasmussen of the Marine Biologiske Laboratorium of the University of Copenhagen. The author has accompanied Rasmussen to the eel grass beds a number of times and was struck by the similarity of the fauna between the beds in Denmark and Woods Hole. Rasmussen also made a brief investigation of the eel grass beds in Woods Hole, and concurred on their similarities. Polychaete species are often identical in the two eel grass communities, and most of the amphipods and isopods are of the same genera and, according to some systematists, even of the same species. Rasmussen also has noted the change in predominance from infaunal to epifaunal species during the return of the eel grass. The amount of seasonal radiant energy is considerably less in the Isefjord than in Hadley Harbor, and there is nowhere near the amount of kinetic energy involved in tidal exchanges in Isefjord as in Hadley Harbor. This may account not only for the higher stands of eel grass, but also for the much denser and more diversified populations of invertebrates in Hadley Harbor as observed by both of us. Diversity is higher in the Hadley Harbor Complex because it occurs at the boundary of two major zoogeographic regions, while the Isefjord is confined to one, and that one is characterized by year-round reduced salinities and low temperatures.

One publication which gives a quantitative evaluation of a Danish community, strikingly similar to the Hadley Harbor eel grass community, concerns the fauna associated with the attached benthic alga *Fucus serratus* (Hagerman, 1966). The area selected for study was in the Danish Øresund, about 10 km northwest of Helsingør at a depth of 2 m, on a stony bottom, where salinities ranged from 16.33‰ to 24.22‰ (mean 20.18‰) and water temperatures ranged from 1 to 17.2°C. Salinity was considerably lower than in Hadley Harbor as were the maximum water temperatures. Most of the data used in this study were collected by quantitative means from the leaves of the *Fucus*, and the residue was washed through a 120 μ mesh sieve.

Hagerman (1966) collected 164 species and identified 148 species of invertebrates (mostly of meiofaunal size) from his *Fucus* leaves. The surface area of the plants examined ranged from about 1/10 to slightly over 1/2 of square meter. Total population counts ranged from about 7,000 to nearly 50,000/m^2, or very close to total populations found by us in the eel grass beds. Even though Hagerman examined *Fucus* plants, it is apparent from his species list that many of these animals also live on eel grass, presumably because the same hydroids and epiphytic algae live on both plants. Of the 148 species identified in the Øresund, 33 species occurred on the eel grass in Hadley Harbor, and the majority of the genera were common to both areas. Some of the more abundant species common to both the *Fucus* and eel grass were: *Nereis pelagica, Harmothoë imbricata, Platynereis dumerili, Nicolea zostericola, Loxoconcha impressa, Dexamine (spinosa), Microdeutopus gryllotalpa, Ampithoe (rubricatum), Corophium insidiosum, Caprella (linearis), Idotea baltica, Pallene (brevirostris), Anoplodactylus (petiolatus), Copidognathus sp., Lacuna vincta, Lacuna pallidula, Littorina littorea, Bittium (reticulatum), Retusa (obtusa), Odostomia (plicata), Mytilus edulis, Hiatella arctica, Mya arenaria, Macoma baltica, Mysella (bidentata), Asterias (rubens)*, and the pipefish *Sygnathus (acus)*. The specific names given parenthetically are the slightly different species of Danish waters, while the other species are the same in the Danish and Woods Hole regions. This list compares favorably with Table III and the species list given in the discussion of the eel grass assemblage of Hadley Harbor, and also with the species heavily loaded on Factors 5, 6, and 12 (the eel grass factors) on Tables V and VII. It is significant that the two completely different sampling methods for collecting plants from the bottom produced not only the same animals, but also approximately the same numbers of individuals per species. Direct comparisons between Hagerman's work and my own can be made by reviewing Nagle (1968). Both papers are devoted to the study of epibiota of a plant community, and both achieved very similar results.

The names of major communities examined by Thorson, and adopted from Petersen (1913, 1914, 1915), were identified by the predominant genus or genera of megafaunal animals. Typical bottom communities of shelf and inshore waters are the *Macoma*, the *Tellina*, the *Syndosmya*, the *Amphiura*, the *Amphiodia—Amphioplus*, the *Turritella* and *Cerithium*, the *Mal-*

dane sarsi—Ophiura sarsi, the amphipod communities, and also a number of communities peculiar to various latitudes and regions of the world. No real equivalent to the *Macoma* community was in the Hadley Harbor region, although *Macoma tenta* was one of the "subdominants" in the Inner Harbor. The *Macoma baltica* community described by Petersen apparently has its equivalent in parts of New England, but not in Hadley Harbor. The sandy bottom community designated as the *Tellina* community is also without a real parallel in the Hadley Harbor Complex. *Tellina agilis* does occur in fairly large numbers on sand bottom, but it also can be found in equal numbers in the silty clays of the Inner Harbor habitat. Thorson (1957) refers to the sand bottom community of Lee (1944) in Menemsha Bight as a typical *Tellina* community, but this is not supported by Lee's original data. No real equivalent can be found for the *Venus* communities of northern Europe in the Woods Hole region, even though the large venerid clam *Mercenaria* abounds in dense beds near the margins of embayments. Other inhabitants of the *Mercenaria* beds do not take the place of the other species in the *Venus* community. The *Syndosmya (Abra)* community seems to be close to the Inner Harbor, clay bottom community, in that *Abra* is probably equivalent to both *Tellina* and *Macoma*, and *Nucula* and *Yoldia* are equal to *Nucula nitida*. The polychaete members of the Danish *Syndosmya* community are almost identical, at least at the generic level, to the polychaetes in the Inner Harbor habitat. Since ophiuroids of any genus were rare within the Complex and actually absent within most of the Complex, no equivalent was found to the host of Danish and other regional ophiuroid communities described by Thorson. Sanders also found ophiuroids rare or absent in Long Island Sound and Buzzards Bay. Salinity is certainly not the limiting factor, as salinities in Buzzards Bay are considerably higher than those of Danish waters. The only other community of Thorson which bears some resemblance to those found in Hadley Harbor is the amphipod community. The factor analysis produced a community grouping which consisted almost entirely of amphipods, plus several other small crustaceans (Table VIII). Unfortunately, the Hadley Harbor amphipod group was really part of the eel grass community living in the deeper part of the channels, while Thorson's amphipod communities were mostly soft-bottom communities and are probably closer to the *Ampelisca* community described by Sanders from Buzzards Bay, so are not comparable.

It is evident from the data collected in this study, therefore, that the broad level-bottom communities conceived by Thorson do not have their exact equivalents in the shallow and dissected habitats of Hadley Harbor. The primary reason for this difference is the absence of large areas of level bottom in Hadley Harbor and the relative instability of environmental factors there which would tend to permit the dominance of a few species. Salinities in Hadley Harbor were close to the normal 34‰ of oceanic waters, thus the region as a whole is not one of great "adversity" which tends to produce communities with certain organisms clearly predominating over others. Also, perhaps the Hadley Harbor Complex is transitory in a geologic time sense, and there has not been time to produce the clearly defined level-bottom communities of the Thorson type.

BENTHIC COMMUNITIES OF THE TEXAS–LOUISIANA COAST AND GULF OF CALIFORNIA

In order to relate similarities and differences between warm- and cold-water benthic communities, the author will next make comparisons between the community organizations found in the Woods Hole region with those "assemblages" described by Parker (1956, 1959, 1964a,c) on the Texas–Louisiana Coast and the Gulf of California. Exact comparisons are difficult to make between the present study and these previous ones, as the warm-water studies were carried out on both the distribution of living organisms and of shells and tests of the former inhabitants. Few soft-bodied animals were included in the former investigations, because of the emphasis in solving geological rather than biological problems. Also, most samples taken in the Hadley Harbor study were quantitative, while investigations in the Gulf of Mexico and Gulf of California included both quantitative and qualitative samples.

The first investigation of warm-water benthic communities was carried out in the vicinity of the Mississippi River Delta (Parker, 1956). A series of assemblages was described to depths of over 75 m, with the majority of assemblages occurring in less than 20 m. Tidal marshes in the Hadley Harbor Complex were not investigated, so cannot be compared to the Delta marshes; however, the Delta Front silt environment of the Mississippi Delta contained many species common to the Hadley Harbor sand flat habitat. Many genera also were common to both habitats. For instance, both had species of *Tellina*, *Macoma*, *Nassarius* and *Lumbrineris*, and *Mulinia lateralis* was occasionally found in both environments. *Crassostrea virginica* also occurred in both the sand flat and Delta Front habitats. The lower sound assemblage of the Mississippi Delta most resembled that of the Inner Harbor, and both were characterized by highly reducing clayey silts and silty clays. Species taken in common were *Mulinia lateralis*, *Retusa canaliculata*, *Tellina versicolor* (closely related to *Tellina agilis*), *Macoma tenta*, *Anachis avara* ssp., *Polinices duplicatus*, *Prionospio* sp., *Diopatra cuprea*, and *Anadara transversa*, which appeared to be a transient in both areas.

The upper-sound and inlet assemblages were combined to form a community somewhat similar to the channel and high-current community of Hadley

Harbor. Both regions had mixed, poorly sorted sediments and were characterized by strong bottom currents, considerable marine grass, shelly gravel, and abundant attached algae and *Bugula* (a bryozoan). Like the channels and Outer Harbor of the Hadley Harbor Complex, the inlets and upper-sound habitats contained the maximum diversity of species, presumably because of a more stable physical—chemical milieu and an interchange of forms between the inner shelf and smaller embayments. *Astrangia*, *Sthenelais*, *Anachis*, *Crepidula*, *Libinia*, *Crassinella*, *Mitrella*, *Neopanope*, *Ensis*, *Chaetopleura*, *Turbonilla*, and *Natica* were some of the invertebrate genera which predominated and are common to both regions. Only a few of these genera were represented by the same species in both regions. If one had studied the inlets of the Mississippi Delta region and then gone to the channels of Hadley Harbor, he would feel that he was in familiar territory. The other assemblages in the Mississippi Delta region, typical of much deeper waters, did not resemble those of the Hadley Harbor Complex.

One would expect more resemblance between the assemblages of the Rockport, Texas, area (Parker, 1959) and Woods Hole than the Mississippi Delta and Woods Hole because of the greater influx of fresh water from the Mississippi River. No equivalent was discerned in the Hadley Harbor Complex for the low-salinity, river-influenced assemblage of the Texas coast, inasmuch as there are no low-salinity habitats in the Elizabeth Islands chain. The "enclosed bays, variable low to intermediate salinity assemblage" of the Rockport, Texas, region had its closest equivalent in the Inner Harbor habitat. This assemblage is the Texas coast equal of the "Lower Sound assemblage" in the Mississippi Delta. Although neither *Nucula proxima* or *Yoldia limatula*, both deposit feeders, were present in the enclosed bays, *Nuculana concentrica*, a member of the same family as *Yoldia*, and also a deposit feeder, occupied the same niche. Two of the dominant Texas coastal forms, *Retusa canaliculata* and *Mulinia lateralis*, also occurred in the soft clayey-silt bottoms of the Inner Harbor, thus enhancing the resemblance between the two communities. Three more genera from the enclosed bay environment of Texas, the pelecypods *Tagelus* and *Ensis* and the ophiuroid *Amphiodia*, were occasional inhabitants of the Inner Harbor habitat in Hadley Harbor. Although *Macoma tenta* was also taken in the enclosed bay habitat in Texas, another species of *Macoma*, *M. mitchelli*, was more common and probably occupied the same niche as *Tellina agilis* in Hadley Harbor.

There was some resemblance between the "high-salinity shell reef assemblage" of Texas and the channel or current-influenced habitat grouping in Hadley Harbor. Major differences between the two are based on the fact that the channels of Woods Hole were characterized by stands of eel grass (*Zostera*), while the major spermatophyte on the high-salinity shell reefs and inlets of the Texas coast was turtle grass (*Thalassia testudinum*), a related but warm-water marine plant. Common inhabitants of both environments were two species of *Anachis*, *Mitrella lunata*, a small chiton, the pelecypod *Anomia simplex*, a mytilid, various species of small caridean shrimp, and a species of bryozoan *Bugula*.

Few studies have been carried out on the invertebrate fauna of the turtle grass beds in Texas, although one paper by Hoese and Jones (1963) contains a discussion of the seasonality of larger crustaceans and fish within the turtle grass community of Redfish Bay, Texas, one of the small embayments discussed by Parker (1959). Quantitative samples for biomass were taken by Hoese and Jones of the larger organisms on a twice monthly basis throughout one annual cycle. Correlations were evident between the numbers, weights, and water temperature for *Neopanope texana texana*, but this species was not abundant in the Hadley Harbor eel grass beds. Hoese and Jones (1963, p.45) state that the grass community is a distinctive one on the Texas coast, but there are insufficient data on the characteristic smaller organisms of these beds to make any valid comparison between them. The author made a few small collections of amphipods, polychaetes, and gastropods from some turtle grass beds near the Institute of Marine Science, University of Miami, Florida, in the fall of 1964, and found roughly the same genera of amphipods and polychaetes and some of the same species of gastropods in the turtle grass of Miami that also occur in the eel grass of Woods Hole.

The "high-salinity bay margins assemblage" of the Texas coast also has its equivalent in Hadley Harbor in the sand flats and channel margins community. Extensive tidal flats are missing in the Rockport area, as the amplitude of the astronomical tides are only 15—25 cm. Therefore, the just subtidal sand habitat is relatively narrow and surrounds the margins of the larger bays in the Texas coastal bays. Species of mollusks characterizing this habitat in both regions were: *Tagelus divisus*, *Mysella planulata*, and *Lyonsia hyalina*. Several species of mollusks in Hadley Harbor had closely related species and subspecies living in the sandy margins of the Rockport high-salinity bays. These included such genera as: *Nassarius*, *Vermicularia*, *Aequipecten*, *Mercenaria*, *Macoma*, and *Bittium*.

The final assemblage typical of the Rockport area, which has a near equivalent in Hadley Harbor, is the "inlet assemblage". As expected, the inlet assemblage had a superficial resemblance to the Outer Harbor and channel community of Hadley Harbor, although the Texas inlets were characterized by a greater diversity of fauna than Hadley Harbor, at least on the megafaunal level. Jointly occurring invertebrates for the two habitats were: the gastropods *Anachis avara* ssp., *Turbonilla interrupta*, *Crepidula fornicata*, *Natica pusilla*, *Polinices duplicatus*, and *Caecum pulchellum*; the pelecypods *Crassinella mactracea (lunulata?)*, *Petricola pholadiformis*, and closely related species of *Pandora*, *Tellina*, and *Macoma*; the echinoid *Arbacia punctu-*

lata, and the solitary coral *Astrangia*. It is surprising that so many of the species found in Hadley Harbor are also considered the same species or very closely related species over 5,000 miles of coastline and four or five zoogeographic provinces to the south on the Texas coast. A further dimension is added in terms of paleoecological research in that they occupy more or less the same habitats in these two very different climatic regions, thus presenting opportunities for large areal correlations in older sediments.

A discussion of "parallel" Rockport Bay and Hadley Harbor communities is given in Parker (1969). Each Rockport area assemblage is examined in depth and new boundaries, based on knowledge gained in the Hadley Harbor investigation, derived for Texas communities, and re-illustrated. This study also sets forth for the first time some hypotheses regarding diversity, stability (see also Slobodkin and Sanders, 1969), and larval settlement and development as they relate to marine benthic community composition.

The second large area investigated for the existence of broad assemblages of mega-invertebrates characteristic of specific marine benthic habitats was the Gulf of California (Parker, 1964a,c). Most of the shallow portions of the Gulf of California can be considered as truly tropical, and its fauna should thus differ considerably from that of Hadley Harbor. The study of the Gulf of California was concerned primarily with faunas in much greater depths than those found in the Woods Hole region. Only two habitats in the Gulf of California show any resemblance to habitats studied in Hadley Harbor: the intertidal sand beaches and sand flats to 10 m, and the sand bottom nearshore shelf, 11—26 m deep. Although higher taxa other than mollusks were described from the Gulf of California, such soft-bodied groups as the amphipods and polychaetes were not. Sampling methods were different in the two investigations, only animals larger than two or three millimeters being taken in the Gulf of California. One technique employed in both studies was the use of the computer as an aid in forming community aggregations. Major differences resulted from this type of analysis in that no distinction was made among living organisms and the shells and tests of formerly living forms was made, and numbers of individual species were not calculated for the Gulf of California stations.

Only 27 species of living invertebrates including mollusks and the shells of 41 other species of mollusks characterized the intertidal sand beach and sand flat habitat of the Gulf of California. Of these 68 species, only six species at the generic level could be considered to occupy the same niche in both regions: *Tellina* and *Macoma* (but different subgenera), *Tagelus*, *Mulinia*, *Nassarius*, and *Thyone*. However, less effort was expended in the study of the intertidal sand flats of the Gulf of California than to the sand flats of Hadley Harbor. The major difference found between the two regions was the greater diversity of molluskan life in the Gulf of California.

The second habitat in the Gulf of California containing organisms which resembled those living in Hadley Harbor was the "nearshore sand bottom of the continental shelf from 11 to 26 meters deep". In physical characteristics this resembled the sand bottom habitat of Buzzards Bay or Vineyard Sound. Over 130 species of large invertebrates (corals, gastropods, scaphopods, pelecypods, crustaceans, echinoids, ophiuroids, and asteroids) were collected alive in this habitat. In terms of animals of comparable size and taxa, this was ten times the number found on the same type of bottom and comparable depths by Sanders (1958) and by Lee (1944) in the Cape Cod area and Thorson (1957) in European Boreal waters. The author has noted also that, where a genus is represented by one or at the most two species in the northern waters, the same genus in the warm waters of the Gulf of California was represented by as many as seven species, and most genera had two or three species living in the same habitat. The diversity of organisms living on level bottoms in the tropics is unquestionably much greater than the diversity found in the colder latitudes. Similar tropical diversity is reported from one haul of an epibenthic sled in 15 m of water off the coast of Madras, India, in the Bay of Bengal by Sanders (1968). They found 6236 individuals belonging to 201 species. Twenty-one genera (8 of which were of the same subgenus) of the megafaunal invertebrates occurring in the shallow-shelf sand bottom habitat of the Gulf of California were taken also in the Hadley Harbor Complex; they were also common in the sand bottom community in Buzzards Bay and Vineyard Sound. A comparison of twin species of mollusks occurring on opposite sides of Central America made during the investigation of the Gulf of California (Parker, unpublished manuscript), showed that 14 of the genera common to both the Gulf of California and Woods Hole region have species which are probably of the same ancestral stock in the Miocene of the Americas. In fact, the resemblance between the 14 species listed below in Woods Hole and in the shallow waters of the Gulf of California is so great that one is tempted to give them the same names:

Gulf of California	Woods Hole
Crepidula incurva	*Crepidula fornicata*
Crepidula perforans	*Crepidula plana*
Polinices reclusianus	*Polinices duplicatus*
Anachis varia	*Anachis avara*
Nassarius versicolor	*Nassarius trivittatus*
Eupleura muriciformis	*Eupleura caudata*
Anadara nux	*Anadara transversa*
Chlamys (Aequipecten?) circularis	*Aequipecten irradians*
Laevicardium elenense	*Laevicardium mortoni*
Tellina felix	*Tellina agilis*

Mulinia palida	*Mulinia lateralis*
Ensis californicus	*Ensis directus*
Tagelus politus	*Tagelus divisus*
Lyonsia gouldi	*Lyonsia hyalina*

A comparison between the Woods Hole Inner Harbor fauna and the benthic fauna of a small harbor in southern California (Alamitos Bay Marina) can also be made (Reish, 1961). The size of the Marina was about the same as that of the Inner Harbor. The same-size quantitative samples, about 1/20 of a square meter, were taken with an Orange Peel grab. Reish's samples were washed through a screen with a mesh diameter of about 0.78 mm (another odd size and a further complication in making meaningful comparisons between quantitative benthic invertebrate studies). Seven polychaete, amphipod, and pelecypod species were taken in both harbors, and 26 species of Californian invertebrates belonged to the same genera found in Hadley Harbor. Numbers of individuals for the polychaete species were similar to the concentrations of the same species found in Hadley Harbor (Reish is a polychaete specialist), but further comparisons do not seem to be evident.

Comparisons can be made also between the Hadley Harbor study and an investigation of Bogue Sound, North Carolina, by Brett (1963). Again, sampling methods were so different from those of the Hadley Harbor investigations that the useful comparisons which can be made are limited. Brett used a suction dredge operated by hand under water, which washed out only the very large organisms. Only those invertebrates with hard parts were considered, as this was a geological rather than a biological study. Of the 43 megafaunal species (mostly mollusks) taken by Brett, 12 species were common to Hadley Harbor. Brett assigned these 43 species to some 11 habitats, several of which could be considered similar to Hadley Harbor habitats. Only one will be considered here, the "Lagoon, marsh island, grassy bottom" which appears to be similar to the eel grass habitat. Brett listed 10 species of mollusks as indicative of the grassy bottoms, although only *Laevicardium mortoni*, *Cumingia tellinoides*, and *Aequipecten irradians* might be considered to occupy the same habitat in Hadley Harbor.

There are many more studies on benthic communities of small coastal estuaries and embayments which have been reported for other parts of the world, including those published by Jones (1961), Keith and Hulings (1965), Day (1967), Green and Hobson (1970), Stanton and Evans (1971), and Wade (1972), but space does not permit the inclusion of all of them. A review of the literature indicates that the four major communities representing the four habitats in Hadley Harbor have their equivalents in one form or another in most of the Boreal, temperate, and warm-temperate regions of the world. Until techniques for studying these communities are standardized by all of the workers in this field, rigorous comparisons will not be possible.

CHAPTER 6

APPLICATION OF BENTHIC COMMUNITY STUDIES TO PRACTICAL
ENVIRONMENTAL PROBLEMS

The study of benthic ecology has always been a fascinating one for young
people, as it involves boats, diving, discovering attractive sea shells and other
creatures, plus getting lots of sunshine. This set of conditions has produced a
large and eager group of young marine biologists within every generation
since the 1880's.

Although the practicality of studying aggregations of animals on the sea
bottom for "profit" had not been evident during the years of richly endow-
ed basic research of the 1950's and 1960's, this special branch of marine
biology had its real start as an applied science through efforts of the Danes in
the early 1900's. These people, with a strong dependence upon the sea,
realized that productivity of the benthos was intimately concerned with
production of sea food, especially when it concerned the abundance of the
plaice and other flat fishes. The systematic attack on the identity and composition of bottom communities by Petersen (1914, 1915) and his co-
workers was soon followed by research in this field by workers in Norway,
The Netherlands, England, and the United States. Later, the Americans,
Russians, Germans, and other nationalities with close dependence upon the
sea initiated thorough studies of "fish food" in the bottom which support
seafood species.

There was no doubt as to the practical application of benthic studies
towards improving bottom fisheries, although man is not yet able to control
(improve) benthos in the open sea by direct intervention except to limit
harvests. On the other hand, he can contribute towards destroying benthic
crops through massive pollution, particularly through major oil spills. The
past few years (1967—73) has shown a marked decline in funding for basic
research in the marine environment in America, particularly as to delving
into the systematics and life histories of small, little known groups of invertebrates. During periods of emphasis on man and his environment, basic
research on other types of organisms is deemphasized and research is concentrated in the applied fields.

The establishment of Coastal Ecosystems Management Inc. at Fort Worth,
Texas, was promoted primarily by the need for applying the knowledge of
benthic community structure to practical problems; such as, detecting an oil

brine pollution, establishing baseline conditions before environmental modification, and aiding land and marina developers in environmental planning. Within the last three years, at least 10 major contracts have required study of benthic communities to achieve answers to practical problems. In these days of practical and applied research and funding, it is worthwhile to enumerate and describe some of these projects, in which the study of bottom faunas and floras played an important part. Perhaps there can be a wedding of applied and basic research, through knowledge of how science can solve a problem with thinking rather than just doing.

BRAZOS—COLORADO ESTUARINE SURVEY FOR DOW CHEMICAL COMPANY

Soon after completing the Hadley Harbor study, the author was privileged to obtain an industrial contract from Dow Chemical Company at Freeport, Texas, to study the ecology of two estuaries, the Colorado and Brazos River mouths, on the central Texas Gulf of Mexico coast (Fig. 87). This comparative study of two estuarine ecosystems (Parker et al., 1969) provided an excellent opportunity to test some of the principles and methods gained in this present study. Quantitative $1/25 \text{ m}^2$ benthos samples were collected once a month for 9 months at 0.5-mile and 1-mile intervals from river mouth to the head of tidal excursion. At each station sampled for benthos, chemical—physical data — including Eh, pH, salinity, trace metals, light penetration, dissolved oxygen, and major ions — were measured at surface and bottom. Attempts were made to sample both rivers within the same time period and at the same spacing.

The purpose of this study was purely practical or applied: to identify differences between the highly disturbed (by industrialization) Brazos River Estuary and the almost completely undisturbed Colorado Estuary. The differences, or lack of differences, were used to determine environmental controls for Dow Chemical discharges into the Brazos Estuary. Although the data were collected and compiled by the summer of 1969, they were not released to the public until a hearing of the Texas Water Quality Board in 1971.

Since the results of this study took nearly 400 pages of final report, only the conclusions can be reported here. The complete report was "read into" the hearing, but is not generally available as it was not printed. Some of these results are reported here.

(1) The two estuaries were significantly different in the range of physical—chemical variables. Salinities were higher upstream in the Brazos River because salt water was discharged directly into the river 9 miles from its mouth. Calcium values were higher in the Brazos, and likewise, pH and Eh values differed considerably from those measured in the Colorado River.

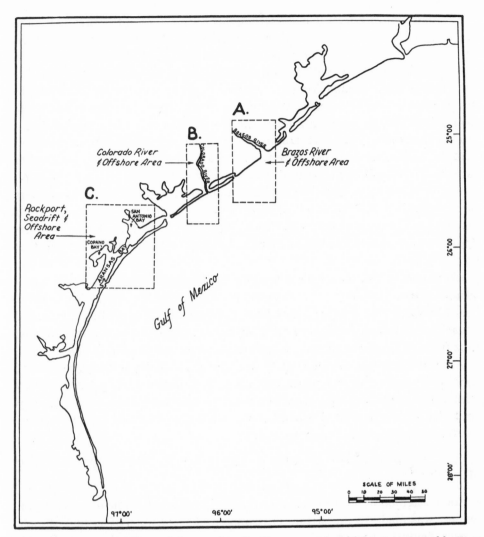

Fig. 87. Locations of three of the areas on the Texas coast in which concentrated bottom sampling was carried out.

Trace-element concentrations were similar in both rivers. At times, water temperatures were higher in the Brazos, but these were of short duration and did not appear to harm the fauna.

(2) The number of organisms found in bottom sediments were higher in the Brazos Estuary than in the Colorado Estuary, often an order of magnitude higher. The major difference in distribution of populations between the two rivers was that most of the living bottom invertebrates were found in the first 5 miles of the Colorado Estuary, while the majority of the animals taken from the Brazos occurred 6 miles above its mouth.

(3) Many more kinds of benthic animals were found in the Brazos than in the Colorado. Highest diversity was observed at Dow Chemical Company's outfalls and intakes, while low diversity characterized most of the Colorado stations. Low-diversity indices characterized both river estuaries suggesting that they are unsuitable for most marine organisms. Diversity is related to environmental stability, thus the rapidly fluctuating environmental conditions of narrow, shallow estuaries promote low diversity.

(4) Crustaceans (such as amphipods, cumaceans, and ostracodes) and nematodes (motile animals) were the most abundant animals found in either estuary, while mollusks (non-motile) were relatively scarce.

(5) An index of pollution, applicable upon testing in other areas of stress or "pollution", was determined through the application of the ratio of benthic copepods to nematodes. Under disturbed conditions, copepods predominate at their trophic level, while under normal conditions nematodes predominate.

(6) Wherever and whenever stress conditions were evident, bacterial populations were high and invertebrate populations were low. In addition, these conditions of stress produced high bacterial diversity, but low benthic animal diversity. High stress may impart high mortality rates to benthic animals, thus furnishing varying organic substrates for bacterial populations.

Additional results of this study were related to the hydrodynamics of narrow estuaries and the relationship between these special conditions and population levels of organisms. Neither the hydrography nor the biology could have been neglected, since both of the disciplines were needed to find answers to questions asked by the client.

STUDY OF BASELINE CONDITIONS TO ESTABLISH FUTURE INDUSTRIAL USE OF AN ESTUARY

Soon after completion of the study for the Dow Chemical Company, a request was made to investigate environmental conditions of a small estuary (Cedar Bayou) entering Galveston Bay, Texas (Culpepper et al., 1969). Although the upper end of the small bayou was contaminated by salt dome brine, conditions were relatively undisturbed by man throughout much of its 10 mile length. On the other hand, Cedar Bayou was selected for intensive industrial use by U.S. Steel Corporation and the Houston Light and Power Company, even though it was still relatively "clean". It was our task to determine baseline conditions and to predict the impact of future industrialization upon the natural biological populations and environmental conditions. The same techniques used for the Brazos—Colorado and Hadley Harbor studies were used. Results of the study as related to benthic ecology are summarized here.

(1) Environmental conditions for the first ten miles upstream from the

mouth of the bayou into Galveston Bay were similar to those of Galveston Bay. Salinities were low, ranging from 7 to 14‰, typical of the bay. Oxygen, nutrient levels, and pH were normal for this type of an estuary.

(2) The upper end of the estuary was severely disturbed by brine discharges, which resulted in salinity values up to 61‰, well above tolerances of the low-salinity faunas found there.

(3) Low numbers and few kinds of living organisms were taken past 5 miles up the bayou. The benthic populations and diversity were highest at the mouth of the bayou and decreased rapidly towards the region of high-salinity fluctuations and extremes at the upper end.

(4) The relationship between numbers of benthic copepods and nematodes was the same for the disturbed portions of Cedar Bayou as it was for the disturbed portions of the Brazos River estuary. Copepods far outnumbered nematodes, indicating that portions of the estuary were stressed.

(5) Further deterioration of the bayou by planned industrialization would have little more effect upon the already depauperate fauna.

EFFECTS OF OIL FIELD BRINE DISPOSAL ON ESTUARINE ECOSYSTEMS

At the request of a number of major oil companies, a survey and study of the effects of oil field brines on estuarine faunas were carried out (Parker and Blanton, 1970). Although much of the data used to defend the oil companies before the Texas Railroad Commission was obtained from the literature and Coastal Ecosystems Management Inc. data files, some field work on benthic standing crops and diversity was performed. Review of published and unpublished data produced information on benthic community aggregations and controls not considered previously.

(1) In order to put various portions of the Texas coast into proper climatic and environmental perspective, climate and hydrography as controlling forces for benthic ecosystems were summarized for the entire Gulf of Mexico region as shown on Fig. 88. Note that benthic community composition is examined in the light of predominant trophic levels or feeding types and larval development. Interactions between climate, sediment type, physical factors, and number and diversity of benthic organisms are given in this illustration.

(2) Relationships between stability, extreme ranges of physical factors (typical of the Texas coast), and types of benthic communities were established from the wet, subhumid climate and low-salinity bays of east Texas and Louisiana to the semiarid climate and hypersaline waters of the southwest coast of Texas. Benthic communities representing geomorphic areas of habitats similar to those previously described for Hadley Harbor are illustrated on Fig. 89 through 91.

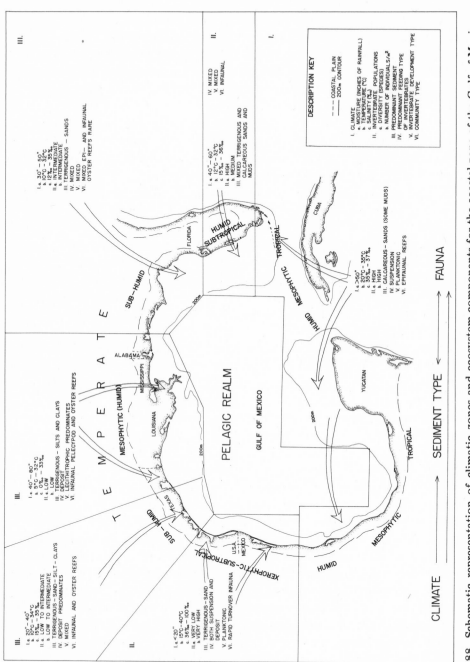

Fig. 88. Schematic representation of climatic zones and ecosystem components for the coastal zone of the Gulf of Mexico.

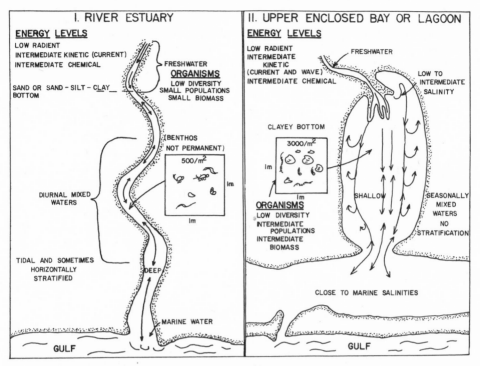

Fig. 89. Diagrammatic representation of estuarine habitats in temperate latitudes. I. River estuary with typical ecosystem energy levels, sediments, and bottom community type. II. The upper enclosed bay or lagoon habitat and typical characteristics of the environment and fauna.

(3) Faunal counts were made from a series of samples taken in Texas coastal habitats and compared with counts taken from Hadley Harbor samples (Fig. 92). Highest counts for all stations in Texas and Massachusetts habitats were found in the grass flats of Cape Cod, averaging 110,000 animals/m². Second highest counts were made on samples of the same size taken from grass flats within south Texas bays (those with greatest environmental stability). Lowest counts characterized samples from the highly unstable river and bayou estuaries and the low-salinity secondary and tertiary bays of the upper Texas coast.

(4) Clayey sediments produced the lowest number of organisms in both the Cape Cod and Texas studies, while mixed sediments characterized areas of high benthic standing crops in all areas sampled.

(5) Finally, it was proved that the natural populations and diversities of benthic infaunal animals were no lower in areas of brine disposal than in areas of high natural stress and no brine disposal. Fluctuations of natural environmental factors were more important in regulating benthic animal populations and diversity than man-made stresses.

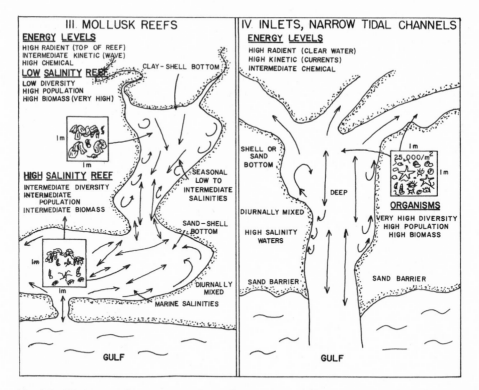

Fig. 90. Diagrammatic representation of two dynamic ecosystems. III. Mollusk reefs (oyster, mussel, or serpulid) with typical environmental and faunal characteristics. IV. Inlets or narrow tidal channels. Note highest diversities and population levels, accompanied by highest energy levels.

BIOLOGICAL ASSESSMENT OF MAJOR OIL SPILL DAMAGE

One of the more important uses of benthic animal studies was to use number and diversity of benthic organisms as a key to environmental disturbance by oil spills. At various times, our scientific personnel were called out to assess damage to biotic ecosystems by major spills. The overall studies were guided by Texas Instruments Inc. of Dallas, Texas, for a spill in the northeast Pacific Ocean off the coast of the state of Washington and by Resources Technology Corporation of Houston, Texas, for a major oil platform fire off southern Louisiana (Resources Technology Corporation, 1972).

The first response to a call for damage assessment was in reference to a Number 4 diesel oil spill in the Straits of Georgia and Rosario Strait near Puget Sound, Washington (Watson et al., 1971). Over 5,000 barrels of diesel fuel escaped from a loading barge at Anacortes, Washington. Tidal currents swept this highly poisonous substance into gravel and sandy intertidal and tidal bottoms nearby, which were known from previous studies to be ex-

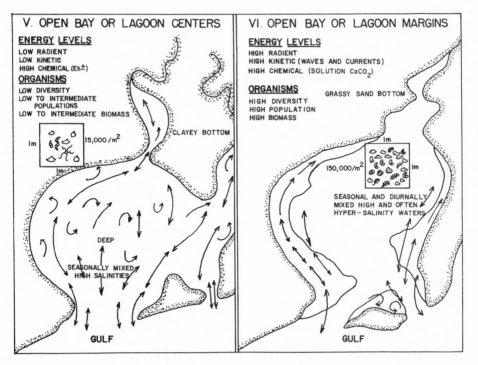

Fig. 91. Diagrammatic representation of lagoonal or bay ecosystems within temperate latitudes. V. Open bay or lagoon centers, with low energy input and low diversity and abundance of benthos. VI. Open bay or lagoon margins with high energy levels and an order of magnitude larger benthic population.

tremely rich in benthos. The same sampling methods used in the previously mentioned studies were used here, in order to provide valid comparative data.

Samples from half-meter quadrats were taken in the intertidal region for assessment of megafaunal benthic population and diversity, while regular $1/25$ m^2 Van Veen grabs were taken in both the intertidal and subtidal bottoms for meiofauna. As large benthic animals, such as starfish, echinoids, holothurians, and crabs, were more characteristic of the meter quadrat samples, data were accumulated for two faunal size classes. Results of the damage assessment survey were as follows:

(1) Subtidal collections of animals taken after the spill were not as rich as those taken thirteen years prior to the 1971 samples. Faunal diversity increased with depth (contrary to the usual results of this sort), suggesting damage in the upper part of the subtidal zone. Large numbers of the megafaunal species listed in previous studies of the intertidal areas were missing altogether.

(2) Samples taken from control areas, with the same habitat types outside

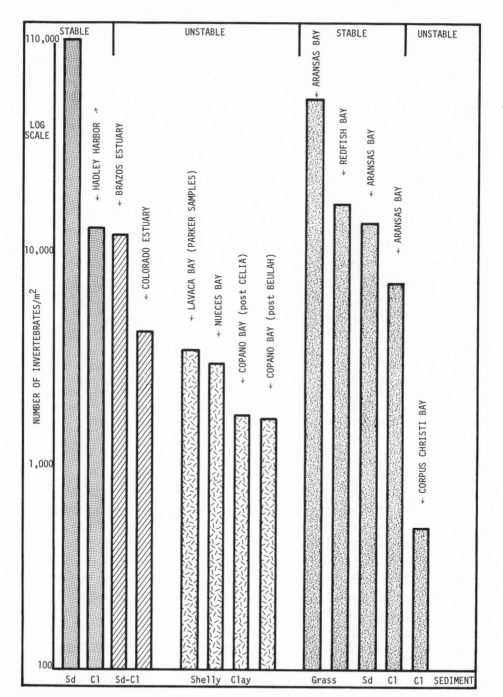

Fig. 92. Comparisons of invertebrate counts from 1/25 m² Van Veen bottom grab samples taken from various bays and estuaries, ranging from Woods Hole, Massachusetts, to Corpus Christi, Texas. Counts represent averages of five samples from each locality.

of the spill area, were richer in bottom fauna than those samples taken in the affected region.

(3) Diversity indices were highest in stable subtidal or lowest tidal habitats and lowest in the upper intertidal areas, especially in areas with fresh-water seepage.

(4) Lowest standing crops of meiofauna were found in the areas with largest amounts of diesel fuel still in evidence. Highest meiofaunal counts were found in the control areas. Likewise, lowest meiofaunal diversity occurred in areas with the highest visible amounts of oil.

This particular study proved that quantitative benthic faunal studies are extremely valuable for determining damage from major industrial chemical spills. Although the presence of some oil in sediments was determined, the rapidity with which the oil disappeared through tidal action precluded the possibility of finding direct evidence of damage, especially as our samples were taken ten days after the spill. It was the lack of living animals, which if killed would already have been decomposed, that provided information needed to establish true damage levels. As benthic infaunas provide one of the major trophic levels for this dynamic ecosystem, the damage to that population could be disastrous to the whole system.

Results of the faunal damage assessment required for the Louisiana oil platform fire were not determined by us, although data were collected and analyzed by our firm. Using the same sampling techniques described here, it was possible for us to determine (unofficially) that some changes were wrought within the normal inshore Louisiana bottom communities.

(1) Several normally abundant megafaunal species were absent and some of the smaller infaunal species of mollusks and other invertebrates were reduced in number.

(2) The relatively slow leaking of crude oil and distillate over a period of nearly 120 days did bring out some major changes in trophic structure. Invertebrate species with high tolerance for environmental stress became extremely abundant, apparently replacing species with low tolerance to oil or turbidity.

(3) Most of the tolerant species were determined to be detritus or deposit feeders, which apparently thrived on the increase in organic matter in the sediments. Brittle stars, certain mollusks, crabs, and fish that feed on infauna attained higher than normal population levels.

One could draw conclusions from this assessment that crude oil spills (off Louisiana) may change the diversity and trophic structure, but also may actually increase organic-matter levels and thus standing crops of many organisms. Our studies further indicated that overall production of life probably increased somewhat over the pre-spill conditions, although we did not personally pursue this suggestion, as the interpretation and verification of the results were not within our province of the study.

DETERMINATION OF RIVER DISCHARGE CONTROLS ON FAUNAL PRODUCTIVI-
TY OF ITS ESTUARY

The present major project, involving the study of benthic communities, involves the investigation of the affect of Trinity River (east Texas coast) flow on the flora and fauna of Trinity Bay, an arm of Galveston Bay, Texas. In order for the U.S. Corps of Engineers to establish guidelines for river basin management, it was necessary for them to obtain data as to how much fresh water is needed to maintain normally operating estuarine ecosystems. This question was answered through a year-long study by Parker et al. (1972) and Solomon and Smith (1973).

Again, the same sampling techniques were employed to measure both the environmental parameters thought to be important in controlling plant and animal growth and reproduction, and the size and diversity of living populations. Some of the results obtained from this study, more basic than applied, are given here.

(1) Waters of Trinity Bay are extremely turbid at all times resulting in low phytoplankton populations. Commercial fish and shellfish catches, on the other hand, are very high. This is puzzling, since primary phytoplankton production was determined to be low, yet it is thought that the primary trophic level (plankton) is needed to support this high megafaunal population.

(2) Investigation of bottom trophic levels indicated that sediment bacterial populations are extremely high at all times of the year, yielding counts of 1 to $3 \cdot 10^{10}$ bacteria/cm^3. Organic matter from the surrounding marshes, bayous, plus industrial wastes from the Houston Ship Channel may provide the high organic-matter content needed to support the high bacterial populations.

(3) Populations of benthos from 1/25 m^2 Van Veen grab samples were higher in Trinity Bay than in comparable habitats in other Texas bays (25,000/m^2). Average counts ranged from 1,700/m^2 on clayey bottoms to 140,000/m^2 on shelly bottom. These high infaunal populations (mostly polychaetes, oligochaetes, and nematodes) feed on organic detritus, reduced to refractory matter by the large bacterial populations. In turn, these soft-bodied invertebrate communities provide the food base for the very large populations of bottom fish and crustaceans which characterize the greater Galveston Bay system.

(4) Overall benthic diversity is low compared to other Texas bays and Hadley Harbor. However, it remains extremely stable throughout the fluctuating and relatively adverse environmental conditions typical of the Trinity Estuary. This stable diversity, regardless of environmental extremes, may be attributed to genetic adaptability of these organisms throughout nearly

3,000,000 years of similar adverse conditions in the same region.

The above examples of the practical uses of benthic animal studies to solve management problems of our aquatic ecosystems are only a few of the applications we have tested. A major practical use for benthic community investigations was devised by the author in his consulting work for oil companies and arose as an outgrowth of his research for the American Petroleum Institute at Scripps Institution of Oceanography in La Jolla, California. Knowledge of the composition of benthic faunal assemblages (living organisms plus dead shell remains) as they relate to marine habitats is useful in interpreting the environments of ancient sediments that were sources or have become reservoirs of oil. Relative abundances and taxa composition of shelled invertebrates are extremely characteristic of specific habitats, not only those of Hadley Harbor but also similar ones throughout the world. What is more important is that these basic assemblage compositions hold true for both Recent sedimentary environments and apparently for past ones as far back as early Mesozoic times. Data supporting this practical aspect of benthic ecology are contained in a number of papers by this author (Parker, 1956, 1959, 1960, and 1964a,c).

In summary, the practical uses to which the knowledge of benthic community structure can be applied are as follows:

(1) Diversity and abundance of infaunal animal species, as deduced from quantitative samples, can be used to determine the stability of aquatic environments or habitats. Low diversity and high population levels of a few organisms denote some major stress condition which eliminates many species, but promotes survival of a few. High diversity and little dominance of species in numbers of individuals of each species characterizes areas of relative environmental stability. Using this concept, diversity indices can be used to denote stress conditions in industrialized waterways. They also can be used to characterize undisturbed areas (establish baseline conditions) before planned changes in water use are made.

(2) Knowledge of the reproduction and feeding types of the predominant members of benthic communities can be used to assess trophic levels in already disturbed estuaries. Once the food chain has been established for a "useful" coastal bay or estuary, plans can be made to either implement its improvement biologically or maintain the normal level of biological productivity. Intimate knowledge of food chain structure is needed for intelligent management of coastal waters, where most marine production exists.

(3) Changes in community composition within the six or seven well-defined bottom animal habitats described throughout this work can be used to pinpoint environmental disturbance. Overall generic faunal composition seems to be relatively uniform from the middle Atlantic coast of America to the Texas Gulf of Mexico coast. Disappearance of any of the major genera

characterizing the various communities and their habitats would suggest a major change in the ecosystem, which could be traced to either natural causes or to man's interference with nature. Knowledge of the normal community makeup makes the job of finding the cause of major changes easier.

(4) Knowledge of the total composition (meiofauna and megafauna) of bottom communities is essential in managing commercial sea food crops, especially in confined waters where some environmental factors can be manipulated by man. If the fresh-water requirements for growth and reproduction of benthos can be determined adequately within an estuary, it may be possible to manipulate or increase standing crops of sea food species by controlling river discharge and runoff into that estuary. An extension of this corollary is the ultimate farming of sea food species in estuaries by controlling both fresh-water input and nutrients needed to sustain the base of the food chain.

(5) Finally, knowledge of bottom community composition can help solve problems relating to past communities and their habitats. Using the principle of uniformitarianism, it can be assumed that benthic faunal aggregations of today's habitats are similar to those which existed in the past. Inasmuch as benthic communities contain many organisms with hard parts, they leave an adequate fossil record for interpretation of past habitats. Oil accumulates in ancient sand deposits, difficult to find by usual oil exploration means. These sand deposits have characteristic benthic assemblages which reveal how the sands got there and direction to the ancient shoreline. Using these clues supplied by benthic animal studies, it has been possible to help discover new deposits of oil and gas.

CHAPTER 7

CONCLUSIONS

This investigation in the Hadley Harbor Complex was designed to examine, by statistical means, the validity of "community" organizations of subtidal benthic invertebrates and their biological interdependence as well as their dependence on the physical environment. In addition, it was intended to explore the internal consistency of these aggregations relative to environmental conditions and its relation to normal reproductive cycles of component species. Because the subtidal area selected for examining these hypotheses was small and the hydrography was complex resulting in restricted habitats, the problem of identifying true "communities" was further complicated. The magnitude of data gathered (200,000 variate values) precluded conventional means of data reduction, and so computer programs were utilized and thus proved invaluable.

The primary hypothesis that community organization exists and is influenced by multiple environmental stresses is supported by the data presented and discussed in this book. At least four major aggregations of organisms, more or less confined to specific habitats, were recognized by both subjective and statistical treatment of these data. These four communities — found on the clayey-silt bottoms of settling basins of Inner Harbor, the outer sand flats at the entrances to the Complex, in the deep current-influenced channels, and within the permanent eel grass beds — are characterized by the combination and density of certain species. Furthermore, evidence supports the concept that most species found in Hadley Harbor were derived from one or two major communities which occupy the broad, level sandy and clayey bottoms of Buzzards Bay and Vineyard Sound. The remaining Hadley Harbor species were derived from intertidal portions of the Complex and surrounding shores of the region. The community concepts formulated by Thorson (1957), Sanders (1958, 1960), and others are validated by these results, and they also demonstrate that small confined bodies of water, influenced by complex circulation patterns and varying physical—chemical factors, are characterized by small discrete patterns of species distributions. Biotic interactions (commensalism, mutualism, parasitism, predation, and others) are extremely important toward *maintaining* the organization of these communities. The data presented suggest that individual environmental factors (particularly current, depth, substrate composition, the chemical state of the organic matter and water, and amount of radiant energy) cause the separation or fragmentation of larger outlying and deeper biotic communities into smaller units which may occupy the dissected embayments of larger stable bodies of water. It is suggested from these data that it is the total amount of radiant and kinetic energy which regulates the internal composition of these unique aggregations.

Not only do whole populations shift their centers of abundance from one habitat to another, but also they increase or decrease in a single locale in response to seasonal fluctuations of temperature, Eh, pH, turbulence, and light penetration. Individual components of these populations were examined for cyclic changes in their abundances, although only two major taxa (amphipods and mollusks) provided sufficient detail to study this problem. Preliminary results (Nagle, 1968 and A. Sharp, personal communication, 1968), showed that, at least within the amphipods and mollusks, species oscillations may or may not correlate with temperature changes, but may be attributed to biological interactions and interspecific competition. It is obvious that the next step in unravelling the complexities of community organization must be detailed long-term investigations of the life cycle and autecology of the individual species making up these communities.

It is hoped that the techniques for collecting and reducing the biological and environmental data obtained in this study might serve as a model for future studies in ecology, oceanography, and certain of the earth sciences. Greater emphasis is now being placed by governmental agencies and private institutions on large-scale, multidisciplinary sampling programs involving the marine environment. Major problems in marine ecology can no longer be solved with the "one shot" collection of a few samples of the biota and a scattering of environmental measurements on water samples brought back and stored in the laboratory. Recent advances in technology permit in situ measurements of physical and chemical variables with such rapidity that thousands of values are now obtainable where ten had been taken previously. Because of increased contract support for systematic and ecological investigations related to environmental disturbances, larger numbers of organisms are being collected and identified. It is obvious that with the acquisition of such large volumes of raw data, new techniques must be used to reduce these data to a level which permits easier problem solving. The use of computers and data reduction programs as evolved in the present study is suggested as a means for treating the problems of large data storage and analysis.

For the first time in my experience, it was possible to delineate communities or aggregations of organisms by a completely objective process. Description of the composition of these groups was based entirely on the correlative relationships between population density, distribution, and size classes of each species in relation to similar data for other species at every station through time. Thus, not only the presence of certain species but also the concentration of that species within the community (in relation to its and other species' concentrations throughout the whole Complex) and its relative size (one large clam is more important than one tiny nematode) determined the validity of the aggregation. The application of factor analysis to these ecological data also revealed with some mathematical certainty the physical factors which appeared to be most closely associated with the internal and areal fluctuations of the communities, and also the degree to which they influenced individual species. Factor analysis also delineated the areas that these communities occupied, both as areas with special combinations of species in special areas and as areas of overlap of these species combinations. With the use of factor scores, it was possible to examine the distributional patterns of entire groups of organisms in a purely numerical sense. High positive factor scores denoted the centers of population and regions where most of the abundant species were living together at the same time. Low negative scores (depending upon the sign of the factor loadings) indicated regions of "adversity" for these communities. By using large correlation matrices, this large mass of data (no longer a novelty in these days of rapid data collection) revealed, to some extent, the structure (size-frequency distribution of species) within groups of organisms. The essentially heuristic approach to interpretation of factor analysis revealed combinations of organisms (Factors) related to biological function, such as trophic levels. Some combinations of species (Factors 2 and 4) were certainly derived from their relationship to each other as deposit feeders, filter feeders, and herbivores.

Most previous studies in marine benthic ecology were sufficiently subjective that interpretation of their data depends entirely upon the philosophy of the ecologist treating those data. However, data from the present research may be analyzed mathematically by any number of investigators, and, because of this objective treatment, results should produce identical conclusions substantiated by identical numerical answers.

The results of our investigation are not conclusive, even though objective analysis supported the subjective conclusions. There were some gaps in the collection of physical—chemical data, and three of the most abundant groups of organisms were not identified to the species level and therefore did not enter into the factor analysis. However, results of this study provide much of the basic information necessary for future ecologists who may wish to apply the ecosystem concept to Woods Hole waters, or who may be interested in the autecology of one of the predominant species within the Complex. It is my premise that the principle value of this research is as a model for collecting and reducing large masses of data which can be handled by relatively few persons at any one time. During most of the period covered by this project, only two people were working full time. During the two summers, when collecting the data occupied most of our efforts, as many as four persons were actively engaged in research. Similar problems on organization of plankton communities, defining composition of commercial fisheries populations, analyses of catch efforts, and even predictions of catches can be approached with the methods evolved in this study. Objections are often raised on the amount of time spent in devising storage methods for computer analysis, and even more so, on the time involved in finding errors in computer programs. Offered here is a means of organizing and reducing data, already devised, and in which the investigator need only to "fill in the blanks".

Future ecological studies will depend more and more upon machines, not only to collect but also to analyze the data. Possibilities exist even now for in situ electronic sensing of organisms in the bottom, just as they are now counted in the overlying waters, using resistance or conductance or very narrow sound beams. Several cations and some anions in sea water are being measured electronically, and eventually it will be possible to make continually recorded analyses of many, or possible most, of the components of sea water, including the so-called ectocrine substances, which are thought to regulate many of the biological interactions within communities. Unfortunately, electronics as applied in the marine environment leaves much to be desired in terms of continual and trouble-free operation. It is also true, as Hedgpeth (1967, p.708) remarked: "As expensive as they may be, however, fancy black boxes are not better than the watcher of the box". In fact, there is no computer now, or likely to be in the future, which can integrate and correlate with the speed and accuracy of the human brain the hundreds of variables noted within a single human glance. It may be possible therefore to collect the magnitude of data represented by this study and to reduce it to simpler and correlated form, but it still takes the interest and the imagination of the scientist to bring forth new ideas and information from these sterile numbers.

REFERENCES

Allee, W.C., 1922a. The effect of temperature in limiting the geographical range of invertebrates of the Woods Hole littoral. *Anat. Rec.*, 23: 111.

Allee, W.C., 1922b. Some physical factors related to the distribution of littoral invertebrates. *Anat. Rec.*, 23: 109—110.

Allee, W.C., 1922c. *Studies in Marine Ecology. II. An Annotated Catalog of the Distribution of Common Invertebrates of the Woods Hole Littoral.* Marine Biological Laboratory, Woods Hole, Mass., and The University of Chicago, Chicago, Ill., 123 pp. (Unpublished manuscript.)

Allee, W.C., 1923a. Studies in marine ecology. I. The distribution of common littoral invertebrates of the Woods Hole region. *Biol. Bull.*, 44: 167—191.

Allee, W.C., 1923b. Studies in marine ecology. III. Some physical factors related to the distribution of littoral invertebrates. *Biol. Bull.*, 44: 205—253.

Allee, W.C., 1923c. Studies in marine ecology. IV. The effect of temperature in limiting the geographical range of invertebrates of the Woods Hole littoral. *Ecology*, 4: 341—354.

Boss, K.J., 1968. The subfamily Tellinidae in the western Atlantic, the genera *Tellina* (Part II) and *Tellidora. Johnsonia* (Mus. Comp., Harvard Univ.), 4(46): 274—344.

Bousfield, E.L., 1965. Haustoriidae of New England (Crustacea: Amphipoda). *Proc. U.S. Natl. Mus.*, 117: 159—240.

Bousfield, E.L., 1973. *Shallow-Water Gammaridean Amphipoda of New England.* Comstock Publ. Assoc., Division of Cornell Univ. Press., Ithaca, N.Y., and London, 312 pp.

Bradley, W.H., 1957. Physical and ecological features of the Sagadahoc Bay tidal flat, Georgetown, Maine. In: H.S. Ladd (Editor), *Treatise on Marine Ecology and Paleoecology. Mem. Geol. Soc. Am.*, 2(67): 641—681.

Bradley, W.H., 1959. Living and ancient populations of the clam *Gemma gemma* in a Maine coast tidal flat. *U.S. Fish Wildl. Serv., Fish. Bull.*, 58(137): 304—334.

Brett, C.E., 1963. *Relationships Between Marine Invertebrate Infauna Distribution and Sediment Type Distribution in Bogue Sound, North Carolina.* Dissertation, Univ. N. Carolina, Chapel Hill, N.C., I—VII, 202 pp. (Unpublished manuscript.)

Burbanck, W.D., Pierce, M.E. and Whiteley Jr., G.C., 1956. A study of the bottom fauna of Rand's Harbor, Massachusetts: an application of the ecotone concept. *Ecol. Monogr.*, 26: 213—243.

Buzas, M.A., 1966. Systematics and distribution of the Foraminifera of Hadley Harbor and adjacent waters. *Rept. on Progress — Systematics-Ecology Program — 1966, 4th Ann. Rept.*, 35 pp. (Marine Biological Laboratory, Woods Hole, Mass.; multilith printed 1967.)

Buzas, M.A., 1968. Foraminifera from the Hadley Harbor Complex, Massachusetts. *Smithson. Misc. Collect.*, 152(8): 1—26. (Publ. 4727).

Carriker, M.R., 1967. Ecology of estuarine invertebrates: A perspective. In: G.H. Lauff (Editor), *Estuaries.* A.A.A.S., Washington, D.C., 83: 442—487.

Conover, J.T., 1958. Seasonal growth of benthic marine plants as related to environmental factors in an estuary. *Publ. Inst. Mar. Sci., Univ. Texas*, 5: 97—147.

Cory, R.L. and Davis, H.F., 1965. Automatic data systems aids thermal pollution study of Patuxet River. *Water Sewage Works*, April 1965: 6 pp. (Reprinted by Honeywell, Inc.)

Culpepper, T.J., Blanton, W.G. and Parker, R.H., 1969. *A Study of the Effects of the United States Steel Effluent on Cedar Bayou.* For: U.S. Steel Corp., Turner, Collie and Braden, Consulting Engineers, Houston, Texas, 150 pp.

Day, T.H., 1967. The biology of Knysna estuary, South Africa. In: G.H. Lauff (Editor), *Estuaries.* A.A.A.S., Washington, D.C., 83: 397—407.

Dexter, R.W., 1947. The marine communities of a tidal inlet at Cape Ann, Massachusetts. *Ecol. Monogr.*, 17: 261—294.

Driscoll, A.L., 1964. Relationship of mesh opening to faunal counts in a quantitative benthic study of Hadley Harbor. *Biol. Bull.*, 127: 368.

Fenchel, T., 1969. The ecology of marine microbenthos, IV. Structure and function of the benthic ecosystem, its chemical and physical factors and the microfauna communities with special reference to the ciliated Protozoa. *Ophelia*, 6: 1—182.

Gilbert, W.H., 1970. Territoriality observed in a population of *Tellina agilis* (Bivalvia: Mollusca). *Biol. Bull.*, 139: 423—424. (Abstract.)

Ginsburg, R.N. and Lowenstam, H.A., 1958. The influence of marine bottom communities on the depositional environment of sediments. *J. Geol.*, 66: 310—318.

Green, R.H. and Hobson, K.D., 1970. Spatial and temporal structure in a temperate intertidal community, with special emphasis on *Gemma gemma* (Pelecypoda: Mollusca). *Ecology*, 51(6): 999—1011.

Gunter, G., 1945. Studies on marine fishes of Texas. *Publ. Inst. Mar. Sci., Univ. Texas*, 1(1): 1—190.

Hag, J., 1965. Records of some interstitial mites from Nobska Beach together with a description of the new genus and species *Psammonsella nobskae* of the family Rhodacaridae (Acarina Mesostigmata). *Acarologia*, 7: 411—419.

Hagerman, L., 1966. The macro—microfauna associated with *Fucus serratus* L., with some ecological remarks. *Ophelia*, 3: 1—43.

Harris, R.P., 1972a. The distribution and ecology of the interstitial meiofauna of a sandy beach at Whitsand Bay, East Cornwall. *J. Mar. Biol. Assoc. U.K.*, 52(1): 1—18.

Harris, R.P., 1972b. Seasonal changes in the meiofauna population of an intertidal sand beach. *J. Mar. Biol. Assoc. U.K.*, 52(2): 389—404.

Hedgpeth, J.W., 1967. The sense of the meeting. In: G.H. Lauff (Editor), *Estuaries.* A.A.A.S., Washington, D.C., 83: 707—710.

Hessler, R.R. and Sanders, H.L., 1967. Faunal diversity in the deep sea. *Deep-Sea Res.*, 14: 65—78.

Hoese, H.D. and Jones, R.S., 1963. Seasonality of larger animals in a Texas turtle grass community. *Publ. Inst. Mar. Sci., Univ. Texas*, 9: 37—47.

Holme, N.A., 1961. The bottom fauna of the English Channel. *J. Mar. Biol. Assoc. U.K.*, 41: 397—461.

Holme, N.A., 1964. Methods of sampling the benthos. In: F.S. Russell (Editor), *Advances in Marine Biology, 2.* Academic Press, London, pp. 171—260.

Hope, D., 1966. A systematic study of marine nematodes from the Cape Cod region and an ecological investigation of marine nematodes of the Hadley Harbor Complex. *Rept. on Progress — Systematics-Ecology Program — 1966, 4th Ann. Rept.*, 39 pp. (Marine Biological Laboratory, Woods Hole, Mass.; multilith printed 1967).

Hough, J.L., 1940. Sediments of Buzzards Bay, Massachusetts. *J. Sediment Petrol.*, 10: 19—32.

Hulings, N.C., 1969. The ecology of the marine Ostracoda of Hadley Harbor, Massachusetts, with emphasis on the life history of *Parasterope pollex* Kornicker, 1967. In: J.W. Neale (Editor), *The Taxonomy, Morphology and Ecology of Recent Ostracoda*. Oliver and Boyd, Edinburgh, pp. 412—422.

Imbrie, J. and Van Andel, Tj. H., 1964. Vector analysis of heavy-mineral data. *Bull. Geol. Soc. Am.*, 75: 1131—1156.

Inman, D.L., 1949. Sorting of sediments in the light of fluid mechanics. *J. Sediment. Petrol.*, 19: 51—70.

Jones, M.L., 1961. A quantitative evaluation of the benthic fauna off Point Richmond, California. *Univ. Calif., Publ. Zool.*, 67(3): 219—320.

Keith, D.E. and Hulings, N.C., 1965. A quantitative study of selected near-shore infauna between Sabine Pass and Bolivar Point, Texas. *Publ. Inst. Mar. Sci., Univ. Texas*, 10: 33—40.

Keyser, A.H., 1967. Water quality characteristics and their measurement. *Instrumentation*, 20: 6—11.

Klovan, J.E., 1966. The use of factor analysis in determining depositional environments from grain-size distributions. *J. Sediment. Petrol.*, 36: 115—125.

Krumbein, W.C. and Pettijohn, F.J., 1938. *Manual of Sedimentary Petrography*. Appleton—Century—Crofts, New York, N.Y., 252 pp.

Lee, R.E., 1944. A quantitative survey of the invertebrate fauna in Menemsha Bight. *Biol. Bull.*, 86: 83—97.

Lie, U., 1968. A quantitative study of benthic infauna in Puget Sound, Washington, U.S.A., in 1963—1964. *Fiskeridir. Skr. Ser. Havunders.*, 14(5): 229—556.

Longhurst, A.R., 1958. An ecological survey of the West African marine benthos. Colonial Office (Br.). *Fish. Publ.*, 11: 1—102.

Longhurst, A.R., 1964. A review of the present situation in benthic synecology. *Bull. Inst. Océanogr. Monaco*, 63 (1317): 1—54.

Lynts, G.W., 1966. Relationship of sediment-size distribution to ecologic factors in Buttonwood Sound, Florida Bay. *J. Sediment. Petrol.*, 36: 66—74.

Manheim, F.T., Trumbull, J.A., Tagg, A.R. and Hulsemann, J., 1964. *Bottom Sediments of Woods Hole Great Harbor*. Woods Hole Oceanographic Institute Ref. No. 64-38: 6 pp. (Unpublished manuscript.)

McNulty, J.K., Work, R.C. and Moore, H.B., 1962. Some relationships between the infauna of the level bottom and the sediment in South Florida. *Bull. Mar. Sci. Gulf Caribb.*, 12(3): 322—332.

Michael, A.D., 1971. Biology of *Leptocheirus* and other amphipods in Cape Cod Bay. In: M.R. Carriker (Editor), *Biology of the Whole Organism. Rept. on Progress — Systematics-Ecology Program — 1970, 8th Ann. Rept.*, 240: 19. (Marine Biological Laboratory, Woods Hole, Mass.)

Mills, E.L., 1964. *Ampelisca abdita*, a new amphipod crustacean from eastern North America. *Can. J. Zool.*, 42: 559—575.

Mills, E.L., 1967. A reexamination of some species of *Ampelisca* (Crustacea: Amphipoda) from the east coast of North America. *Can. J. Zool.*, 45: 635—652.

Milne, L. and Milne, M., 1951. The eelgrass catastrophe. *Sci. Am.*, 184: 52—56.

Moore, J.R., 1963. Bottom sediment studies, Buzzards Bay, Mass. *J. Sediment. Petrol.*, 33(3): 511—558.

Nagle, J.S., 1965. Distributional aspects of Cape Cod eel grass epibiota. *Biol. Bull.*, 129: 417—418.

Nagle, J.S., 1968. Distribution of the epibiota of macroepibenthic plants. *Contrib. Mar. Sci., Univ. Texas Mar. Inst.*, 13: 105—144.

Ockelmann, K.W., 1965. An improved detritus-sledge for collecting meiobenthos. *Ophelia*, 1(2): 217—222.

Oppenheimer, C.H., 1960. Bacterial activity in sediments of shallow marine bays. *Geochim. Cosmochim. Acta*, 19: 244—260.

Oppenheimer, C.H. and Kornicker, L., 1958. Effect of microbial production of hydrogen sulphide and carbon dioxide on the pH of recent sediments. *Publ. Inst. Mar. Sci., Univ. Texas*, 5: 5—15.

Parker, R.H., 1955. Changes in invertebrate fauna, apparently attributable to salinity changes in the bays of central Texas. *J. Paleontol.*, 29(2): 193—211.

Parker, R.H., 1956. Macro-invertebrate assemblages as indicators of sedimentary environments in east Mississippi Delta region. *Bull. Am. Assoc. Pet. Geol.*, 40(2): 295—376.

Parker, R.H., 1959. Macro-invertebrate assemblages of central Texas coastal bays and Laguna Madre. *Bull. Am. Assoc. Pet. Geol.*, 43(9): 2100—2166.

Parker, R.H., 1960. Ecology and distributional patterns of marine macro-invertebrates, northern Gulf of Mexico. In: F.P. Shepard, F.B. Phleger and Tj. H. van Andel (Editors), *Recent Sediments, Northwest Gulf of Mexico, 1951—1958*. Am. Assoc. Pet. Geol., Tulsa, Okla., pp. 302—337.

Parker, R.H., 1964a. Zoogeography and ecology of some macro-invertebrates, particularly mollusks, in the Gulf of California and the continental slope off Mexico. *Vidensk. Medd. Dansk Nat. Foren. Bd.*, 126: 1—178.

Parker, R.H., 1964b. A new approach to the ecological study of marine benthic communities and its relationships to previous studies. In: *Conference on Estuaries, Jekyll Island, Ga*. National Academy of Sciences, Washington, D.C., p.49. (Abstract.)

Parker, R.H., 1964c. Zoogeography and ecology of macro-invertebrates of Gulf of California and continental slope off Western Mexico. *Am. Assoc. Pet. Geol., Mem.*, 3: 331—376.

Parker, R.H., 1965. A multi-environmental sensing system developed for *in situ* study of small scale variations in sublittoral habitats. In: *Ocean Science and Ocean Engineering Conference, Wash., D.C.* Mar. Tech. Soc., p. 780. (Abstract.)

Parker, R.H., 1969. Benthic invertebrates in tidal estuaries and coast lagoons. In: A. Ayala-Castañarea and F.B. Phleger (Editors), *Lagunas Costeras, un Simposio*. Mem. Simp. Int. Lagunas Costeras. UNAM—UNESCO, Mexico, D.F., pp. 563—590.

Parker, R.H. and Blanton, W.G., 1970. *Environmental Factors Affecting Bay and Estuarine Ecosystems of the Texas Coast*. For: Humble Oil Company. Coastal Ecosystems Management Inc., Fort Worth, Texas, 182 pp.

Parker, R.H., Nagle, J.S., Williams, A.B. and Kaufman, R., 1965. Seasonal aspects of Hadley Harbor benthic ecology. *Biol. Bull.*, 129(2): 418. (Abstract.)

Parker, R.H., Blanton, W.G., Slowey, J.F. and Baker, J.H., 1969. *Comparative Study of Two Estuarine Ecosystems: the Brazos and Colorado River Estuaries*. For: Dow Chemical Corporation. T.C.U. Research Foundation, Texas Christian University, Fort Worth, Texas, 283 pp.

Parker, R.H., Solomon, D.E. and Smith, G.D., 1972. *Environmental Assessment of the Trinity River Discharge on Productivity in Trinity Bay*. For: Fort Worth District, U.S. Corps of Engineers. Coastal Ecosystems Management Inc., Fort Worth, Texas, 162 pp.

Pennak, R.W., 1942a. Ecology of some copepods inhabiting intertidal beaches near Woods Hole, Mass. *Ecology*, 23: 446—456.

Pennak, R.W., 1942b. Harpacticoid copepods from some intertidal beaches near Woods Hole, Massachusetts. *Trans. Am. Microsc. Soc.*, 61: 274—285.

Petersen, C.G., 1913. Valuation of the sea. II. The animal communities of the sea bottom and their importance for marine zoogeography. *Rep. Dan. Biol. Stat.*, 21: 44 pp.

Petersen, C.G. 1914. Appendix to Report 21. On the distribution of animal communities of the sea bottom. *Rep. Dan. Biol. Stat.*, 22: 7 pp.

Petersen, C.G., 1915. On the animal communities of the sea bottom in the Skagerrak, the Christiania Fjord and the Danish waters. *Rep. Dan. Biol. Stat.*, 23: 3—28.

Pratt, D.M., 1953. Abundance and growth of *Venus mercenaria* and *Callocardia mor-rhuana*, in relation to the character of bottom sediments. *J. Mar. Res.*, 12: 60—74.

Redfield, A.C., 1953. Interference phenomena in the tides of the Woods Hole region. *J. Mar. Res.*, 12: 121—140.

Reish, D.J., 1959. A discussion of the importance of the screen size in washing quantitative marine bottom samples. *Ecology*, 40: 307—309.

Reish, D.J., 1961. A study of benthic fauna in a recently constructed boat harbor in southern California. *Ecology*, 42: 84—91.

Reish, D.J., 1963. A quantitative study of the benthic polychaetous annelids of Bahia de Quintin, Baja California. *Pac. Nat.*, 3(14): 399—436.

Resources Technology Corporation, 1972. *Fate and Effect Studies of Shell Oil Spill — December 1970.* For: Environmental Protection Agency, Washington, D.C., U.S. Government Printing Office, Washington, D.C., 55 pp.

Rhoads, D.C. and Young, D.K., 1970. The influence of deposit feeding organisms on sediment stability and community trophic structure. *J. Mar. Res.*, 28: 150—178.

Sanders, H.L., 1956. Oceanography of Long Island Sound, 1952—1954. X. Biology of marine bottom communities. *Bull. Bingham Oceanogr.*, 15: 345—414.

Sanders, H.L., 1958. Benthic studies in Buzzards bay. I. Animal—sediment relationships. *Limnol. Oceanogr.*, 3: 245—258.

Sanders, H.L., 1960. Benthic studies in Buzzards Bay. III. The structure of the soft-bottom community. *Limnol. Oceanogr.*, 5: 138—153.

Sanders, H.L., 1968. Marine benthic diversity: A comparative study. *Am. Nat.*, 102(925): 243—282.

Sanders, H.L., Goudsmit, E.M., Mills, E.L. and Hampson, G.E., 1962. A study of the intertidal fauna of Barnstable Harbor, Mass. *Limnol. Oceanogr.*, 7: 63—79.

Sanders, H.L., Mangelsdorf, P.C. and Hampson, G.R., 1965. Salinity and faunal distribution in the Pocasset River, Massachusetts. *Limnol. Oceanogr.*, 10: R216—R229. (Supplement, Redfield Volume.)

Segerstråle, S.G., 1933. Studien über die Bodentierwelt in südfinnländischen Küstengewässern. II. Übersicht über die Bodentierwelt, mit besonderer Berücksichtigung der Produktionsverhältnisse. *Sci. Fenn. Comment. Biol.*, 4(8): 1—62.

Segerstråle, S.G., 1960. Fluctuations in the abundance of benthic animals in the Baltic area. *Sci. Fenn. Comment. Biol.*, 23(9): 1—19.

Sellmer, G.P., 1959. Studies on the anatomy and life history of the gem clam *Gemma gemma* (Totten). Dissertation, Rutgers University, New Brunswick, N.J., 237 pp. (Unpublished manuscript.)

Sellmer, G.P., 1967. Functional morphology and ecological life history of the gem clam *Gemma gemma* (Eulamellibranchia, Veneridae). *Malacologia*, 5: 137—223.

Shelford, V.E., 1932. Basic principles of the classification of communities and habitats and the use of terms. *Ecology*, 13: 105—121.

Shepard, F.P., 1954. Nomenclature based on sand—silt—clay ratios. *J. Sediment. Petrol.*, 24: 151—158.

Slobodkin, L.B., 1960. Ecological energy relationships at the populations level. *Am. Nat.*, 94: 215—236.

Slobodkin, L.B. and Sanders, H.L., 1969. On the contribution of environmental predictability to species diversity. In: G.M. Woodwell and H.H. Smith (Editors), *Diversity and Stability in Ecological Systems. Brookhaven Symposia in Biology, 22.* Assoc. Univ. Inc. Brookhaven Natl. Lab., Upton, N.Y., pp. 82—95.

Solomon, D.E., 1965. Basic research in benthic ecology in Hadley Harbor, Woods Hole, Massachussetts, with special emphasis on the Order Cumacea. Senior Project, Kalamazoo College, Kalamazoo, Mich., 84 pp. (unpublished).

Solomon, D.E. and Smith, G.D., 1973. *Seasonal Assessment of the Relationship Between the Discharge of the Trinity River and the Trinity Bay Ecosystem.* For: Fort Worth District, U.S. Corps of Engineers. Coastal Ecosystems Management Inc., Fort Worth, Texas, 147 pp.

Stanton, R.H. and Evans, I., 1971. Environmental controls of benthic macrofaunal patterns in the Gulf of Mexico adjacent to the Mississippi Delta. *Trans. Gulf Coast Assoc. Geol. Soc.*, 21: 371—378.

Stauffer, R.C., 1937. Changes in the invertebrate community of a lagoon after disappearance of the eel grass. *Ecology*, 18: 427—431.

Sumner, F.B., 1910. An extensive study of the fauna and flora of a restricted area of sea bottom. *U.S. Fish Wildl. Serv., Fish. Bull.*, 28 (Part 2): 1225—1263.

Sumner, F.B., Osborn, R.C., Cole, L.J. and Davis, B.M., 1913. A biological survey of the waters of Woods Hole and vicinity, 1. Physical and zoological. *U.S. Fish Wildl. Serv., Fish. Bull.*, 31 (Part 1): 11—442.

Thorson, G., 1957. Bottom communities (sublittoral or shallow shelf). In: J.W. Hedgpeth (Editor), *Treatise on Marine Ecology and Paleoecology. Mem. Geol. Soc. Am.*, 1(67): 461—534.

Valentine, J.W. and Peddicord, R.G., 1967. Evaluation of fossil assemblages by cluster analysis. *J. Paleontol.*, 41: 502—507.

Verrill, A.E., 1873. Report upon the invertebrate animals of Vineyard Sound and the adjacent waters with an account of the physical characters of the region. *Rep. U.S. Comm. Fish., 1871—1872*, pp. 295—522.

Verrill, A.E., Smith, S.I. and Harger, O., 1873. Catalogue of the marine invertebrate animals of the southern coast of New England and adjacent waters. *Rep. U.S. Comm. Fish., 1871—1872*, pp. 537—778.

Verrill, A.E. and Smith, S.I., 1874. *Report Upon the Invertebrate Animals of Vineyard Sound and Adjacent Waters, with an Account of the Physical Features of the Region.* U.S. Government Printing Office, Washington, D.C., VI, pp. 1—478. (Reprinted version of Verrill et al., 1873.)

Wade, B.A., 1972. A description of a highly diverse soft-bottom community in Kingston Harbour, Jamaica. *Mar. Biol.*, 13(1): 57—69.

Watson, J.A., Smith, J.P., Ehrsam, L.C., Parker, R.H., Blanton, W.G., Solomon, D.E. and Blanton, C.J., 1971. *Biological Assessment of Diesel Spill, Anacortes, Washington.* For: Environmental Protection Agency. Texas Instruments, Services Group, Dallas, Texas, 84 pp. (Final Report.)

Wieser, W., 1960. Benthic studies in Buzzards Bay. II. The meiofauna. *Limnol. Oceanogr.*, 5: 121—137.

Wieser, W. and Kanwisher, J., 1961. Ecological and physiological studies on marine nematodes from a small salt marsh near Woods Hole, Massachusetts. *Limnol. Oceanogr.*, 6: 262—270.

Wigley, R.L. and McIntyre, A.D., 1964. Some quantitative comparisons of offshore meiobenthos and macrobenthos south of Martha's Vineyard. *Limnol. Oceanogr.*, 9(4): 485—493.

Williams, A.B., 1965. Marine decapod crustaceans of the Carolinas. *U.S. Fish Wildl. Serv., Fish. Bull.*, 65: 1—297.

Williams III, G.E., 1972. *Species Composition, Distribution, and Abundance of Macrobenthic Organisms in the Intake and Discharge Areas of a Steam-Electric Generating Station Before and During Initial Startup.* Thesis, Texas A and M University, College Station, Texas, 260 pp.

Woodworth, J.B. and Wigglesworth, E., 1934. Geography and geology of the region including Cape Cod, the Elizabeth Islands, Nantucket, Martha's Vineyard, No Mans Land and Block Island. *Mem. Mus. Comp. Zool., Harv. Univ.*, 52: 322 pp.

Yentsch, A.E., Carriker, M.R., Parker, R.H. and Zullo, V.A., 1967. *Marine and Estuarine Environments, Organisms and Geology of the Cape Cod Region, an Indexed Bibliography, 1665—1965.* Systematics-Ecology Program, Marine Biological Laboratory, Woods Hole, Mass., 178 pp.

Zeigler, J.M., Whitney, G.G. and Hayes, C.R., 1960. Woods Hole rapid sediment analyzer. *J. Sediment. Petrol.*, 30: 490—495.
Zeigler, J.M., Hayes, C.R. and Webb, D.C., 1964. Direct readout of sediment analyses by settling tube for computer analysis. *Science*, 145: 51.
Zobell, C.E., 1946. Studies on redox potential of marine sediments. *Bull. Am. Assoc. Pet. Geol.*, 30: 477—513.

INDEX